CW00741318

Grímsey

Hraunhafnartangi

Raufarhöfn

Melrakkaslétta

Kópasker

ÖXARFJÖRÐUR

PISTIL

Þórshöfn

BAKKAFLÓI

SIGLUFJÖRÐUR

EYJAFJÖRÐUR

Flatey

ÓLAFSFJÖRÐUR

SKJÁLFANDI

Tjörnes

HÚSAVÍK

Ásbyrgi

Bakkafjörður

DALVÍK

Hrísey

Grenivík

VOPNAFJÖRÐUR

Árskógssandur

Hauganes

Dettifoss

Krafla

Laugar

Svalbarðseyri

Goðafoss

Vopnafjörður

HÉRAÐSFLÓI

AKUREYRI

Reykjahlíð

Grímsstaðir

Fnjóská

Skjálfandafljót

Mývatn

Jökulsá á Fjöllum

Borgarfjörður

Möðrudalur

Herðubreið

Jökulsá á Brú

SEYÐISFJÖRÐUR

Ódáðahraun

Lagarfljót

EGILSSTAÐIR

Dyngjufjöll

NESKAUPSTAÐUR

Hallormsstaður

Gerpir

Askja

Grímsá

ESKIFJÖRÐUR

Reyðarfjörður

Fáskrúðsfjörður

HOFS
JÖKULL

Sprengisandur

Trölladyngja

Snæfell

Stöðvarfjörður

Breiðdalsvík

Dungnafells-
jökull

Djúpivogur

Papey

VATNAJÖKULL

Eystrahorn

Grimsvötn

Þórisvatn

HÖFN

Vesturhorn

Hornafjörður

Tungn
aá

Lakagígar

Skaftafell

Öræfajökull

laugar

Eldgjá

Hvannadalshnúkur

Skeiðarársandur

Ingólfshöfði

Kirkjubæjarklaustur

Þorleifur Einarsson

Geology of Iceland

Rocks and Landscape

Translated by Georg Douglas

Mál og menning

Books by Þorleifur Einarsson

Gosið í Surtsey. [The Surtsey Eruption.] 1965. 30+23 pp. In English, Danish and German.
Gosið í Surtsey. Revised ed. 1966. 32+23 pp. In Danish, English and German.
Jarðfræði – saga bergs og lands. 1968. 335 pp.
Jarðfræði. 254 pp. 1971, 1973, 1978, 1980, 1985.
Gosið á Heimaey. [The Heimaey Eruption.] 1974. 56+30 bls. In English, Norwegian, German and Polish.

Geology of Iceland. Rocks and Landscape. 1994.
Original title: *Myndun og mótun lands – Jarðfræði.* First published 1991. Reprinted 1992 and 1994. Also available in German.

© Þorleifur Einarsson, 1991
© English translation: Georg Douglas
Published by Mál og menning, Reykjavík 1994, 1999

All rights reserved
No part of this publication may be reproduced, stored in a retrieval system or transmitted, in any form or by any means, electronic, mechanical, photocopying, recording or otherwise, without prior written permission of the publishers.

Picture Researcher: Gunnar H. Ingimundarson
Cover: Næst . . .
Cover photo: Þorleifur Einarsson. The picture is taken in Hnappadalur, Snæfellsnes. In the foreground are the volcanic craters Rauðamelskúlur and the lavas Rauðamelshraun. In the background are interglacial lavaflows on Rauðamelsheiði and the palagonite (móberg) mountain Þrífjöll.
Prentsmiðjan Oddi hf.
Printed in Iceland

ISBN 9979-3-0689-0

Contents

Introduction

Geology is one of the youngest branches of the very wide range of natural sciences. The name *geology* is taken from the Greek words geo = earth and logia = study.

The study of geology deals with the earth's crust, while the subject matter is divided into two main areas. One deals with *general geology* which is concerned with the formation, structure and shaping of the earth's crust by natural forces, on the one hand *internal or endogenic forces* such as volcanic eruption and earthquakes which originate within the earth, and on the other hand *external or exogenic forces* especially frost, river, glacier, wind and wave action, whose energy source is the sun. The other main area of study is *stratigraphy* which recounts in chronological order events and changes which have occurred on the earth, both due to internal and external forces, as well as the history of life.

Geology depends heavily on various related subjects. In general geology physics and chemistry are of prime importance, while based on them are *mineralogy* which deals with the structure and composition of minerals, the basic building units of rocks and *petrology* which deals with the study of the composition and origin of the rocks themselves. *Geochemis-*try is related to these subjects and deals with the chemical composition of the earth and the cycles of materials in nature. *Geophysics* investigates inaccessible strata indirectly using for example seismic, resistivity, magnetic and gravity measurements. Stratigraphy is mainly based on *palaeontology*, i.e. research on the fossils of organisms, from which their evolution and living conditions in the past can be deduced.

In more recent years geological research has attained economical value; in Iceland research has concentrated on raw materials, geothermal energy and hydro electric power, as well as on research connected with construction such as power schemes, harbour and road works, while environmental studies have been given increasing attention.

The first mention of a volcanic eruption in Iceland appears in Völuspá, a poem written long before 1104 A.D., the time of Hekla's first historical eruption. It is evident from the poem that the author had an experience of a volcanic eruption.

Medieval European literature frequently refers to Icelandic natural phenomena, such as volcanic eruptions both on land and in the sea, hot springs and geysers and glacial bursts. Some of the accounts are quite unrealistic and more akin to folklore. In his book on Iceland, bishop Oddur Einarsson (1559-1630) mentions drift ice and volcanic eruptions and that in his time glaciers were advancing. The books of Arngrímur the learned (1568-1648) contain similar material. Bishop Guðbrandur Þorláksson's map of Iceland, published in 1590, was the first to show realistic outlines of Iceland and to show glaciers on a map. Sveinn Pálsson (1762-1840) was first to understand the movement of glaciers when he climbed Öræfajökull in 1794 and realized that glaciers flowed like a viscous liquid. The parson Jón Sæmundsson wrote a clear description of the Mývatn eruption 1725-29. However, by far the best contemporary description of a volcanic eruption in Iceland is the work of the parson Jón Steingrímsson, in which he describes the Laki eruption in 1783-4 and the traumatic aftermath. The first Icelander to study geology at university level was Jónas Hallgrímsson (d. 1845). During the period 1801-18 Norwegian geodesists drew an accurate map of the coastline of Iceland. During the years 1831-43 Björn Gunnlaugsson drew maps of the lowland areas and much of the interior. These maps were updated in this century first by the Danish Geodetic Survey and more recently by the Iceland Geodetic Survey. There was a turning point in Icelandic geology in 1881 when Thorvaldur Thoroddsen began his researches in Iceland. He travelled around the country for eighteen summers and wrote numerous books of great value on the geography and geology of Iceland. His geological map of Iceland, in the scale 1:600,000, the first modern one, based on Gunnlaugsson's map, was published in 1901. In 1989 it was replaced by a map compiled by Haukur Jóhannesson and Kristján Sæmundsson. At the turn of last century Helgi Pjeturss (d. 1949) began his geological research. He showed how hyaloclastic mountains had formed in subglacial eruptions and that the ice age had not been one continuous long winter.

Up to the nineteen seventies only a handful of Icelandic geologists worked in geology. Guðmundur G. Bárðarson (d. 1933) worked in palaeontology and on the geology of Tjörnes; Jóhannes Áskelsson (d. 1961) in palaeontology and stratigraphy; Tómas Tryggvason (d. 1965) in petrology and economic geology; Guðmundur Kjartansson (d. 1972) in glacial geology. He explained the formation of subglacial volcanoes and started work on geological map of the country in the scale 1:250,000; Sigurður Þórarinsson (d. 1983) worked in glaciology and volcanology. He was the father of tephrochronology. Trausti Einarsson (d 1984) and Þorbjörn Sigurgeirsson (d. 1988), pioneered geophysics in Iceland and were among the first workers in palaeomagnetic field mapping. In 1968 the University of Iceland started an Earth Sciences Department. In the seventies this led to a sharp increase in the number of geologists in Iceland (over 200 at present). As a result, research, both scientific and applied, was increased at various research institutions.

The earth, size and shape

2

The Earth in space

Counting from the sun, the Earth is the third of the 9 planets which revolve in almost circular orbits around the sun, which is one of virtually countless solar systems in a huge galaxy of stars known as the *milky way*. The Earth rotates from west to east on its axis in 23 hours and 56 minutes relative to fixed stars or in 24 hours in relation to the sun., i.e. a sidereal day. This time difference is due to the earth's travel around the sun, each revolution taking 365 days, 5 hours and 49 minutes, i.e. one year. The Earth's orbital velocity is around 30 km/sec. So that the year is based on complete days a leap year is added every fourth year.

The Earth's orbit around the sun is an almost circular ellipse, its *radius,* being about 149,5 million km. The Earth is closest to the sun on 2nd January and furthest on 3rd July each year. The earth's axis is inclined at 23,5° in relation to the vertical with its orbital plane. The direction of inclination is practically constant, towards the Pole Star. The inclination of the axis causes the seasons and variations in the length of day and night.

The sun is the central point of the solar system and a source of energy. Its surface temperature is about 6000° C and it radiates heat energy on the earth's surface equivalent to 1,92 calories per cm^2 per minute. It is 109 times greater in diameter than the earth, 1.300.000 times greater in volume and 330.000 times heavier, i.e. its density being only one quarter of the average density of the earth.

The celestial bodies which revolve around the sun and whose orbits are maintained by its force of gravity are as follows (figures in brackets give the distance of the planets from the sun based on the radius of the earth's orbit, 149.5 million km.):

1) *Planets* , counting from the sun: Mercury (0.38), Venus (0.72), Earth (1.00), Mars (1.5), Jupiter (5.2), Saturn (9.5), Uranus (19.2), Neptune (30) and Pluto (39.5). Jupiter is by far the biggest planet, being about 1300 times larger in volume and 318 times heavier than the Earth.

2) *Asteroids*: About 5000 asteroids revolve in known orbits around the sun. In addition there are several thousand asteroids which have seldom been observed. The largest asteroid, Ceres, is about 800 km in diameter. The orbits of most asteroids lie between Mars and Jupiter.

3. *Moons*: 64 moons revolve around the planets. Of these 16 moons revolve around

Jupiter, 21 around Saturn, 15 around Uranus, 8 around Neptune, 2 around Mars and one each around the earth and Pluto.

4. *Comets*: Altogether about 700 comets are known in the solar system. They occupy very elongated orbits around the sun. They are composed of cosmic dust and minutely crystallised gases.

5. *Meteorites*: Meteorites move rapidly around space in groups. They enter the atmosphere at great speed (30–70 km/sec) where they heat up due to friction and glow (shooting stars) while most of them burn up before reaching the earth's surface. On rare occasions meteorites reach the surface. The largest which has been found weighing about 60 tons. It is composed of iron mixed with nickel and was found at Hopa in Southwest Africa. Most (90%) meteorites however are composed of rock, similar to that believed to be in the earth's mantle.

From the above it can be seen that the distance between the planets increases fairly regularly. There is though one gap in the series, between Mars and Jupiter, precisely in the area where there are most asteroids. It is generally believed that they and most meteorites which fall to earth are the remains of planets which have disintegrated in the distant past.

Shape and size of the earth

Because of rotation on its axis and the effect of the centrifugal force, the earth is not perfectly spherical, but flatter at the poles. The circumference of the earth at the equator is 40,076 km and the diameter 12,714 km. The average radius of the globe is 6371 km. The difference in diameters is 43 km and the deviation from sphericity therefore 1/297. Amongst other effects, the deviation causes gravity to vary according to latitude. It is least at the equator and greatest at the poles. The volume of the earth is about $1,083 \times 10^{21}$ km^3 and its mass is believed to be just under 6×10^{24} tons. The density of the earth is 5,52.

The surface area of the earth is about 510 million km^2, of which oceans cover 361 million km^2 or 71% and dry land about 149 million km^2 or 29%.

Compared to the globe in general, irregularities on the surface of the earth are insignificant. If the world was reduced so that its diameter was 2 m, the difference in height between the highest mountain, Mt. Everest which is 8882 m and the greatest ocean depth, The Vítias trench off the Marianna islands in the western Pacific which is just over 11,000 m, would be just under 2 mm. The average height on dry land is 875 m and the average ocean depth about 3800 m. If all the irregularities on the earth were smoothed out, the ocean depth on this surface would be 2430 m.

Chemical composition of the earth's crust

The composition of rocks in the upper part of the earth's crust is well known and tens of thousands of chemical analyses have been carried out on various types of rock from the surface layers.

Altogether about 100 elements are now known and as the accompanying table shows, their amount varies greatly. The table shows the percentage by weight of the main elements in the surface rocks:

oxygen, O	46.6%
silica, Si	27.7%
aluminium, Al	8.1%
iron, Fe	5.0%
calcium, Ca	3.6%
sodium, Na	2.8%
potassium, K	2.6%
magnesium, Mg	2.1%

These 8 elements are predominant in the surface rocks of the earth and altogether amount to 98%. Although there is most oxygen by weight in the surface rocks, its proportion is even greater if calculated by volume. Thus in one ton of rock there are on average 466 kg of oxygen and 277 kg of silica. Luckily the valuable earth materials have separated out and been concentrated in various ways, such as by volcanism, mountain building, metamorphism and denudation and are therefore exploitable are exploitable by mining.

Spectroscopy has revealed that the elements found on earth also occur on the sun as well as on the fixed stars, which are actually also solar systems. The proportions of the elements on the sun are admittedly different than on earth. Hydrogen and helium dominate, whereas they occur only in small amounts in the earth's atmosphere. They are the lightest elements and probably the earth's gravity is not sufficient to hold them. Hydrogen is however fairly common in compounds (0.13%), mainly in water. The gravity of the sun is on the other hand so strong that it holds even the lightest elements. The same applies to the planets. The heavier planets have larger and denser atmospheres than the lighter planets. Jupiter has for example a thick atmosphere while Mercury has none. If the densities of the earth (5.52) and the sun (1.4) are compared, it is also obvious that the light elements are more common in the sun than on earth. Solar energy is indeed a result of the fact that hydrogen atoms combine to form helium. It is estimated that about 4 million tons of solar material is converted to energy every second. This fusion results in a release of energy, solar energy, which makes life on earth possible and benefits its inhabitants.

Properties and structure and composition of minerals

3

The earth's crust is composed of rocks which vary in composition and properties. They include unconsolidated rocks, e.g. sand, consolidated, e.g. sandstone, or solidified, e.g. basalt. Sometimes rocks consist of one chemical compound, e.g. limestone, but much more often they are made up of different grains, minerals or crystals which each has its own particular properties and composition. Basalt is, for instance, composed mainly of four mineral types. These smallest rock units are known as minerals.

A mineral is a crystallised solid element or chemical compound occurring independently in the natural state.[1]

Examples of minerals composed of a single element are gold, sulphur, graphite and diamond. Minerals composed of elements bonded together as so-called compounds are however much more common. Examples are quartz (SiO_2), which contains the elements silica (Si) and oxygen (O), or rock salt (NaCl), which is composed of sodium (Na) and chlorine (Cl), or potassium feldspar ($KAlSi_3O_8$) which contains potassium (K), alumini-

um (Al), silica (Si) and oxygen (O). The numbers show the proportion of the elements in the compound.

Crystal structure

In minerals the elements are arranged in an ordered way as a so-called crystal lattice. The chemical composition of each mineral is usually strictly defined, although in complex compounds it is often variable so that elements having similar properties can replace one another.

The organisation of the elements in the lattice of rock salt is one of the simplest cases. When rock salt is dissolved in water, a salt brine is formed. The solution contains charged ions of positively charged sodium (Na^+) and negatively charged chlorine (Cl^-), which are in constant movement. Slow distillation of the brine results in the solution becoming gradually saturated, so that the two ions pair, form molecules and crystallise in a cube shaped lattice. Chlorine and sodium ions alternately occupy the corners of the lattice and the distance between them is always the same (Figure 3-1). With continued distillation the cubic crystals gradually increase in size, as new layers are added on to those already formed, until the crystals are visible to the naked eye.

---

1 Materials of organic origin, such as coal and oil, are generally not classified as minerals. The same applies to man-made materials such as window glass.

13

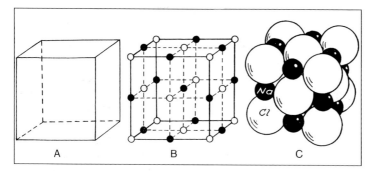

Figure 3-1. Cubic salt crystal (left). Crystal lattice at centre. The circles represent chlorine ions (Cl⁻) the filled circles sodium ions (Na⁺). On the right the size ratio of the ions is shown.

From the above it is obvious that in every grain of salt added to a meal, there are millions of molecules of table salt. Crystals of other minerals are formed in the same way, although the crystal lattices vary. In silicate minerals the lattice is formed of equal-sided tetrahedral with oxygen ions occupying the corner sites and silica ions in the centres. Conditions for crystallisation do not always permit the crystals to grow equally in all directions however so that they become prismatic or elongated. The angles between crystal faces of a particular mineral are however always constant, as the Dane Nikulas Steno demonstrated as early as 1669. The crystal lattice controls both the structure and properties of the various minerals.

When crystallisation occurs unrestricted, the crystals are beautifully formed and large, as for instance is the case with crystals in rock cavities and fissures, which often form beautiful *crystal groups*. If many types crystallise at the same time, the crystals are generally smaller and irregular, since they interfere with each other and sometimes even grow within each other. This is the case for example when liquid magma solidifies.

Mineral identification

As indicated above, minerals differ from one another as regards chemical composition and structure. If sufficiently large,

minerals can be identified with the naked eye, with hand equipment or with acid. Smaller crystals can also often be identified with a magnifying glass. In addition to structure there are various physical crystal properties which are important in their identification, such as hardness, density, colour, lustre, cleavage, fracture surface etc.

Crystals. Crystals can be classified into seven main groups according to form although in each group there are many variations. This method is mainly practical for large and well formed crystals. For instance quartz, which forms hexagonal crystals, can be easily distinguished from calcite, which forms rhomboids (c.f. illustrations in Chapter 4).

Cleavage and fracture surfaces. Many minerals break regularly on receiving a blow, in one or more directions along straight and smooth planes. Rock salt

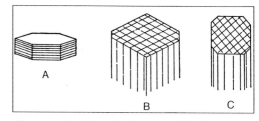

Figure 3-2. Mineral cleavage. A) shows mica which cleaves into sheets, B) hornblende which cleaves into right angled prisms and C) augite which cleaves into diamond-shaped prisms.

cleaves for instance in three directions so that the cleavage planes intersect at right angles. Calcite also cleaves in three directions but the intersection angle is either 75° or 105° so that the cleavage planes are diamond shaped and the fragments trapezoidal. Mica and gypsum on the other hand have only one cleavage direction, i.e. cleavage into sheets or plates. Certain minerals show no cleavage and their fracture surfaces are conchoidally fractured, e.g. in quartz, or jagged, such as in some ore minerals.

Colour. Minerals are either clear or coloured. Colour is not a diagnostic property, only a little extraneous material being sufficient to impart colour. It is easy to decide if the colour is true by for example rubbing the mineral on a corrugated ceramic plate – the *streak*. Jasper, which is usually red, green or brown, has a white streak.

Lustre. Minerals can be classified into two main groups according to lustre, on the one hand metallic lustre, e.g. metal ores, and on the other hand minerals with no metallic lustre. Minerals without metallic lustre are divided into several types such as glassy lustre (quartz), diamond lustre (diamond), pearly lustre (zeolites) and greasy (talc).

Hardness. Measurement of hardness of minerals is made on a scale of 1 to 10. Certain minerals are used to represent each stage on the scale. The softest minerals are at the bottom of the scale and the hardest at the top. The hardness scale is chosen so that a mineral with a higher value clearly scratches one immediately below it.

1 *talc*	6 *feldspar*
2 *gypsum*	7 *quartz*
3 *calcite*	8 *topaz*
4 *fluorspar*	9 *corundum*
5 *apatite*	10 *diamond*

Minerals with a hardness of 1 are so soft that they rub off in the fingers, while those with hardness 2 can be scratched by fingernail. Minerals softer than 5 1/2 can be scratched by glass, while those with hardness 6 or more are capable of scratching glass. A knife will scratch minerals up to a hardness of 6. Minerals of between 8–10 are known as precious stones and few everyday materials are capable of scratching them. An example of a soft mineral with hardness 1 is graphite, which is composed of pure carbon, as is diamond which is the hardest of all minerals. The difference in hardness lies in the crystal structure. When hardness is measured, the scratch should always be rubbed over with the finger to ensure that it is not confused with streak.

Density. Most common minerals have densities of 2.0–3.0, the metal ores 4 or more.

Some minerals which contain iron are *magnetized* and have an effect on the compass needle. The main types are magnetite. Magnetite occurs in basalt which therefore has an effect on the compass (c.f. geomagnetic time scale). *Acids* react with various minerals. For example when cold, dilute hydrochloric acid is allowed to trickle on to calcite, $CaCO_3$, the mineral fizzes and carbon dioxide (CO_2) is released.

Modern mineralogical research involves the use of complicated instruments and chemical analyses. *Microscopy* is particularly useful in examining minerals and rocks. Slices of mineral or rock are cut thinly enough for light to pass through and the minerals are then identified by their behaviour in transmitted light (Figures 6-4 and 6-10). In more recent years *X-ray diffraction* has gained importance in mineralogical research. X-rays are passed through the crystal and are either refracted or reflected by particular atoms according to lattice structure, thus enabling mineral identification.

The chief minerals

4

Altogether about 3000 minerals are known but only 9 of them are common in rocks. These 9 types comprise about 95% of all the minerals at the surface of the earth. Another 200 minerals are rather common in rocks, but most of them are not very remarkable although they can characterise the rock in certain areas. In addition around 200 minerals are important economically and are found in such quantities in limited areas that they can be mined.

There are rather few mineral types in Iceland and this chapter deals with the main rock-forming minerals as well as the main amygdule minerals (found in gas cavities etc.) A few other minerals are also dealt with, especially those of economic value.

Rock-forming minerals

The minerals of igneous rocks are known as *rock-forming minerals*. They have in common that they contain silica, SiO_2, and are known as silicates. These minerals are admittedly also common in sediments or sedimentary rocks, e.g. sand or sandstone abroad and metamorphic rock, e.g. gneiss.

Quartz. Crystalline quartz (SiO_2, H 7, density 2.65)[2] is one of the main minerals in acid igneous rocks , i.e. granite, granophyre and rhyolite. It is usually clear but in granite it is also often greyish in colour. Quartz is also a common mineral in metamorphic rocks such as gneiss. The rocks crumble on weathering, but because of its hardness and resistance to chemical weathering quartz breaks down and disintegrates less and later than other minerals in the rock so that it accumulates and forms thick sediments. Light-coloured beach, aeolian and alluvial sand in other countries is composed mainly of quartz grains.[3] Quartz sand is used in glass manufacture, also as an abrasive, e.g. in sandpaper, in polishes and soap, as well as in concrete. Sandstone formed mainly of lithified quartz grains is frequently used abroad as building stone or as dressing stone in buildings. Sandstone rich in quartz is often brown or red stained due to traces of iron.

Feldspar is formed of potassium-, sodium-, or potassium-aluminium-silicate, H 6,

---

2 Hardness is represented here by H.

---

3 The dark colour of Icelandic sand is on the other hand due to the fact that the sand grains are either ground down basalt or dark basalt rock fragments. Light coloured beach sand in Iceland is almost entirely of shell fragments, shelly sand.

density 2.6–2.8. Feldspar is the most common rock-forming mineral in igneous and metamorphic rocks. There are two main types of feldspar (cf. Figures 6-4, 6-5, 6-10 and 6-11).

a. *Orthoclase* is *potassium feldspar* (KAl Si_3O_8). This is a very common mineral in acid igneous rocks. In granite it is usually grey-white or light red in colour but in rhyolite it is clear. Very large crystals of potassium feldspar is often found in dikes surrounding granite plutons or batholiths, where it has crystallised from magma gas or magmatic liquids, released from the cooling granite magma (pegmatite). Potassium feldspar is mined and then often from crushed coarse-grained granite and used in glass manufacture, the china industry and in pottery as a glazing material.

b. *Plagioclase* is a mixture of *sodium feldspar* (NaAlSi_3O_8) and *calcium feldspar* (CaAl_2Si_2O_8). It is clear or white in colour. Various varieties of it are common minerals in igneous rocks, calcium-rich in basalt and gabbro, or sodium-rich in rhyolite, granophyre and granite. Intermediate igneous rocks e.g. andesite contain almost equal amounts of each. Sometimes basalt contains so many white plagioclase phenocrysts that it resembles blood pudding. The extensive Þjórsá hraun lava in S-Iceland is an example.

Mica is a mineral composed of hydrolysed potassium-aluminium-silicate, H 2, density 3. It breaks down into thin, flexible, shiny and often transparent sheets. Two of the most common varieties are *dark mica (biotite)* and *light mica (muscovite)* which are both common minerals in metamorphic rocks, especially gneiss and schist, as well as in acid plutonic rocks e.g. granite. Large sheets of mica often occur in dikes (pegmatite) in connection with acid batholiths. Mica is a good insulator and was often used in electrical equipment. It is also heat resistant and is therefore used as window material in furnace doors. It is also used ground, as a paint filler and for decoration in for example "Christmas snow". The best mica mines in the world are in the Madras province of India.

Olivine is a magnesium-iron-silicate, $(Mg,Fe)_2SiO_4$, H 6–7, density 3.2–4.3. It has a glassy lustre and is yellow green in colour. Olivine is a common mineral in gabbro and basalt and often occurs as phenocrysts e.g. in Reykjavík Pleistocene basalts, Búðahraun, (Snæfellsnes) and Búrfellshraun lavas in Hafnarfjörður.

Pyroxene is a diverse group of minerals composed of magnesium-iron-calcium-aluminium silicates. It is sufficient to mention *augite* which is a common mineral in basalt and gabbro, H 5–6, density 3,5. It is usually dark or black in colour. Pyroxene-phenocrysts are very common in lavas on the Snæfellsnes peninsula e.g. the Berserkjahraun lava.

Iron compounds occur in all igneous rocks, mainly as (magnetite), which causes magnetism. Magnetite is the fourth most common mineral in basalt and gabbro. The grains are generally too small to be discernible to the naked eye.

Amygdules

Through time various precipitates form from hot solutions in holes, cavities and fractures in the rock. Water which sinks through the bedrock becomes heated with depth in accordance with the local geothermal gradient, although most of all if it comes in contact with cooling intrusions e.g. underneath active volcanoes. Hot water which percolates through the rock dissolves material from the minerals

Figure 4-1. Rock crystal (quartz). The longest crystal is 7.5 cm in length. Þorgeirsfell, Snæfellsnes peninsula. (Photo Sigurður Sv. Jónsson.)

in it. This results in the formation of new minerals which remain in the rock. These are mainly clay minerals. The dissolved materials, on the other hand are carried away with the hot water and precipitate in holes and cavities in the colder surrounding rock in accordance with falling temperature, thus forming amygdules. The type of amygdules depends on the temperature of the solution they are precipitated from. At 50–150°C *low temperature* minerals form such as zeolites, while *high temperature* minerals form at up to 350°C, e.g. calcite (Iceland spar).

Amygdules are mainly found in the Tertiary Basalt Formation and in rock sequences from the early part of the Pleistocene period. These are heavily eroded ar-

19

Figure 4-2. Agate with in-fill of small quartz crystals. Size 7 cm. Eastern Iceland. (Photo Sigurður Sv. Jóns-son.)

eas with high mountains and deep valleys. In these areas it can be seen that the amygdules are arranged in belts in accordance with the fossil temperature gradient, the most variety being at the roots of long extinct central volcanoes. Icelandic amygdules can be classified by crystal structure and chemical composition into 6 groups: *quartz minerals, zeolites, calcite* and other salts, *ore minerals* (e.g. iron pyrites, FeS_2, galena, PbS and copper-iron-sulphide (chalcopyrite)), *clay minerals* and *high temperature minerals* (e.g. epidote and garnet).

QUARTZ MINERALS are composed of pure silica oxide, SiO_2. In their purest form quartz minerals are clear and colourless, but they are often coloured due to contamination. Quartz minerals are either micro-crystalline (chalcedony) or coarsely crystalline and form hexagonal crystals with a six sided pyramid top (rock crystal, Figure 4-1). Quartz minerals usually have a glassy lustre, H 7, density 2.7.

Rock crystal is crystal-clear quartz (Figure 4-1). It is common in fractures and as amygdules and is generally easily recog-

nised by its structure and hardness. In Iceland the crystals are occasionally a few centimetres in length, but abroad, mainly in Brazil, they sometimes reach tens of centimetres in length. Nowadays quartz crystals are used a lot in electrical and radio equipment, as well as for accurate time keeping (quartz watches). Rock crystal which contain contaminating materials are beautifully coloured and are used in jewellery. The main varieties are: Amethyst, purple. Has been found in Iceland e.g. in Hornafjörður, Lón, Borgarfjörður (eastern) and Gerpir. Smoky quartz, smoke coloured, or brown. Quite common.

Chalcedony (tinder stone) is semi-transparent and grey in colour and was used in Iceland for fire lighting. They are very finely crystalline. When ground down by river or marine erosion they resemble white glass. Chalcedony is very common as amygdules in Iceland, one of the best known localities being Glerhallavík at Reykjaströnd in Skagafjörður. It is often coloured by other materials, e.g. *rose quartz* which is bright red. It is often banded, with differently coloured layers, which can be horizontal grey and white

Figure 4-3. Scolesite (zeolite). Size 3 cm. Eastern Iceland. (Photo Sigurður Sv. Jónsson.)

bands as in *onyx*, or white, red, brown and green concentric bands as in *agate*. Onyx is fairly common in Iceland but agate less so. Chalcedony is used in jewellery. The name tinder stone comes from the fact that when knocked together the stones produce a spark (Figure 4-2).

Jasper is very similar to chalcedony in structure but always mixed with other materials, mainly iron compounds and is green, red or brownish-coloured. Jasper is common as amygdules in the Tertiary Basalt Formation. It is used in jewellery.

Petrified wood was originally wood which has become (turned into stone). Silica has replaced organic material and the wood texture and growth rings are clearly preserved. Fossilised tree trunks are commonest in ancient rhyolite ash, e.g. in Reykhólasveit, Loðmundarfjörður and Drápuhlíðarfjall.

Flint resembles chalcedony in structure. It is grey or dark in colour and is mainly found in chalk strata, e.g. in Denmark and the British Isles. The silica in flint has its origins in silica sponges and radiolarian shells (Figure 23-19). Flint was used to light fires before the discovery of match-

es. For a long time it has also been one of the chief raw materials used by man for tool making, prehistory being known as the stone age and being divided into periods according to polishing and type of tools.

Opal is composed of silica oxide like other quartz minerals, but in addition they contain some water ($SiO_2 + n.H_2O$). Opal is amorphous and lighter than other quartz minerals and not as hard, H 5 1/2, density 2.2. Opal is generally milky white and semitransparent, although sometimes it is contaminated and then grey, greenish brown or red. It is used in jewellery, especially the *fire-opal* variety which displays beautiful colours. Opal is common in Iceland as amygdules and fracture infill.

Geyserite crusts are formed when silica oxide precipitates from geothermal solutions on cooling. It is frothy and light or grey in colour. In many geothermal areas there are great areas of sinter, e.g. at Geysir, in Hveragerði and in Hveravellir (Figure 9-4). It often contains replicas of leaves and other plant remains. Through time the sinter consolidates and forms denser opal. A good example can be seen

21

Figure 4-4. Stilbite (zeolite). Size 3 cm. Eastern Iceland. (Photo Sigurður Sv. Jónsson.)

in a stream section in the north of Geysis-skálin. Sinter is usually known as geyse-rite and owes its name to Geysir in Haukadalur.

ZEOLITES are composed of potassium-, sodium-, or calcium-aluminium-silicate and closely resemble the feldspars, except that they contain water. An example is scolesite, $Ca(Al_2Si_3O_{10})\cdot3\ H_2O$, which close-ly resembles calcium feldspar, $CaAl_2Si_2O_8$ (Figure 4-3). Zeolites are very common as amygdules in rocks in Iceland. Their crys-tal structure is very varied and 20 types are now known here. Their hardness va-ries, H 3.5–5.5, and density 2–2.4. Zeolites are usually transparent or white and have a glassy or pearly lustre. Most zeolites dissolve in hot hydrochloric acid to form a gel. On heating slightly they lose water but absorb it again in damp conditions.

Figure 4-5. Iceland spar (calcite). Helgustaðir in Reyðarfjörður, E-Iceland. Size 7 cm. (Photo Sigurður Sv. Jónsson.)

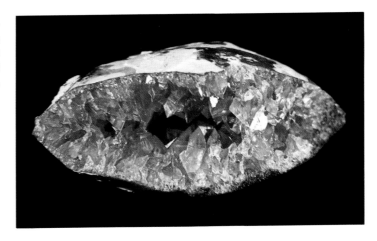

Figure 4-7. Sykurberg (candy sugar-stone), calcite in a cockle shell from the Tjörnes sediments. Size 5 cm. (Photo Sigurður Sv. Jónsson.)

On heating they boil or foam from which fact their name of zeolites or boiling stones is derived.

Identification of zeolites is difficult, but they can be roughly divided into three groups: radiating or prismatic or needle-like, e.g. scolecite, plate or sheet forms, e.g. heulandite and stilbite (Figure 4-4 and 4-5), rhomboidal or cubic forms, e.g. chabasite and analcime. One of the best known localities in the world for zeolites is at Teigarhorn in Berufjörður and most of the larger collections have examples from there. The locality at Teigarhorn is now protected as an area of outstanding natural interest. Zeolites are used in industry to remove unwanted materials from liquids.

CALCITE (Iceland spar) is composed of calcium and carbonate, $CaCO_3$. The crystals are rhomboidal with diamond shaped faces and have a glassy lustre (Figure 4-5), H 3, density 2.7. In its pure

Figure 4-6. Double refraction of light in Iceland spar.

form it is transparent. Calcite foams in cold dilute hydrochloric acid producing carbon dioxide.

There are various varieties of calcite. In Iceland a transparent variety is found, *Iceland spar*, which is common as amygdules in fractures and cavities. The most important occurrence of calcite is at Helgustaðir in Reyðarfjörður and in Hoffellsdalur in Hornafjörður and mining was carried out in both places for many decades. In other languages calcite is associated with Iceland, e.g. in English Iceland spar, and most mineral collections contain examples. It is still used in various very accurate optical equipment, such as in the polarising microscope and in laser technology, although it has largely been replaced by synthetic materials except in the best equipment. The value of calcite lies mainly in its ability to cause double refraction of light better than most other minerals, i.e. to polarise light. This is well illustrated when a calcite crystal is placed on a book, when the writing appears to be double (Figure 4-6). This property of calcite from Helgustaðir was first described by the Erasmus Bartholin from Denmark in 1669 and was the first step in understanding the properties of light and its wavelike behaviour. *Sugarstone* is a yellow brown or brownish coloured variety

23

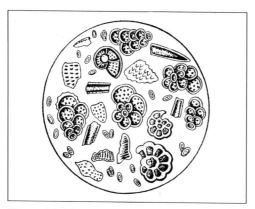

Figure 4-8. Thin section of blackboard chalk, show-ing shell fragments, spiricules from sponges, fora-minifera shells and chalk platelets from coccoliths. Magnification approximately 200X.

of calcite (Figure 4-7). It is mainly found in hollow shells in the Tjörnes strata. *Ara-gonite* is a needle-like, white variety of calcite. It has been found in various local-ities in Iceland, e.g. in Stöðvarfjörður, in Fljót and on Snæfellsnes. White coloured calcite is common in cavities and frac-tures in rocks in Iceland though the crys-tals are usually small. At Mógilsá on the south of the Esja mountain north of Reykja-vík is for example a thick chalk vein which was mined at the turn of the centu-ry and roasted in the chalk furnaces on Kalkofnsvegur (lime kiln road), in Reykja-vík. It was used as mortar.

Various minerals

Here follows an account of various min-erals which do not contain silica oxide (SiO_2), e.g. *salts*, i.e. compounds of light metals and acid residue (e.g. table salt NaCl), and *ore minerals*, i.e. rather simple compounds of heavier metals with sul-phur (e.g. FeS_2, iron pyrites) or oxygen (e.g. Fe_2O_3, hematite) and pure elements (e.g. gold). For various reasons the miner-als have been concentrated in workable quantities. Ore minerals can for example

sink to the bottom of magma chambers because of their density (nickel iron mine at Sudbury in Canada), separate from gas and magmatic fluids from cooling mag-ma (sulphur and copper pyrites), concen-trate due to metamorphism (ironstone at Kiruna in northern Sweden) or due to weathering and erosion (e.g. Rhine gold) or precipitate from solutions (e.g. bog iron and rock salt).

Rock Salt, sodium chloride (NaCl) has a vitreous lustre and is clear but is often contaminated and is then yellow or red in colour. The crystals are cubic (Figure 3-1), H 2, density 2. Rock salt dissolves easily in water. Its most easily recognised prop-erty is its salty taste. The sea contains about 2.7% rock salt in solution but in salt lakes it often reaches around 20%. Rock salt occurs in thick strata widely through-out the world, e.g. in Poland, Germany, the Alps (Salzkammergut, Hallstadt), the Ural mountains and the United States. These thick layers were formed by rapid evaporation of inland seas, lagoons or salt lakes in dry hot climates of earlier ge-ological periods and the salt beds are clear evidence for the climate during their formation. In earlier times salt was mined on a large scale but nowadays it is ob-tained from the sea in southern latitudes such as in Spain by evaporation in the sun. In Iceland salt was obtained for a long time by burning seaweed and for a time by boiling brine using the heat from natural hot springs such as at Reykjanes in Ísafjarðardjúp. Rock salt is now ob-tained in the salt works on the Reykjanes peninsula using heat from geothermal steam. Salt is extensively used in food processing as well as for preserving foods (salt fish, salted meat), as well as in vari-ous types of industry such as in chlorine and sodium production by electrolysis.

Practically the only salt now mined is potassium salts which are important nu-tritional salts, as fertilizer for plants. Potassium is also widely used in industry. It is mainly obtained in Germany and the United states.

Sulphur (S) forms yellow clear crystals or yellow coatings and is common in natural steam spring areas or geothermal clay areas in Iceland. It melts at 110°C. It burns on ignition with a blue flame producing a strong smell (SO_2). In earlier times sulphur was mined in Iceland such as at Krýsuvík and at Námafjall in the Mývatnssveit district. Sulphur was used for gun powder but nowadays it is extensively used in industry such as in rubber production, fertiliser production for pesticides and matches. Sulphur is now mainly obtained from gypsum beds on the crowns of salt domes in Texas where it occurs in fairly pure form. Large quantities are also obtained from iron pyrite, FeS_2. Most sulphur is produced in the United States, the former Soviet Union, Mexico and France.

Gypsum is a white or clear mineral composed of hydrated calcium sulphate ($CaSO_4 + 2H_2O$). H2 density 2.3. Outside of Iceland it occurs widely in thick beds along with rock salt. In Iceland it occurs as clear, tabular crystals in steam and clay hot springs in solfatara areas such as at Krýsuvík and Námafjall. Gypsum is used for instance in the building industry and in cement production. The mineral *anhydrite* has the same composition as gypsum but is without the water.

Limestone is composed of calcite. Limestone is dealt with in this chapter although it is not a mineral but rather a rock type. It is very common outside Iceland where it forms thick beds and even entire mountains such as in the Alps. It is formed mainly in the sea, particularly from the remains of microscopic remains of animals, calcalgae and organisms such as shells and corals. When uncosolidated it is known as *chalk* (writing chalk) a lot of which occurs in Denmark (Møns Klint)

and England (White Cliffs of Dover). Chalk is largely composed of the calcium shells of micro organisms (foraminifera and coccoliths) and the calcium plates of microscopic coccoliths. Another variety of limestone is *marble* which is coarsely crystallised metamorphosed chalk. The best marble mines in the world are at Carrara in Italy. Yet another type of chalk is *travertine* which precipitates from calcium rich solutions (hard water) where it emerges at the surface in mineral springs and the carbon dioxide evaporates. On boiling, still more chalk precipitates, forming kettle fur. In Iceland chalk coatings are formed around mineral springs such as at Lýsuhóll on the Snæfellsnes peninsula. Limestone is an important raw material in various industries such as in cement production. The Icelandic Cement Factory in Akranes uses chalk obtained from shelly sand deposits on the sea floor in the Faxaflói bay. Chalk is used widely abroad in the construction industry as a dressing stone. It is also used to neutralise acid soils.

Cryolite, sodium-aluminium-fluoride (Na_3AlF), was formerly the chief ore used for aluminium production until bauxite mining began. It was then used in aluminium production by electrolysis from bauxite, but has now been replaced by artificial cryolite. Cryolite is found in pegmatite veins at Ivigtut in western Greenland.

Clay.[4] When ground water containing carbon dioxide and humus acids comes in contact with minerals or rocks, they are gradually dissolved to form clay. Such chemical weathering takes place in warm humid climatic conditions.

In a constantly humid hot climate *kao-*

---

4 Clay here refers to plastic materials which can absorb or release water. Clay particles are smaller than 0.002 mm. What is usually referred to as clay in Iceland is very fine grained rock debris.

lin-clay is formed from acid igneous rocks and gneiss, while light metals such as potassium and sodium. Kaolin or China-clay is mainly used in the ceramics industry and in paper manufacture. Most kaolin occurs in China, Czechoslovakia, Cornwall in England and in the United States. Traces of kaolin have been found in Mókollsdalur in the Strandasýsla district of Iceland.

In hot countries where dry and humid seasons alternate chemical weathering is somewhat different than in a constantly humid and hot climate. When igneous rock weathers under these conditions, the silicate and various metals are removed leaving either an iron rich clay known as *laterite*, or aluminium-rich clay known as *bauxite* which in time can form thick beds. It is named after Les Baux in southern France where there were large bauxite mines. Aluminium was first extracted from these clays in 1821. Large bauxite mines occur for instance in Guyanna in South America, in the United States, the former Soviet Union, Guinea, Ghana, Australia and Indonesia. Aluminium production requires a lot of electricity, the metal being extracted from the raw material using electrolysis. Bauxite is therefore transported over long distances to where there is sufficient electric power, e.g. to the Icelandic Aluminium Plant from Australia.

The bauxite and kaolin being mined today was formed in warmer climates in earlier geological periods especially during the Tertiary.

In fact kaolin, laterite and bauxite are each composed of many clay mineral types which closely resemble mica in crystal structure (thin layers).

Limonite and bog iron ore (limonite, iron oxide with water, FeOOH or $Fe_2O_3H_2O$, iron content 60%) is red-coloured or dark and often unconsolidated. Humus acids, especially in bog water dissolve iron com-

pounds in the rock. They are then mobilised in solution and precipitate as bog iron ore where the solution is neutralised. Bog iron ore is common in Icelandic bogs and was extracted in the first centuries of settlement and up until the 15th century (iron ore smelting) when import of better quality iron began. Limonite occurs in sediments in the Tertiary Basalt Formation of Iceland such as in Önundarfjörður but can not be extracted. Limonite is for instance mined in north-east France, Luxembourg and at Bilbao in Spain. *Rust*, which is formed when iron rusts, has the same composition as limonite.

Siderite, (iron carbonate, $FeCO_3$, iron content 48%) has a vitreous lustre, and is brownish in colour and crystallises like calcite (rhomboidal). It occurs in Iceland at, for instance, Lón, SE-Iceland in association with copper and sulphur minerals, as well as in nodule form in inter basaltic sediments in Steingrímsfjörður. Siderite is either formed directly from magma dikes and veins or where iron has replaced calcium in limestone deposits.

Hematite , (iron oxide, Fe_2O_3, iron content 70%) is a dark or red coloured ore which occurs in large quantities at Kirovoi Rog in Ukraine and at Lake Superior in the United States and Canada. The hematite there occurs in Precambrian rocks and is thought to have been precipitated in a marine environment by iron-fixing bacteria.

Magnetite (iron oxide Fe_3O_4, iron content 72%) is the most economical iron ore for extraction and is mined in large quantities in northern Sweden (Kiruna) and in the Urals (Magnitaja). Magnetite is one of the four main rock forming minerals in basic igneous rocks.

Pyrite, (iron sulphide FeS_2, iron content 46%), often forms cubic crystals, H6, density 5, which are brass-or golden-coloured and thus often mistaken for gold (fool's gold). Pyrite is formed from magmatic

26

fluids i.e. hot aqueous solutions (c.f. the sulphur smell of geothermal springs). Pyrite is common in Iceland wither in calcite or quartz veins or surrounding them, as well as in rocks altered by geothermal heat. Pyrite is weathered rather rapidly to form bog iron ore. Where it occurs in quantity the rock can acquire a brown-or red-coloured sheen on weathering. Abroad, pyrite occurs in quantity and is mined. Extensive mines occur in Spain, Japan and Sicily. Pyrite is mainly used for production of sulphuric acid. Also occurring in association with it, apart from sulphur, are iron, copper, lead, zinc and even gold and other precious metals.

Copper is occasionally found in pure form in rock cavities. It occurs much more often in sulphur compounds in veins in igneous rocks as for instance *copper pyrite* (copper-iron-sulphur, $CuFeS_2$, with 35% copper) from which copper is mainly extracted. It is yellowish in colour, H4, density 4. Copper minerals weather in surface strata, the copper combining with carbon dioxide in the atmosphere to form *malachite* ($CuCO_3$ + $Cu(OH)_2$), a light green mineral used in jewellery or from which copper is extracted. *Spanish green* resembles malachite. In Iceland copper pyrites occurs at Svínhólanáma, Lón, where it is found in veins with other metal ores and has formed from magmatic fluids.

Lead occurs mainly associated with sulphur as galena which occurs in small quantities with other ores in Lón.

Zinc occurs mainly as *zincblende* (ZnS) which is found with other sulphur associated metals in veins formed from magmatic fluids.

Silver occasionally occurs in pure form, but more often in sulphur compounds as silver glance (Ag_2S) which has formed from magmatic fluids .

Mercury although occurring in pure form as a liquid, mainly obtained from a bright red sulphur compound cinnabar (HgS) which occurs mainly around ancient or young volcanoes. Most mercury is produced in Spain at Almaden. Traces of it have been found at eroded central volcanoes in Iceland

Tin occurs mainly as tin oxide (SnO_2, cassiterite) and is found chiefly in veins associated with granite batholiths such as occur in Cornwall. A mixture of tin and copper known as *bronze* was probably the first alloy (successful) to be produced by man and lends its name to a period in the history of mankind, the bronze age which preceded the iron age.

Uranium occurs mainly as *pitchblende* (UO_3 UO_2) which is mainly found associated with other metal ores in ore veins connected with plutonic batholiths and as *uranium compounds* which had precipitated from ground water. Uranium is used in the production of atomic power.

Gold occurs either as elemental gold or mixed with silver and mercury /amalgam) or as compounds with tellurium (gold-silver-tellurium, AuAgTe). Gold is also often mixed in metal ore deposits such as in copper and sulphur pyrite and can be extracted by smelting. Elemental gold is gold-coloured and produces a gold streak. It is soft, easily scratched and pliable. It is therefore easily distinguishable from iron, copper and sulphur pyrite by its softness although the colour can be similar. It is also considerable heavier with a density of 19.4. On mixing with other materials it becomes hard and even brittle. Gold is carried by magmatic fluids from granite plutons and is often found in quartz veins as microscopic flecks and is mined from this source. Gold is also extracted by washing fluvial sand where it accumulates due to its density and reluctance to combine with other materials (Rhine gold). Most gold is mined in South Africa (50% of world production) and the former Soviet Union (25%). Traces of gold have been found in Iceland at Mógilsá, Esja, Þormóðsdalur in Mosfellssveit and Þvottá in Álftafjörður.

Diamonds are composed of pure carbon. They are the hardest of all the minerals, hardness 10 and are also inert (resistant) to most materials. In their pure form they are clear and have a sharp diamond lustre. Clear diamonds refract light and reflect it better than other materials (refractive index 2.4) producing the specturm. They are polished and cut to make the best use of their optical properties. The largest diamond mines in the world are in ancient volcanic feeder conduits at Kimberly in South Africa and are also the deepest mines in the world at about 3000 m depth. When diamonds are coloured by contamination they loose their refractive properties and are used for industrial purposes such as in grinding products and drill crowns. Most industrial diamonds are produced in Zaire. Diamonds are now being produced in research laboratories. Diamonds are found mainly in very ancient, basic igneous rocks and metamorphic rocks as well as in sand and gravel beds where they remain after the weaker rocks have been removed by denudation.

Graphite like diamonds is composed of pure carbon but has a hardness of only 1. The explanation for this difference in hardness lies in the crystal structure. Graphite is black, as is the streak. It occurs mainly in rocks which have been strongly metamorphosed. The main localities are in Czechoslovakia, Ceylon and Madagascar. It occurs quite widely in Greenland as for instance at Julianehåb and Upernavik. Graphite is used for example as a lubricant in bearings, in smelters and in pencils. It is now produced in quantity industrially. Graphite has been found in Iceland in fossilized wood at a volcanic dike in Siglufjörður.

The main classification of rocks

5

The earth's crust is formed of rocks of very varied origin. Most of them are composed of many minerals as for instance basalt which consists of four mineral types i.e. feldspar, olivine, pyroxene and magnetite. Certain rocks are on the other hand composed of only one mineral type such as limestone which is composed of calcite. Rocks are usually consolidated such as sandstone and móberg (pyroclastite), or solidified as for instance basalt, but they can also be unconsolidated such as clay, sand and gravel. Rocks vary greatly in appearance either due to their *internal structure* or grain size or crystal size on the one hand, or to their *external structure* such as bedding, flow banding, or columnar structure.

Rocks are classified into three main groups according to origin.

1. *Igneous rocks* which are formed by solidification of magma, either at depth forming *plutonic rocks*, at shallow depth forming *dike rocks*, or at the surface forming *volcanic rocks* (cf. chapter 6).

2. *Sedimentary rocks* are formed by accumulation of rock debris, sediments or clastic rocks (e.g. sandstone) (cf. chapter 15), by evaporation (e.g. rock salt) or pre-cipitation, *chemical sediment* (e.g. geothermal precipitates), or from organic remains, *organic sediment* (e.g. peat or lignite) (cf. chapter 22).

3. *Metamorphic rocks* which are formed by recrystallisation of igneous or sedimentary rock deep within the earth's crust, especially during fold mountain movements (cf. chapter 12).

The greater part of the earth's crust is formed of igneous rock. It is the primary rock of which other rocks are formed through weathering, erosion or recrystallisation. Down to a depth of 15 km around 95% of the crust is composed of igneous rocks or metamorphic rocks. This ratio is, however, reversed if the dry land surface of the earth is considered, since 75% of the surface rock is sediment or sedimentary rock which forms a thin cover over the igneous rocks or metamorphic rocks. The average thickness of this cover is only 1.5–2 km (cf. chapter 12 and 23).

The main classes of rocks will not be treated here, but in connection with the internal and external conditions prevailing during their formation.

29

Classification and appearance of igneous rocks

6

Magma is a mixture of melted rock and gases which originate in the earth's interior. With solidification of the magma the gas separates while the magma solidifies as *igneous rock*. The internal and external appearance of igneous rocks depends on the conditions of formation and in particular where the magma has solidified (Figure 6-2).

Texture of igneous rocks

The outward appearance of igneous rocks is mainly the result of the molten rock while it was cooling and solidifying, as well as of the external conditions in the final cooling stages.

Flow-banding is produced when viscous magma flows after it has started to solidify. Incipient crystals, glassy granules and small gas bubbles are carried with the magma and are aligned in bands in accordance with the flow direction much like a log in a stream. Rhyolite is frequently flow-banded and its surface often resembles wood as a result (Figure 6-1 and 6-5). Frost weathering causes flow-banded rock to break down into flakes or slabs.

Figure 6-1. Flow-banded rhyolite. (Guðmundur G. Bárðarson 1945.)

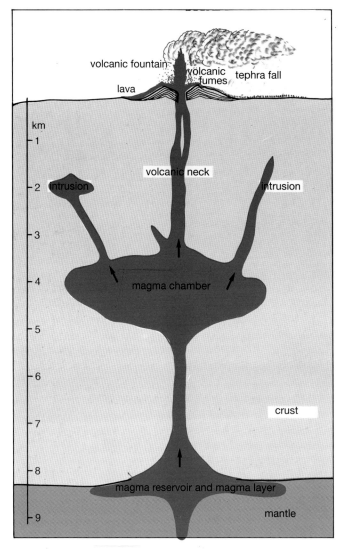

Figure 6-2. Cross section of volcano, magma chamber and magma reservoir or magma "layer". Magma rises from the asthenosphere and accumulates first in a layer or reservoir at the junction of the crust and mantle. It then rises into a magma chamber from which it forces its way to the surface and erupts causing lava flow and tephra fall. Part of the magma is intruded into the rocks around the magma chamber to form plutonic intrusions. (Guðmundur P. Ólafsson 1990 and G.H.I.)

Columns. When the solidification is complete the rock cools gradually and contracts, forming columns which are frequently hexagonal. Columns are always at right angles to the cooling surface and are thus vertical in lava flows and sills (Figure 6-3), horizontal in dikes (Figure 7-16) and radiate outwards from the centre of pillow lavas (Figure 7-7).

Gas cavities. The rapid solidification of volcanic rocks does not give gases suffi-

cient time to escape from the magma before it becomes solid. The magma thus solidifies around the gas bubbles and the rock is *vesicular*. Scoria and tephra in particular are highly vesicular, both being formed from little lava splashes which solidify rapidly. Pumice is so vesicular that it resembles foam and floats on water. In time various minerals precipitate in the gas cavities and if all the vesicles are completely filled the rock is *amygdaloidal*. Gas cavities do not form with the slow

Figure 6-3. Columnar formation. Svartifoss in the Skaftafell National Park, SE-Iceland. Height probably around 10 m. (Photo Gunnar H. Ingimundarson.)

solidification of plutonic rocks, the gases gradually escaping before solidification is complete.

Structure and appearance of igneous rocks

The internal appearance of igneous rocks depends mainly on the manner of solidification.

If the magma solidifies very rapidly by cooling in air or in water, the rock becomes *glassy*. Solidification is then so rapid that the rock can not crystallize. The surface of lava flows and the contact surfaces of sills is thus always glassy. Volcanic ash and pumice are also glassy since they have both solidified rapidly when ejected from volcanoes.

On solidifying slowly on the other hand the rock becomes *crystalline*, the crystals or crystal grains being bigger the more slowly the magma cools (Figures 6-4 and 6-10).

Microcrystalline refers to igneous rock when the crystals are so small as to be indiscernible to the naked eye. This is the case in for example thin lava flows.

Finely crystalline refers to igneous rock in which the crystal grains are sufficiently large to be discernible to the naked eye. The crystals are then more than 1 mm in diameter. Rock in thick lava flows or sills is usually *finely crystalline* e.g. in Reykjavík, Pleistocene interglacial lava flows.

Coarsely crystalline is the term used it the crystals can be easily detected with

Figure 6-4. Granophyre from Flyðrur, Hafnarfjall at Borgarfjörður, W-Iceland. Greatly magnified thin section in polarized light. Actual width only 2 mm. The crystals are mainly feldspar, either pure when they are light in colour and spotted or mixed with quartz and then dark. The multicoloured crystals are epidote formed by the geothermal alteration of the rock. (Photo Sigurður Steinþórsson.)

the naked eye, in which cases they are often several millimetres or centimetres in diameter. Plutonic rocks, e.g. gabbro and granite, are usually *coarsely crystalline* since they have formed deep within the earth where heat loss was slow.

Porphyritic refers to glassy, fine or microcrystalline rocks in which larger crystals of the chief minerals are widely distributed. This applies mainly to dike rocks and volcanic rocks, but also to lavas e.g. the Holocene Þjórsárhraun lava and lavas on Snæfellsnes. The phenocrysts form in the magma deep in the crust and are carried by it to the surface.

Classification of igneous rocks

The two most important factors in classifying igneous rocks are the *silica content* (SiO$_2$) and the *solidification* environment.

According to silicate content igneous rocks are classified as *basic* with less than 52% silica content, *intermediate* with 52–65% silica and *acid* with more than 65% silica content.

Magma solidifies either at considerable

depth as *plutonic rock*, at less depth as *dike rock* or it erupts and solidifies as *extrusive rock*. In keeping with this igneous rocks are classified as shown in the table.

From the table it can be seen that granite, granophyre and rhyolite are formed from acid magma while gabbro and basalt are formed from basic magma. It is only their solidification environment which distinguishes the main groups into subgroups. Of the plutonic rocks granite is most common and basalt of the extrusives.

Granite

Granite is an acid plutonic rock the main minerals being *quartz* (orthoclase) and *mica*, either light (muscovite) or dark (biotite). Granite is always coarsely crystalline (Figure 6-4), while finely crystalline acid plutonic rock is known as *granophyre.* Most of the essential minerals are light, although potassium feldspar is often red and biotite dark. Granite is thus usually light grey or reddish with dark patches.

Granite has solidified as large batholiths deep within the crust. It is most common in formations from the Precambrian era, e.g. in Scandinavia, Scotland, Canada and in Greenland, where erosion has had a long time to remove strata covering the batholiths

Granophyre occurs in Iceland in a few small batholiths and laccoliths but coarsely crystalline granite is however rare. The largest intrusions are in Eystra- and Vestrahorn (Figure 7-12), Reyðarártindur in Lón and Ketillaugarfjall in Hornafjörður, but other smaller examples occur e.g. at Lýsuhyrna on the Snæfellsnes peninsula and at Flyðrur in Hafnarfjall in Borgarfjörður. Granophyre in Iceland is usually found in the same areas as gabbro and generally occurs in intrusions as "layers" of gabbro and granophyre (Figure 6-7).

Classification of igneous rocks

		SiO$_2$-silica content ——>		
		acid >52% SiO$_2$	intermediate 52-65% SiO$_2$	basic <65% SiO$_2$
Site of emplacement	Volcanic rock	Rhyolite	Andesite	Basalt
	Dike rock			
	Plutonic rock	Granophyre/ Granite	Diorite	Gabbro
Rock forming minerals		quartz, orthoclase plagioclase, mica		plagioclase, pyroxene, olivine, magnetite

Granite is resistant to weathering being massive and is therefore used a lot in building as a "dressing" material on walls and floors, as well as for tombstones and suchlike. In warmer and more humid conditions granite breaks down to clay.

Often associated with granite intrusions are dikes of coarsely crystalline "granite" or so-called *pegmatite*, which are formed from magmatic gases or fluids. Sometimes these dikes are almost entirely of feldspar, often of quartz and occasionally of mica. The dikes also often contain metal ores.

Rhyolite

Rhyolite is an acid extrusive rock composed of the same minerals as granite.[5] In Iceland however there is frequently more sodium feldspar than potassium. Rhyolite is usually grey, yellowish or pink in colour and is therefore often conspicuous as light patches on mountains. Mountains indeed often have names which is suggestive of the colour such as Ljósufjöll ("Light mountains"), Hvítserkur ("White gown"), Smjörfjöll ("Butter mountain") and the sun appears to constantly shine on them, even in overcast weather conditions. Rhyolite is always microcrystalline or glassy, vesicular and flow-banded, the bands often being of various colours (Figure 6-1, 6–5 and 6–6). Icelandic rhyolite often contains small phenocrysts, mainly feldspar.

As mentioned above rhyolite is usually light in colour although there are varieties with other colours.

Obsidian is formed when rhyolite magma is cooled rapidly, e.g. on lava surfaces and at the contact surface of intrusions. It is jet black in colour and has a glassy lustre. Obsidian for instance occurs in

---

5 In Iceland it has long been the custom to refer to acid rock as líparít, which is in fact two rock types, dacite and rhyolite.

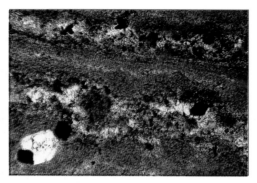

Figure 6-5. Rhyolite from Þingmúli in Skriðdalur, E-Iceland. Thin section in ordinary light, actual width 2 mm. The rhyolite is flow banded, the bands being formed of small crystals, glassy fragments and vesicles which are aligned parallel to the flow. (Photo Sigurður Steinþórsson.)

quantity at Hrafntinnuhraun at Torfajökull and at Hrafntinnuhryggur east of Lake Mývatn.

Pitchstone is another glassy variety of rhyolite which has also formed by rapid solidification. Pitchstone has a greasy lustre, is usually black and resembles coal, but can be greenish or reddish in colour. It is common in rhyolite lavas and at the contacts of intrusions. Sometimes there is so much water in pitchstone glass that it expands on heating to form a glassy foam similar to pumice. Pitchstone of this type is known as *perlite* and is grey in colour. Expanded perlite is for instance used as insulating material. Large quanti-

ties of perlite occur in Loðmundarfjörður and Prestahnúkur in Kaldidalur.

Baggalútar (lava drops or tears) are small spheres which have sometimes formed in groups. They occur here and there in rhyolite and are usually red, grey or green in colour. Being harder then the surrounding rock they become weathered out and can be found in alluvium or on scree slopes, e.g. in Loðmundarfjörður, Álftavík, Húsavík eystra and at Eyri in Hvalfjörður.

Rhyolite lava is usually so viscous that it barely moves and spreads out very little. It thus solidifies either as very thick lava, often 50–100 m thick (Figure 6-8), or builds up as a rhyolite dome (Figure 8-12). In many places rhyolite has intruded older formations to form dikes, e.g. at Grundarmön in Grundarfjörður and at Barnafoss falls on the Hvítá river in Borgarfjörður, or laccoliths, e.g. Sandfell in Fáskrúðsfjörður (Figure 7-14). Sometimes rhyolite magma is so rich in gases that it erupts explosively and forms thick layers of pumice and ash (e.g. Hekla eruption 1104 and Askja eruption 1875) or it erupts as a glowing avalanche (nuée ardente) to form ignimbrite layers.

Rhyolite occurs in all the geological formations of Iceland, mainly in central volcanoes. The amount does vary from place to place the least being in the Vestfirðir (i.e. NW-Iceland) (Figure 6-9).

Compared to basalt lavas, rhyolite la-

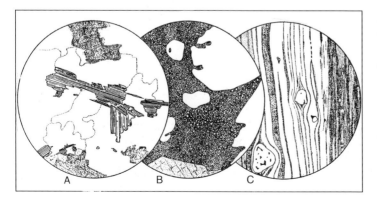

Figure 6-6. Thin sections of acid rocks. A) granite, B) porphyritic rhyolite, and C) flow banded rhyolite. White quartz, mica with strong cleavage, shaded in A and B, feldspar, spotted in B and C, mixture of crystal grains, glassy fragments and vesicles. Actual width around 4 mm. (Baily and Weir 1939.)

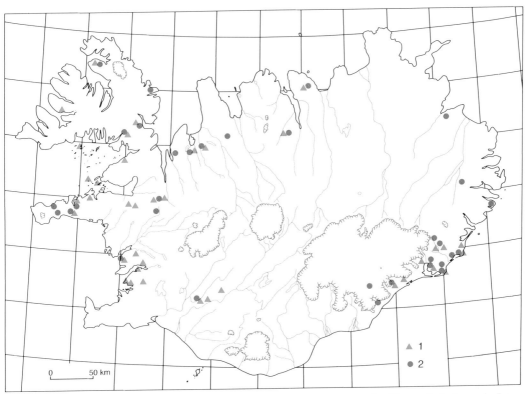

| 1 |
| 2 |

Figure 6-7. Map showing the distribution of plutonic rocks-granophyre and gabbro-main features, in Iceland. Green symbols show gabbro, yellow granophyre. (Þ.E. and G.H.I.)

vas from the Holocene are few. Most are in the Torfajökull area e.g. Hrafntinnuhraun and Laugahraun (Figure 6-8). No rhyolite domes from the Holocene are known with certainty, but Mælifell, above Búðir on the Snæfellsnes peninsula was probably formed after the end of the Pleistocene (Figure 8-12).

In formations from the Pleistocene rhyolite is common as domes, e.g. Hlíðarfjall at Mývatn, or as ignimbrite, e.g. in Þórsmörk, Kerlingarfjöll and the Torfajökull area are the largest rhyolite areas in the country and here it has formed as the result of dome extrusions or explosive eruptions, partly subglacial (Figure 6-8). Móskarðshnúkar in the east of Esja is the remnant of an eroded rhyolite dome from early in the Pleistocene.

Rhyolite is widespread in the Tertiary Basalt Formation and occurs as lava layers (e.g. in Glerárdalur, Oddsskarð and Drápuhlíðarfjall), as volcanic breccia (Súlur in Eyjafjörður) or as ignimbrite (the Skessu bed in Reyðarfjörður).

Frost weathering breaks rhyolite down into slabs of various sizes which are often used for decoration in building. Pumice was used in Iceland as insulating material, but is now exported most being excavated in Þjórsárdalur and at Tröllkonuhlaup on the Þjórsá river (Hekla pumice) and on the sides of Snæfellsjökull. The cement factory at Akranes uses some rhyolite from Þyrill in Hvalfjörður to obtain silicates for its production. Rhyolite aggregate is considered unsuitable for concrete being rich in both sodium and potassium.

Figure 6-8. Landmannalaugur and Laugahraun lava, which is rhyolite (obsidian). The mountains are also composed of rhyolite as their light colour shows. Bláhnúkur (left) and Brennisteinsalda (right) on the eastern side from which the Laugahraun lava was erupted, probably about 1480. (Photo Þ.E.)

Andesite

Andesite is an intermediate eruptive rock and is thus a kind of middle stage between basalt and rhyolite, its essential minerals resembling those of both rocks to some extent. Andesite is always flow-banded, microcrystalline and very dark or black in colour. It is often difficult to distinguish it from dark micro crystalline basalt with the naked eye. Andesite magma is always quite viscous and therefore forms fairly thick lava flows.

A few Holocene volcanoes have erupted andesite, Hekla in particular being worthy of mention since most lavas from the Heklugjá (fissure) (i.e. the true Hekla lavas) are of this composition. Most of the pumice ejected in minor or average eruptions is of andesite, such as in the eruptions of 1947–48, 1970, 1980 and 1991, while in the largest eruptions it has been rhyolite e.g. Hekla 1104. In the Tertiary Basalt Formation and Pleistocene formations andesite is fairly widespread in central volcanoes. Andesite is a common rock type in volcanoes elsewhere in the world, especially in "the ring of fire" surrounding the Pacific.

Plutonic rock formed from intermediate magma is called diorite. It is rare in Iceland but has been found with other plutonic rocks at Lýsuhóll on the Snæfellsnes peninsula (Lýsuskarð). It occurs in large amounts in roots of fold mountains as for instance in Scotland, mid Europe and Norway.

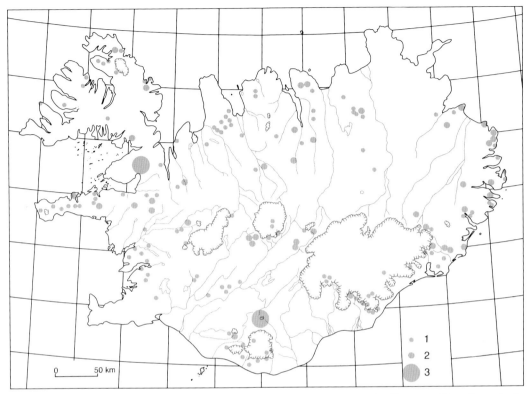

Figure 6-9. Map showing the distribution of rhyolite. Symbols: 1) minor rhyolite areas, 2) medium sized rhyolite areas and 3) major rhyolite areas. (Þ.E. and G.H.I.)

Gabbro

Gabbro is a basic plutonic rock, the main minerals being *plagioclase,* i.e. a mixture of calcium and sodium feldspar, *olivine, pyroxene* (augite) and *magnetite*. Gabbro is always coarsely crystalline. The essential minerals are dark apart from the feldspars and the rock therefore usually dark or greenish in colour.

Gabbro has solidified deep in the earth's crust and forms batholiths or laccoliths which are often to be found in roots of ancient fold mountains, as in Scandinavia and Canada, although to a much less extent than granite.

In Iceland gabbro occurs in a few rather small batholiths or laccoliths and then often with granophyre (Figure 6-9). The largest examples are at Eystrahorn and Vestrahorn in Lón (Figure 7-12), Þorgeirs-fellshyrna and Kolgrafamúli on the Snæfellsnes peninsula. Gabbro is used as dressing stone in buildings.

Basalt

Basalt is a basic extrusive rock with the same minerals as gabbro. Basalt is either micro crystalline and dark or even black in colour, when it is known as diabase or dolerite (in Icelandic *blágrýti* or black stone) or finely crystalline and grey in colour when it is called in Icelandic *grágrýti* (grey stone). Blágrýti is much more common in Iceland than grágrýti.

Grágrýti occurs mainly in lavas extruded during interglacial periods of the

39

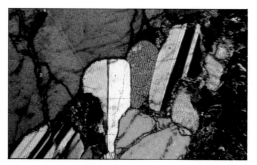

Figure 6-10. Gabbro, thin section of xenolith from Eldfell on Heimaey, thrown up in the 1973 eruption. Thin section in cross polarised light, highly magnified. Actual width 2 mm. The white crystals with black bands are feldspar, the multicoloured crystals olivine. (Photo Sigurður Steinþórsson.)

Figure 6-11. Basalt. Skjaldbreiðarhraun, Þingvellir. Thin section in cross polarized light, highly magnified, actual width 2 mm. The light crystal prisms with black bands are feldspar. Multicoloured crystals are olivine. The black grains are magnetite. (Photo Sigurður Steinþórsson.)

Pleistocene. Most grágrýti lavas erupted from shield volcanoes e.g. Reykjavíkur-grágrýti is from the Mosfellsheiði shield volcano.

Most basalts contain some phenocrysts and are then referred to as feldspar porphyritic (e.g. Þjórsárhraun) or olivine porphyritic (Búrfellshraun near Hafnarfjörður). There are frequently two phenocryst types, usually feldspar and olivine, while occasionally all the essential minerals except magnetite occurs as phenocrysts as in certain Holocene lavas on Snæfellsnes, e.g. Berserkjahraun and Búðahraun.

Basalt magma has a low viscosity and often flows for long distances from the eruptive site, e.g. the great 8000 years old Þjórsárhraun in S-Iceland which is about 130 km in length and with an area of just over 900 km². The longest lava flow in the Laki lavas from 1783 is 60 km in length, these lavas covering 580 km² and having a volume of 12 km³. Basalt lavas are usually rather thin, 10–30 m, and solidify either as pahoe hoe lava (Icel. helluhraun) or as block aa lava (Icel. apalhraun). Basalt is also common in intrusions, mainly dikes and sills.

Rapid cooling of basalt magma, e.g. at dike contacts or on pillow lava surfaces, causes *basalt glass* to form which closely resembles pitchstone in appearance. Lava

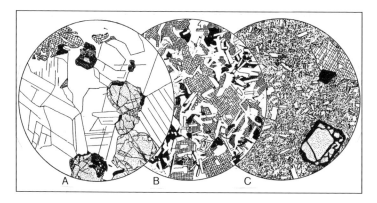

Figure 6-12. Thin sections of basic rocks, highly magnified. A) gabbro, B) diabase, dolerite, C) basalt. White with occasional streaks and needles (in B and C); feldspar, chequered: pyroxene (augite), spotted: olivine and black or dark: magnetite. Actual width about 4 mm. (Baily and Weir 1939.)

bombs, tephra and lava surfaces are always of glassy basalt. Explosive marine or subglacial eruptions as well as vigorous magma fountain activity lead to pumice and ash formation often in large quantities (Surtsey, Katla). Basalt pumice and ash are always dark or black in colour and both are glassy.

Móberg (Hyaloclastites, palagonite tuff). As mentioned, large amounts of basalt ash are formed in subglacial eruptions. During glacial periods of the Pleistocene volcanicity was no less than usual and great masses of pillow lavas and ash were piled up in cavities and fractures in the glaciers, cf. chapter 8. The ash has since generally become altered to *móberg or pyroclastite* a term implying altered, consolidated and cemented ash. Originally the ash was black but has changed to brown. Usually though the ash grains are only altered on the outside and remain fresh within. The altered glass is called palagonite which glues the grains together.

Iceland is one of the largest basalt areas in the world, 80–90% of all igneous rocks in the country being basalt.

The above classification of igneous rocks does not take account of more detailed petrological and geochemical distinctions. Basically, however, Postglacial extrusive rocks in Iceland can be divided into two rock series, the tholeiite-and alkaline series. Volcanic rocks on Snæfellsnes and Vestmannaeyjar belong to the alkaline series, where the most common rock is alkali basalt. Magma in the main active volcanic zone (spreading zone) is rather poor in alkali metals (sodium and potassium) and belongs to the tholeiite series. Basalt in this series is of tow types. on the one had is olivine tholeiite basalt which is mainly associated with eruptions from shield volcanoes. Volcanic rocks on spreading sea floor ridges is similar petrologically. Such basalt is believed to come directly from the mantle and is sometimes referred to as primitive. On the other hand there is tholeiite basalt which erupts mainly in fissure eruptions in the main active volcanic zone. Such magma has probably occupied magma chambers and layers at the mantle crust junction (e.g. Figure 12-6) on its way to the surface. This results in the relative silicate content increasing before the magma erupts. Intermediate and acid volcanic rocks of this series have various names too numerous to mention here.

Types of igneous formations

7

Volcanic materials and formations

When glowing, 1000–1200°C hot magma reaches the surface in eruptions it separates into *volcanic gas* which evaporate mainly in the eruption cloud, and *lava* which either flows from the volcano or explodes as tephra. Volcanic products are therefore often divided into gaseous or *volatile products* (steam, gas), unconsolidated products or tephra and massive solid products, i.e. lava (Figure 6-2).

Gaseous products and volatiles

Gases are a part of the magma and erupt with it. It has proved difficult to collect uncontaminated gas samples from volcanoes. One of the best samples to be collected was taken during the Surtsey eruption in 1964. It contained the following gases: Water (H_2O) 79.2%, hydrochloric acid (HCl) 0.8%, sulphur dioxide (SO_2) 5,4%, carbon dioxide (CO_2) 9.18%, hydrogen (H_2) 4.56%, carbon monoxide (CO) 0.68%, nitrogen + argon (N_2 + Ar) 0.18%. Volcanic gases also contain various fluorine compounds, which cause fluorosis in sheep.

While the eruption is vigorous the gases rush into the air with the eruption cloud, but as it dwindles the gases start to flow downslope along the surface, being heavier than air. This was the case during the Heimaey eruption which began on January 23rd and ended on June 26th 1973. In February the eruption greatly decreased and by the end of the month dangerous gas pollution was evident in the lower part of the town. The pollution was most in March and April and finally stopped in September. During calm weather the gas lay over the lower town like a blue-coloured haze several metres thick. The gas in the town was mainly carbon dioxide (CO_2) 90–98%, but also carbon monoxide (CO) up to 1%, and some hydrogen which reached up to 8%. The gas was fatally poisonous. The gas composition in the town was different from that of the volcano where it resembled that of Surtsey, a result of the fact that sulphur compounds combine with oxygen and moisture in the atmosphere while hydrogen evaporates away. The pollution haze which caused crop failure, loss of livestock and loss of human life during the Laki eruption of 1783–84, was volcanic gas from the Lakagígur fissure. Altogether 75% of the livestock was killed and about 10,000 people died or 20% of the population.

When volcanic gases, especially hydrogen, emerge from escape orifices, they burn at high temperature by combining

Figure 7-1. The eruption cloud from Hekla seen from Vatnsleysuströnd, 120 km southwest of the volcano. The height of the cloud is about 27 km. The picture is taken at 6:59 a.m. on the first day of the eruption, 29th March 1947, or 20 minutes after the eruption started. (Photo Sæmundur Þórðarson.)

with atmospheric oxygen. At such openings close to the eruption craters small but pronounced columns or *hornitos* are thus formed from welded spatter which the burning gases melt from the eruption vent and carry with them. Such hornitos are common on shield volcanoes, e.g. in Surtsey, Kjalhraun and on Selvogsheiði. They can also form in pahoehoe lava. The small craters of Tröllabörn (giants children) at Lækjarbotnar near Reykjavík were formed above a cave in the 4600 years old Leitahraun lava (Elliðaárhraun lava). Part of the gas remains in the magma for long enough to be trapped and form vesicles.

Various *precipitates* often form from the volcanic gases, the most common being beautifully yellow or reddish sulphur compounds.

Magma which solidifies at depth also contains gases, of course. They escape from intrusions while solidification takes place and flow into the surrounding rock as magma gases or fluids to form infilling of cavities or fractures, or metal ore veins.

The eruption cloud is formed of volcanic gases which condense when they enter the atmosphere and produce a cloud column above the volcano. In lava eruptions the eruption cloud is normally small and is probably mainly composed of water vapour and true volcanic gases. Initially however in such eruption the eruption cloud is often quite large since the glowing magma vaporises ground water in the porous layers, especially at the start of the eruption. Thus the eruption cloud from the 1947 Hekla eruption reached a height of 30 km in the first hour. As the eruption continued the cloud became lower and smaller since the volcanic production decreased and the magma had already evaporated much of the ground water at the start. It is also likely that gases collect uppermost in magma chambers during quiescent periods and escape at the start of an eruption. Enormous erup-

Figure 7-2. The Surtsey eruption. Explosive eruption in the northern eruption vent, phreatic eruption in the southern vent. The picture is taken on 21ˢᵗ November 1963. Surtsey was then a week old and 70 m high. The sea was 130 m deep before the eruption which started on 14ᵗʰ November 1963 and continued for 3 ½ years. (Photo Þ.E.)

tion clouds often originate from subglacial eruptions or eruptions in the sea where there are large quantities of water to evaporate. The cloud often reaches as high as the tropopause which is about 10 km over Iceland. In the most vigorous phreatic eruptions eruption clouds can reach the stratosphere, i.e. up to 20–30 km in height (Figure 7-1).

Upward air movement in the eruption cloud can be regarded as a meteorological phenomenon since it is due to the high temperature of the gases. When they have cooled and reached equilibrium with the temperature of the surrounding air the eruption cloud starts to move downwind.

Steam from the eruption cloud often condenses to produce rain or snow showers. Sometimes this precipitation is so much that it mixes with tephra and runs on the surface as mud flows (lahar).

Solid volcanic products

Molten lava either extrudes quietly or explosively from the eruptive vent and flows downslope until it solidifies as lava.

Basalt magma has always such a low viscosity that it frequently flows for tens of kilometres from the eruptive site. in the Surtsey eruption of April 1964 the lava flow reached a maximum of 70 km/hr. On Hawaii lava has flowed 25 km over a period of one hour. In both cases the rates are exceptional being attained only when the lava is as thin as water and the slope of the land great. The usual rate of ap-

Figure 7-3. Pahoehoe lava (helluhraun). Svínahraun (Leitahraun, Elliðaárhraun), at Reykjavík. In the foreground is a ropy surface and at distance is a domed lava surface (tumulus), fractured on the crest. Hengill in the background. (Photo Þ.E.)

pears to be between 1 m/ sec at the start of the eruption and 1 m/min as it continues. Rhyolite magma is on the other hand so viscous that it builds up to form a lava dome (Figure 8-12). Sometimes however rhyolite magma flows to form lavas which are always very thick, often 50–100 m (Figure 6-8). Andesite magma is also viscous and lava flows of this type which reach lowland are quite thick or 10–50 m.

According to appearance lava is classified as pahoehoe lava and aa lava.

Pahoehoe lava or Icelandic *helluhraun* is always on the surface and covered in ropy patterns which have formed in the partly solidified crust on top of the flowing lava. The surface is undulating with many rounded *tumuli*, the crown of which is fractured (Figure 7-3), which form due to lava movement underneath a solidified surface. Magma which solidifies as pahoehoe lava flows in tunnels (caves) from the crater and then often for long distances underneath the solidified lava crust. It then emerges here and there through openings to flow in thin tongues which build up on top of one another. A good cross section through pahoehoe lava can be seen at Almannagjá, Þingvellir. The walls of the chasm consist of a number of thin, columnar flow units extruded in one eruption. Each flow is usually 0.5–2 m thick while the total lava thickness is tens of metres.

From the above it follows that pahoehoe lava often contains many caves. The largest *caves* known in Iceland are the Kalmannshellir cave in the Hallmundarhraun lava which is about 4000 m in length and the Raufarhólshellir cave in the Lambafellshraun lavas (Leitahraun)

Figure 7-4. Lava tunnels in the Hekla lava 1947. (Water colour by Guðmundur Kjartansson.)

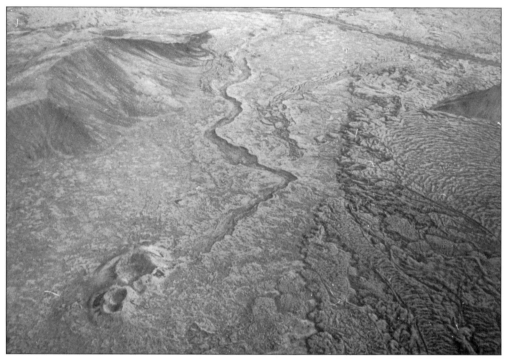

Figure 7-5. Aerial photograph of the edge of the Svínahraunsbruni, an aa lava (apalhraun) on Hellisheiði, SW-Iceland, looking northwards. The youngest lava (right) is covered in arc-like scoria ridges. The older lava (left) was erupted from Nyrðri-Eldborg, which consists of three coalescing scoria craters on a short fissure. From it runs a well-defined lava channel. Both lavas are from early historical times. At the top of the picture can be seen the road from Reykjavík eastwards. Blákollur, a móberg stapi (left) and Lamba-fellshnúkur, a móberg cone with a volcanic plug (right). (Photo M. Schwarzbach.)

of the Ölfus district which is 1360 m long (Figure 7-4).

Lava erupted from shield volcanoes is always pahoehoe in type. Some such lavas are very long and cover large areas. The Bárðardalshraun lava which is erupted from the Trölladyngja shield volcano is about 100 km in length. Other pahoehoe lavas worth mentioning are Þingvalla-hraun, Leitahraun (Svína-, Elliðaár- and Lambafellshraun lavas, Eldá lava of the Mývatn eruption of 1729 (at Reykjahlíð) and the lavas produced during the Krafla eruptions of 1975–84. Pahoehoe lava flows are always basaltic.

Aa lava, also called block lava, (Icelandic *apalhraun*), on the surface is composed of cinders or very porous, unconsolidated volcanic rock which is often a few metres thick while at depth it gives way to coarsely columnar massive lava. Individual aa lava flows are often 10–30 m thick. The magma usually flows out of a break in the crater wall and then flows in channels on the surface. Such channels are called *lava channels* and can be several kilometres in length. There are large lava channels at Búrfell east of Hafnarfjörður (Búrfellsgjá) and at Eldborgir on the edge of the Svínahraun east of the Bláfjöll mountains (Figure 7-5). In aa lavas there are frequently sheets of pahoehoe lava around craters and lava channels.

The lava front of aa lava usually creeps or slides slowly forwards (Figure 7-6). It is covered in slaggy, scoriaceous or clink-

Figure 7-6. A 10 m high aa lava (apalhraun) front moves slowly forwards during the Heimaey eruption. End of January 1973. (Photo Þ.E.)

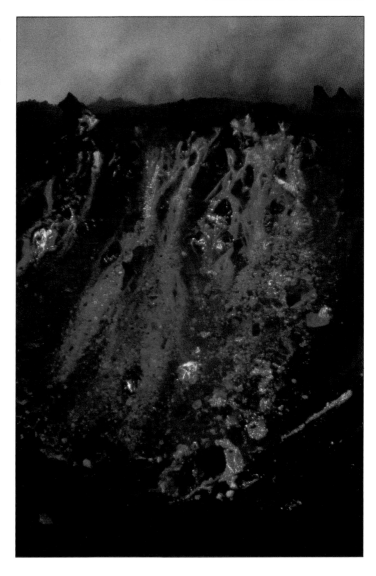

er debris while clinker and blocks constantly collapse from the advancing lava front and disintegrate exposing the glowing interiors. The viscous lava (dough) then creeps over the clinker and covers it. For this reason there is usually a thin clinker layer at the bottom of aa lava.

Aa lava appears to be mainly produced in fissure eruptions. The greatest lava of this type to erupt in the last thousand years is the Laki lava (Figure 8-1) which erupted from the Laki crater row in 1783. It is 580 km^2 and the volume about 12 km^3. Although mainly aa lava, the longest lava flow, Ytra-Eldhraun, is just over 60 km in length. Examples of aa lavas are Kapelluhraun south of Hafnarfjörður, Kristnitökuhraun on Hellisheiði, all of the Hekla lavas, Sveinagjárhraun east of Mývatn from 1875 and the Vikrahraun in Askja from 1961. In other words many basalt lavas and all andesite and rhyolite lavas are of aa type.

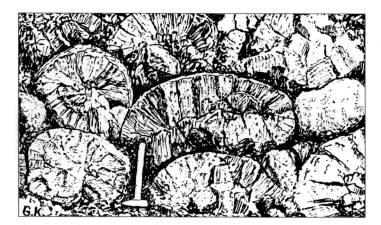

Figure 7-7. Pillow lava from Dyngjur in the Landmannaafréttur district, southern highlands west of Landmannalaugar. The hammer is 40 cm in length. (From a drawing by Guðmundur Kjartansson.)

The reason that some basalt lavas solidify as aa lava while others do not is unknown. Their chemical composition is similar although the magma forming aa lava is probably cooler when it erupts. It is also believed that the amount of volcanic gases is of importance, aa magma being richer in these.

Pillow lava is formed of pillows resembling blown up pillows or bags in appearance. Basalt pillows are usually 0.5–1 m in diameter and elongated. They are often joined together by a narrow neck, the magma having flowed from one to another like toothpaste from a tube. Pillows are glassy on the outside but inside are composed of finely crystalline vesicular rock. They are finely columnar, the columns radiating outwards from the centre (Figure 7-7).

Pillow lavas are formed when magma is extruded from the vent and is cooled suddenly due to the effect of water on the bottom of a lake or in the sea. During subglacial eruptions the magma melts out a cavity or dome in the ice cover and solidifies in meltwater as pillow lava. In pillow lava strata formed in this way the pillows are usually packed closely together. Thus pillow lava in Iceland is mainly found in the lower parts of the Pleisto-

cene móberg (hyaloclastic) mountains. Pillow lava is used as infill material in construction work.

Where andesite or rhyolite magma erupts in water pillows also form. Rhyolite pillows are often many metres in diameter e.g. at Bláhnúkur in Landmannalaugar. In other cases pillow form when lava flows into river channels, lakes or the sea. If the lava flow is slow, cinder and tephra form which then move downslope to form a foundation of dipping foreset beds which builds up the surface and is covered by subaerial lava. Such strata slope rather like gravel layers in delta or offshore deposits. If the lava flow is unhindered the tongues flow downslope and solidify in continuous pillow layers. *Foreset bedded pillow breccia* is quite common in Iceland as for instance underlying the Reykjavík (grágrýti) lavas at Brimnes, at Kjalarnes and underlying the top lava in Hvítárgljúfur canyon at Gullfoss.

Lava domes. Rhyolite magma is often so viscous that it builds up over the eruption vent and sometimes forms a conical lava dome many hundred metres in height. Eruption of this type are termed dome extrusions. The sides are usually very steep and unstable while accumu-

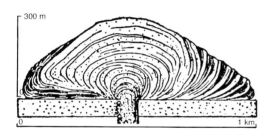

Figure 7-8. Rhyolitic lava dome. They can reach a height of several hundred metres. See Figure 8-12. (Guðmundur G. Bárðarson 1945.)

lation is taking place which makes it difficult to judge the age by appearance alone. The rocks in lava domes are nearly always beautifully flow-banded (figure 7-8). An example of a lava dome is Mælifell at Búdir on Snæfellsnes (Figure 8-12) and Hlíðarfjall at Mývatn. Móskarðshnúkar east of the mountain Esja is an eroded lava dome.

Lava pillars and ignimbrite. In eruptions where the magma is intermediate or acid in composition it can be so viscous that it solidifies in the eruption vent and is blocked by a plug which the magma flow adds to from below while at the same time pushing it upwards. Such obstructions are known as *lava plugs* Occasionally while the eruption is taking place a mixture of volcanic gases and tephra breaks out past the pillar forming a burning hot *glowing avalanche (nuée ardente)* which surges or tumbles down the sides of the volcano. Such glowing clouds often leave thick layers of welded tephra deposits which are termed *ignimbrite or welded tuff.* On their flanks and above or underneath, the deposits tend to be unconsolidated.

No eruptions of this type are known in Iceland from the Holocene. There are thick ignimbrite layers in Pleistocene strata in a few places e.g. in Þórsmörk. The Tertiary lava pile also contains some ig-

nimbrite. One of the most extensive is associated with the mountain Skessa on the southern side of Reyðarfjörður where it appears as a light coloured band which can be traced in the mountain side from the head of Reyðarfjörður and Fáskrúðsfjörður to Breiðdalur and as far south as Berufjörður. It probably originates in an ancient volcano above the head of Breiðdalur valley. The threshold of the Hraunfossar waterfall on the Hvítá river in Borgarfjörður is composed of 2–3 million year old ignimbrite.

In the spring of 1902 the volcano Pelée on the island of Martinique in the West Indies began to erupt after a 50 year interval. During the eruption a 300 m high lava pillar of andesite was built up from the crater but burning hot eruption clouds mixed with glowing tephra burst through the blockage and ran downslope at tremendous speed. One such glowing cloud from the mountain covered the town of St. Pierre destroying it completely and wiped out the population which was around 30,000 before the eruption. A very similar eruption occurred in the volcano Mount St. Helens on the west coast of the U.S.A in 1980. Viscous andesite magma intruded into the mountain and completely blew one side away. Damage was slight in spite of a lot of as fall and mud flow activity.

Tephra or pyroclastic, unconsolidated, eruptive products

When volcanic gases emerge or explode from magma in craters they break off splashes or spatter fragments which are thrown into the air and disintegrate. In flight the lava splashes solidify forming layers of unconsolidated *tephra* when they fall to earth. In flood lava eruptions there is little escape of gas and tephra production is low as a result. In phreatic

Figure 7-9. The Heimaey eruption 1973. Looking across the harbour, the town and new volcano which was later named Eldfell. Helgafell is on the right. Constantly moving lava fountains occur on the eruption fissure. The highest reach 100 m and from them are ejected the scoria and tephra of the eruption cloud. The eruption began just before 2 am on 23ʳᵈ January and lasted for 155 days until 26ᵗʰ June. (Photo Sigurjón Einarsson, 25ᵗʰ January 1973.)

eruptions on the other hand the volatiles escape in such amounts that practically only tephra is produced. In most eruptions however both tephra and lava are produced (mixed eruptions). The tephra is carried various distances from the volcano. The largest fragments either fall back into the crater or accumulate in the immediate vicinity of the volcano, e.g. on the crater walls, while the tephra can be carried for thousands of kilometres by the wind. Tephra is classified into groups according to type and size.

Spatter scoria and cinder are formed mainly when molten glowing magma columns rise tens or hundreds of metres in-

to the air from boiling magma in crater lakes (Figure 7-9). The lava spatter then either falls back into the crater or on the crater rim where it builds up the walls. They fall to earth either solidified to form cinder craters (Rauðhólar, Seyðishólar), or semi solidified when they become flattened and agglutinated in stratified spatter beds. Pseudocraters are also formed of tephra. Sometimes the tephra fall is so great that the accumulated mass creeps as spatter lava. Tephra and cinders are glassy and usually vesicular or even frothy or spongy. The colour of basaltic material is usually black or red, the latter being due to oxidation of divalent iron

Figure 7-10. Lava bombs. (Photo Guðmundur P. Ólafsson.)

compounds to trivalent by atmospheric oxygen while rhyolitic material is grey or white in colour. Cinder or red gravel as it is often known is used as an insulating material and in building blocks, as well as infill material in construction work.

Volcanic bombs are formed when liquid or plastic lava lumps are thrown high into the air. In flight they rotate and become spherical or elongated (Figure 7-10). They are usually glassy on the outside but ve-

sicular inside. Larger bombs either disintegrate on falling to earth or collapse and split, being still hot inside. Smaller bombs on the other hand often maintain their shape being fully solidified when they fall.

Sometimes the volcanic products contain rock fragments which have broken off the feeder conduit deep in the earth. Such fragments are often quite different from the volcanic rocks in which they oc-

Figure 7-11. Tephra eruption in Eldfell on Heimaey 20th April 1973. Looking across the town from the west. The eastern part of the town is buried in tephra. Helgafell is on the right. (Photo Valdís Óskarsdóttir.)

cur and are either found lying loose in the cinders or coated in solidified magma, or incorporated in the lava. They are called *xenoliths* or lithics. In Iceland xenoliths composed of gabbro and granophyre are common and often occur where such rocks are not found on the surface near the volcanoes; as at Víti near Krafla, at Seyðishólar in Grímsnes, Rauðamelskúlur on Snæfellsnes and Grænavatn at Krýsuvík. Sometimes they are sediments as in Surtsey. Xenoliths thus provide information on the nature of the earth's crust and even the mantle.

Pumice is a term used for fragments of frothy, solidified magma foam which is thrown high into the air during erup-

tions, often being carried a great distance from the volcano (Figure 24-25). Pumice is so light that it floats on water but in time becomes saturated and sinks. Near to volcanoes pumice often occurs in thick layers, e.g. the pumice in Tröllkonuhlaup at Þjórsá, 11 km from the top of Hekla is around 10 m thick. In the vicinity of Hekla, the Veiðivötn volcanic area and east of Dyngjufjöll (Askja) the use of the term *vikrar* in Icelandic for large pumice expanses is a direct reference to their composition (pumice = Icel. vikur). Rhyolite pumice is light in colour while basalt pumice is dark. In the past few thousands of years rhyolite pumice has come mainly from Hekla, Snæfellsjökull, Askja (1875)

Figure 7-12. Eystrahorn (Hvalneshorn) at Lón, SE-Iceland, a batholith composed of gabbro (dark screes) and granophyre (light screes). The mountain is scree-covered to half its height. The screes are formed by frost weathering and are composed of rather coarse debris, and as a result are unvegetated. The mountain is 606 m. (Photo Þ.E.)

and Öræfajökull (1362), while the basalt pumice has been produced mainly by Katla and in submarine eruptions. Mýrdalssandur is for instance almost entirely composed of basalt pumice. Pumice and cinder is greatly used in the building industry in building blocks and light concrete, as well as in polishing e.g. in cleaning (scouring) powder.

Volcanic ash refers to the finest dust which can erupt. It is composed of pulverised glass fragments which are usually less than 1 mm in diameter. The tephra is carried upwards in the eruption cloud and is then carried by the wind, sometimes for thousands of kilometres. Tephra from the Hekla eruption of 1947 fell for instance in Finland, from the Askja eruption of 1875 in Stockholm and from the

Laki eruption southwards over Europe. Hekla, Katla and Grímsvötn have been most productive of all the Icelandic volcanoes in producing ash in the Holocene period while Hekla has been the greatest producer of unconsolidated volcanic material in general.

Ash and pumice fall often causes great damage to vegetation and sometimes destroys complete settlements. The most recent example of this was when cinder and tephra as well as lava flow destroyed about one fourth of the town on Heimaey in the 1973 eruption (Figure 7-9). The Hekla eruption of 1104 reduced settlement in the Þjórsárdalur valley and Hreppar district, while the Öræfajökull eruption of 1362 destroyed the Litla-Héraað settlement of 40 farms. This district is

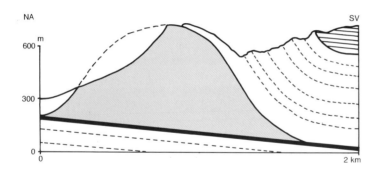

Figure 7-13. Cross section of the laccolith Sandfell in Fáskrúðsfjörður. Clearly shows how the magma has forced its way between the Tertiary basalt lavas and pushed up the overlying beds. The rocks of the laccolith are rhyolite and rhyolitic granophyre (Hawkes 1933.)

now known as Öræfi, or "wilderness". The eruption was also accompanied by catastrophic glacial floods (Icel. jökulhlaup) which caused great damage.

The greatest tephra and pumice eruption in Iceland during the Holocene occurred in Hekla 2800 years ago (H_3) when tephra fell on 80,000 km^2 or 80% of the country, the total amount of newly fallen tephra being about 12 km^3 which is equivalent of 3 km^3 of solid rock. If equally distributed over the entire country the tephra layer would have been 12 cm thick (Figure 24-25).

Tephra layers are useful in geological chronology and in other areas of geological research, forming the study of *tephrochronology* (cf chapter 24).

Through time the tephra and pumice

becomes consolidated as the glass is altered and becomes solid rock, known as *móberg* (i.e. cemented tephra). If this contains a lot of rock fragments it is known as *breccia*.

Plutonic formations

A large part of the magma which comes from within the earth does not reach the surface but solidifies at various depths in the earth's crust as intrusions. It is not possible to observe the manner of formation of intrusions in the same way as extrusive formations since they form at considerable depth. In areas where extensive erosion has occurred it is possible to examine the internal structure of plutonic formations and work out their mode of

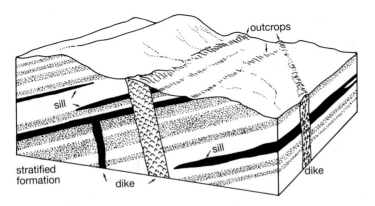

Figure 7-15. Stratified formation with sills and dikes. The stratified formation is oldest, followed by the sills. Dikes shown spotted are youngest, cutting both the other formations.

Figure 7-14. The laccolith Sandfell in Fáskrúðsfjörður. The pushed up Tertiary lavas can be seen on the right, the unaffected dipping beds in the foreground underlie the laccolith. (Photo Bessi Aðalsteinsson.)

formation. Intrusions are classified into several groups according to size and shape.

Batholiths are the largest intrusions and their roots are so deep that the base is not visible. Following erosion of the thick strata under which they have solidified it can be seen that their outline is irregular and the surrounding rock very altered (metamorphosed) and criss-crossed by veins from the plutonic rock. Batholiths vary in size, some being only a few hundred metres in diameter while others are tens or hundreds of kilometres in diameter. A source of debate has long been the question of what has become of the country rock into which the magma has intruded. Some believe that it has been lifted up and then being eroded, but part has sunk into the magma. Others believe that larger batholiths are not intrusions but have been formed by recrystallisation of igneous or sedimentary rocks at high temperature and pressure at the base of fold mountains. Most of the larger batholiths are indeed at the base of old fold mountains, particularly in formations from the older periods of earth history where the agents of denudation have had time to erode the overlaying layers. The base of the sea floor crust appears to be everywhere composed of basic plutonic rock (cf chapter 12).

There are several rather small batholiths in Iceland. The largest occur at Eystrahorn (Figure 7-12), Vestrahorn, Slaufrudalur in the Lón district and in

57

Figure 7-16. Dike at Stöð (Brimlárhöfði) at Grundarfjörður, Snæfellsnes. The dike cuts through the Búlandshöfði beds and overlying lava layers and is almost certainly a feeder conduit to a since eroded volcano. (Photo Þ.E,)

Þorgeirsfellshyrna and Kolgrafamúli on the Snæfellsnes peninsula (Figure 6-7).

The rocks in batholiths are usually gabbro or granite abroad, but in Iceland the acid representative is granophyre and very seldom diorite.

Laccoliths are normally much smaller than batholiths and often only a few hundred metres in diameter and in height. They have formed by intrusion in the upper part of the crust and have pushed the overlaying layers upwards. Sometimes the underlying strata can be observed and it is usually little disturbed (Figure 7-13). Laccoliths are usually composed of rhyolite, granophyre or basalt. Some examples are known in Iceland, e.g. Sandfell in Fáskrúðsfjörður which is rhyolite and one of the most typical laccoliths known (Figure 7-14).

Sills are formed when magma intrudes along bedding planes or through bedded strata. They are frequently concordant with the strata in which they are found (Figure 7-15). In Iceland it is often difficult to distinguish them from lava flows. Sills however usually have glassy contact surfaces and result in red-coloured oxidation of the strata which lie above and underneath. Lava on the other hand only oxidises the underlying layers and are usually cindery or very vesicular on their top surface. Sills vary in thickness from 1–100 m and are often regularly columnar. Thin sills are usually of basalt or rhyolite. Small intrusions can be seen for example in Viðey which lies off Reykjavík as well as underlying pillow lava in some glacial móberg mountains as for example under the cap of the mountain Búrfell in Þjórsárdalur valley.

Dikes and volcanic necks are thin rock layers which have solidified in fractures. They are usually at right angles to the bedding of the country rocks (Figure 7-15 and 7-16). Dikes are very common in Iceland mainly in the Tertiary basalt areas. They are usually rather thin, 1–2 m, but occasionally 30–40 m and are then often in swarms. Dikes are usually glassy on their contact surfaces and often display columnar jointing, the columns being horizontal. Most dikes in Iceland are ancient eruption vents or feeder conduits. They are often very long sometimes being tens of kilometres in length which is hardly surprising since eruption fissures are often of this length. The Laki eruption fissure is for instance 25 kilometres in length. In Iceland dikes are usually composed of basalt but sometimes of rhyolite.

Volcanic necks/plugs are oval or elongated crater-or eruption vents infilled by volcanic materials which often stand out after the volcano has suffered denudation. They are usually composed of dense and mainly non-vesicular rock, with varied columnar joining or, so that they withstand weathering better than the country rock and therefore project as steep peaks. Volcanic necks occur in Iceland e.g. in the mountain ranges between Berufjörður and Breiðdalur and at Þorskafjörður, NW-Iceland (Vaðalfjöll). At Þórðarhöfði and Ketubjörg in Skagafjörður there are funnel shaped necks. Volcanic necks also give rise to conical shaped móberg mountains e.g. Keilir.

Volcanic veins are thin intrusions or network which branch and intertwine irregularly in older rocks and often as extensions from larger intrusions. The outer surfaces are usually glassy while veins often show fine columnar joining. Good examples are to be found at Kleppsskaft and Viðey at Reykjavík as well as in many móberg mountains.

Classification of volcanoes

8

In the last 10,000 years in Iceland volcanic activity has mainly been confined to the two active volcanic zones, i.e. the western volcanic zone which runs from Reykjanes to Langjökull and the eastern volcanic zone, which runs from Vestmannaeyjar right through the country to the peninsula of Melrakkaslétta in the northeast. In the south of the country the eruption fissures run from southwest to northeast, while in the north they lie in a north south direction. There is a smaller lateral volcanic zone on the Snæfellsnes peninsula which runs from Grábrók in the Norðurárdalur valley to Snæfellsjökull. The eruption fissures in this zone strike from eastsoutheast to westnorthwest. Öræfajökull in SE-Iceland is an isolated volcano lying outside the volcanic zones (see Figure 8-1).

Lavas erupted in the last 10,000 years in Iceland cover about 10,000 km^2 (10% of the country) and altogether around 400 km^3 of volcanic products have been produced. Eruptions have probably occurred at 5 year intervals i.e. about 20 eruptions on average every century .

Volcanic activity in Iceland is connected with its position on the mid oceanic Atlantic Ridge which is part of a continuous spreading seafloor ridge system. Here new crust is continually formed as the plates drift apart. Magma from the mantle solidifies as intrusions in the fractures or erupts as extrusive volcanic rock. Iceland lies at the constructive plate margin between the North American and Eurasian plates which drift in opposite directions approximately 1 cm per year i.e. eastwards and westwards as the fracture system in the volcanic belts (drift belts) shows. Volcanic activity and production on mid ocean ridges is not equally distributed but is most on so-called hot spots. One such hot spot occurs under Iceland and nowhere else on earth does so much magma per unit of time reach the surface in eruptions. The characteristics of divergent plate boundaries are nowhere more clearly observable than in Iceland as fracture swarms and volcanoes in the volcanic belts. Within the volcanic belts fracture formation and volcanic activity is not evenly distributed but limited to certain areas or so called volcanic systems.

The volcanic belts can be divided into about 30 *volcanic systems* which can often be delimited petrologically, i.e. according to the chemical composition of the volcanic products (Figure 8-2). Each volcanic system either extends over a limited fracture swarm and associated volcanoes, e.g. the shield volcanoes on the Reykjanes

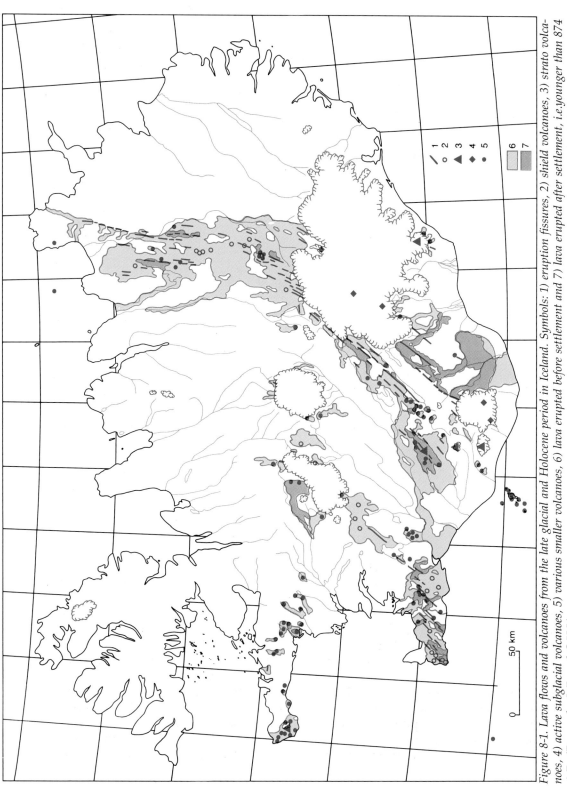

Figure 8-1. Lava flows and volcanoes from the late glacial and Holocene period in Iceland. Symbols: 1) eruption fissures, 2) shield volcanoes, 3) strato volcanoes, 4) active subglacial volcanoes, 5) various smaller volcanoes, 6) lava erupted before settlement and 7) lava erupted after settlement, i.e.younger than 874 A.D. (Drawn by B.E. and G.H.I.)

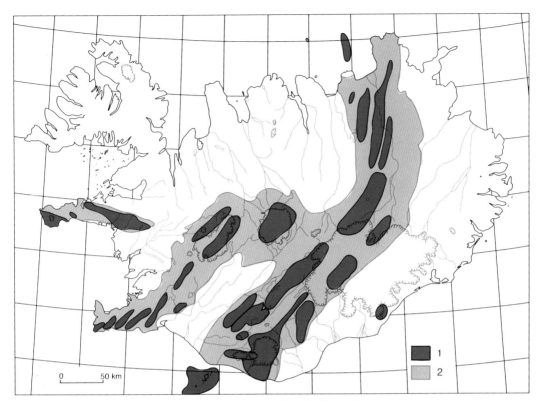

Figure 8-2. Active volcanic systems in Iceland. Symbols: 1) individual volcanic systems and 2) active volcanic zones. (Drawing by Þ.E. and G.H.I., based mainly on Sveinn Jakobsson, 1979.)

peninsula and the crater rows of Stampar and Eldvörp, or a central volcano and a fracture swarm associated with it, e.g. Krafla and the crater rows and fracture swarms south and north of Leirhnjúkur at Mývatn (Figure 8-8), or a strato volcano and volcanoes associated with it, e.g. the ridge-shaped strato volcano, Hekla. Each volcanic system can be many kilometres or even tens of kilometres in length and several kilometres in breadth. The Hekla system is for instance probably about 40 km in length and 5–7 km wide. The Heklugjá fissure itself is just over 5 km in length and the volcanic ridge of Hekla has been built up on it to a height of 1500 m in tens of eruptions during the Holocene period (Figure 8-9).

Volcano refers to a site where magma reaches the earth's surface. Around the eruptive vent the *volcanic structure* is built up and successive eruptions lead to the formation of *volcanoes*.

Until recently Icelandic volcanoes were regarded as being active if they had erupted after the settlement i. e. during the last 1100 years. Helgafell on Heimaey in the Vestmannaeyjar archipelago off the south coast, was for instance not regarded as being active since it had not erupted for 5000 years. Following the eruption of Eldfell in 1973, which is in the vicinity (Figure 7-9 and 7-11), it was obvious that the definition needed revision to include as active, all volcanoes which had erupted in the last 10,000 years.

Volcanic activity has been more varied in Iceland than in any other area of equal

63

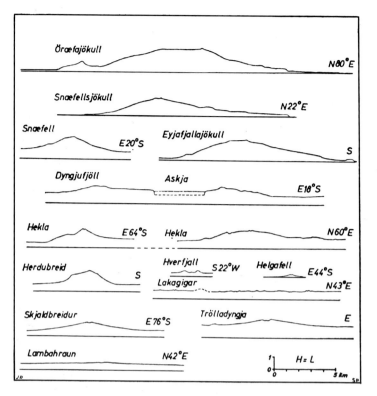

size in the world. Here there are nearly all the known types of volcanic structure and volcanoes. The environmental conditions of eruption in Iceland are also more varied than elsewhere, which have a great effect on the nature of the eruptive products and the shape of craters and volcanoes.

The classification of volcanoes which follows applies mainly to those in which basic magma (basalt) or andesitic magma erupts and only to some extent applies to those which erupt acid magma (rhyolite). The classification is in no way all embracing since on some eruption fissures there are many types of volcanic forms (Figure 8-6).

Three factors most affect the shape and size of volcanic structures and forms which are formed in eruptions on dry land: the shape of the eruption vent, the type of eruptive products and the number of eruptions and finally the amount of eruptive products and the eruption mechanism.

Eruptive vents are either *elongated* (fissures) or *circular* (point). In fissure eruption however it is common for the volcanic activity to be restricted to one place as the eruption progresses.

Volcanic products consist either of layers of lava or pyroclastic tephra or both. In *flood eruptions* only lava is produced while in *explosive* eruptions only tephra is produced. In most eruptions however both are produced, *mixed eruptions*.

An example of an explosive eruption is the Askja eruption of 1875, where in a spell of a few hours about 2 km^3 of pumice and ash were produced or the equivalent of 0.5 km^3 of solid rock. The Hekla 1947–48 eruption may be regarded as a typical mixed eruption and it produced 0.8 km^3 of lava and 0.2 km^3 of tephra, cal-

Figure 8-4. Lava shield volcano forming on Surtsey. The lava is flowing from the crater in countless tunnels and emerging from them as lava springs mainly at the lava surface and newly forming sea cliffs. Looking from the southwest 16ᵗʰ November 1964. Heimaey in the background on left. (Photo Sigurjón Einarsson.)

culated as as solid rock. Purely flood or lava eruptions occur mainly in shield volcanoes and sometimes in eruption fissures. Examples of the latter type are the Laki eruption of 1873, when 12 km³ of lava and about 0.25 km³ of tephra were produced in the 9 eruptions in the Krafla area in 1975–84. The lava covered about 36 km² and the amount of eruptive products 0.25 km³, tephra being practically nothing (Figures 8-8 and 8-11).

The number of eruptions is of great importance to the type of craters and volcanoes. Frequent eruptions in the same volcano produce high mountains which are usually composed of alternating lava-and tephra beds (strato volcanoes, volcanic ridges). If only a single eruption occurs on the other hand, which is very common

in Iceland, the craters and volcanoes are rather low.

Amount of eruptive products and eruption mechanism are of great importance to the shape and type of the volcanic structure. In lava – or mixed eruptions the products build up around the eruption vent producing volcanic structures of various types (Figure 8-3). In vigorous explosive eruptions the products are often thrown high into the air with great force and only build up to a small extent around the eruptive vent (Figure 19-1). Among the best formed are volcanoes produced in weak eruptions.

Shield volcanoes are flat and regularly shaped lava shields formed of thin lava produced in flood eruptions when low

		SHAPE OF ERUPTION VENT	
		Circular	Elongate
Type of eruptive products	LAVA (flood eruption)	*Shield volcano* Example: Skjaldbreiður	
		Spatter ring crater Example: Eldborg í Hnappadal	
	LAVA AND TEPHRA (mixed eruption)	*Scoria and cinder crater* Example: Búðaklettur og Rauðakúla	*Scoria and spatter crater row* Example: Lakagígar and Berserkjahraunskúlur
		Strato volcano Example: Snæfellsjökull	*Linear strato volcano* Example: Hekla
	TEPHRA (phreatic and exlosive eruption)	*Tephra crater* Example: Hverfjall	*Tephra crater row* Example: Vatnaöldur
		Explosion crater Example: Grænavatn	*Explosion crater row* Example: Veiðivötn *Explosion chasm* Example: Valagjá

viscosity lava erupts through a circular vent for months or years at a time. It may also be that such shields are formed by repeated eruptions from a circular vent. Probably shield volcanoes have initially been fissure eruptions in which the activity has become restricted to one place as the eruption progressed. The slope is usually slight, usually less than 8°. At the shield summit there is usually a large crater bowl surrounded by a low crater rim of lava crust. Usually lava has not flowed out of the crater over the rim but rather the magma has flowed out of the vent through tunnels or caves for long distances under the solidified crust, emerging here and there as lava springs. The lava tongues have then solidified as thin pahoe hoe lava beds (Figure 8-4). Shield volcanoes thus consist of many overlapping thin flows, as for instance the Skjaldbreiður lava in the chasm of Almannagjá (the ancient parliament site). In shield volcano eruptions practically no tephra is produced since fountain activity is very little. Altogether 20–30 shield volcanoes have been active in Holocene time, most of them in the Reykjanes-Langjökull area, as

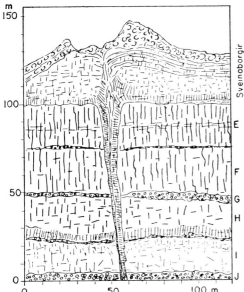

Figure 8-5. Section through the Sveinaborgir cra-ter row as it appears in the eastern wall of the ca-nyon of the Jökulsá á Fjöllum river at Hafragils-foss, just north of Dettifoss, NE-Iceland. The beds E-J are lavas and sediments from late Pleistocene interglacial periods, while a feeder dike cuts through them upwards to the crater row which erupted in the early Holocene period. (Sigurður Þórarinsson 1981.)

for instance Heiðin há, Selvogsheiði and Skjaldbreiður. There are also many shield volcanoes in the Ódáðahraun lava area in middle N-Iceland of which Trölladyngja and Kollóttadyngja are the biggest. Trölla-dyngja (1410m) and Skjaldbreiður (1060 m) are the largest shield volcanoes in Ice-land rising 600–750 m above their sur-roundings, while the amount of eruptive materials from each is around 15 km³. Most shield volcanoes are of early Holo-cene age, Skjaldbreiður being at least 9000 years old and Trölladyngja more than 7000 years. The youngest shield volcano is the lava cap on Surtsey, which was formed 1964–1967 (Figure 8-4).

Also of shield volcano type are a few volcanoes which have erupted during in-terglacial periods of the Pleistocene, such

as Mosfellsheiði, Ok, Vaðalda and Grjót-háls.

Outside of Iceland shield volcanoes are rare except on Hawaii. The shield volca-noes Mauna Loa and Mauna Kea have coalesced, rising from a sea floor depth of 5000 m to over 4000 m above sea level. They are thus in reality around 9000 m high and have formed in repeated erup-tions over a long period of time.

Spatter ring craters (Icel. eldborg) are formed when lava of low viscosity erupts from a circular vent or short fissure in rather short lived eruptions with little or no lava fountain activity. Steep crater walls of very thin lava crust are formed around the vent when lava splashes from the boiling lava lake, while a very low dome of pahoe hoe-or aa lava surrounds the volcano. Eldborg on the flanks of the mountain Geitahlíð east of Krýsuvík and Eldborg in Hnappadalur, Snæfellsnes, are typical examples.

Scoria and cinder craters are the result of mixed eruptions in circular vents or short fissures. Fountain activity in the crater throws lava lumps into the air which land as either half solidified lava splashes which flatten out to form welded scoria walls, or almost completely solidified to form cinder craters. Usually the lava flows through a break in the crater wall and then for long distances in lava chan-nels. An example of a scoria crater is Eld-borgir on the edge of the Svínahraun lava east of Bláfjöll (Figure 7-5) while Rauða-kúla on Snæfellsnes and Eldfell on Heimaey are examples of cinder craters.

Crater rows. In Iceland fissure eruptions are very common and have been from the beginning of the country's geological his-tory in the Tertiary period. Classification of volcanic structures on fissures is diffi-cult especially since the several types of-ten overlap.

67

Figure 8-6. Lakagígar crater row. Looking northeastwards along the crater row. The móberg mountain Laki is in the centre of the picture. In the foreground is a tephra ring crater (of Hverfjall type) while other craters visible are either cinder or scoria craters. (Photo Þ.E.)

Eruption fissures vary greatly in length, one of the longest being the Laki fissure which is about 25 km in length (Figure 8-6). It erupted over the entire length in the summer of 1783, although not everywhere at the same time. A common feature of fissure eruptions is that different sections erupt at different times during the same eruption. On the 8th June the southwestern part of the fissure began to erupt and the lava flowed into the channel of the Skaftá river and spread out over the lowlands in Síða, Skaftár-tunga, Meðalland and Landbrot. These lavas are known as Ytra-Eldhraun. At the end of July the northeastern part of the fissure erupted and the lava followed the Hverfisfljót river course and spread out over the lowland in the eastern parts of

Síða and in the Fljótshverfi area. This part of the lavas is known as Eystra-Eldhraun (Figure 8-1).

Purely flood lava eruptions on fissures are rather rare, since lava fountain activity is common and results in the build up of spatter scoria and cinder cones or craters straggling along the eruption vent and forming a crater row (Figure 8-6). Occasionally however the magma flows quietly from almost the entire length of the fissure in which case a scoria and cinder wall is absent but a long low rim forms on the side opposite to that from which the lava flows. Few such *lava fissures* are known in Iceland, but examples are those of the eruption fissures in the Krafla fires of 1975–84 at Mývatn (Figure 8-8). It should be noted in this connection

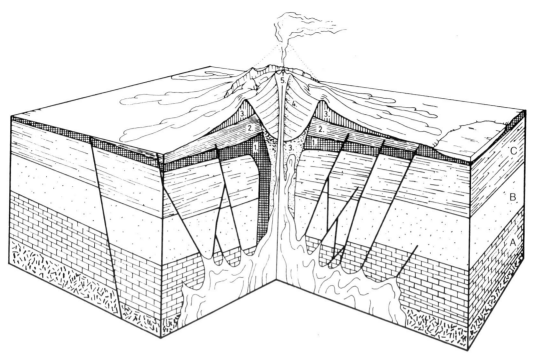

Figure 8-7. Section through the strato volcano Vesuvius. The lower part of the mountain was formed in the early Holocene (series 1, 2 and 3). In the eruption in 79 AD the top of the mountain exploded (hatched) forming a large caldera which has since been filled by volcanic products (4 and 5) as activity continued, most recently in 1944. A magma chamber is shown deep in the bedrock which is in sedimentary beds from the Triassic (A)-Cretaceous (B)-and Tertiary periods (C). The caldera rim (Mt. Somma) is 1132 m high, the present crater rim 1276 m. (Rittmann.)

that Eldgjá in the Skaftártunga district can hardly be regarded as a lava fissure but rather that the wide chasm itself was probably formed by downfaulting. Probably an eruption took place over its entire length of at least 40 km around the year 930. A great amount of lava has erupted from Eldgjá e.g. in Landbrot and on Mýrdalssandur, probably 700 km².

Usually lava fountain activity or even explosive activity accompanies lava flow resulting in a *mixed eruption* and producing the commonest type of Icelandic volcano, *the scoria and cinder crater row*. The volcanic cones then form either a continuous crater row along a fissure, or a discontinuous row with crater groups at various intervals. The Laki crater row which is 25 km in length (Figure 8-6), consists of just over 100 craters, the highest being about 100 m. Other examples of spatter and scoria-crater rows are Þrengsla- and Lúdentsborgir at Mývatn and of cinder crater rows Berserkjahraunskúlur, Grábrókargígar, Seyðishólar and Eldfell and the crater row south of it on Heimaey.

A large amount of lava has flowed from fissures, the Laki lava which erupted from the Laki crater row in 1783–84 being the greatest lava to have been witnessed directly in recent centuries. The longest lava flow, Ytra-Eldhraun is about 60 km long and the total area of lava about 580 km².

Lava from fissures usually solidifies as aa lava. The fissure lavas from the Krafla

69

Figure 8-8. The Krafla fires, 1975–84. An eruption on a fissure north of Leirhnjúkur on 8ᵗʰ September 1977. Low viscosity lava flows to both sides. Looking southwards. The steam columns rising in the foreground at Leirhnjúkur, those furthest away at Bjarnarflag in the Námafjall geothermal area with the diatomite factory and small steam power plant. (Photo Sigurður Þórarinsson.)

fires of 1975–84 were though mainly pahoe hoe lava.

Strato volcanoes. Repeated mixed eruptions at various intervals from a circular vent gives rise to a massive conical volcano or *strato volcano*. They are built up of alternate lava and tephra beds. Magma which erupts in strato volcanoes or volcanoes related to them varies in composition, i.e. basic, intermediate or acid (basalt, andesite or rhyolite). Strato volcanoes are the commonest of all volcanoes outside of Iceland, well known examples being Mt. St. Helens, Fujiyama, Etna and Vesuvius (Figure 8-7). In Iceland only four strato volcanoes have erupted in the Holocene: Snæfellsjökull, Öræfajökull, Eyjafjallajökull and Tindafjallajökull.

As mentioned earlier there is normally only one eruption on the same fissure, although there are exceptions which produce *linear strato volcanoes* (Figure 8-9). They are elongate parallel to the fracture orientation but pyramidal in cross section. Hekla is the best known of all such volcanoes and is built up of lava and tephra beds in repeated mixed eruptions from the Heklugjá fissure which is just over 5 km in length and runs from southwest to northeast. In large eruptions the fissure opens along its entire length and a crater row forms on it as the eruption progresses.

In the last few thousands of years Hekla has either erupted acid or intermediate magma while nearby volcanoes have erupted basic magma. The silica

Figure 8-9. Looking from the south over Hekla three days after the start of the eruption on 17ᵗʰ January 1991. The eruption started at the southern end of the Heklugjá (fissure) and in a few places on the flanks of the volcano. The eruption shown is on the eastern flanks and lasted for 50 days. Lavas covered just under 30 km² and the volume was around 1.5 km³. (Photo Ágúst Guðmundsson, 19ᵗʰ Jan. 1991.)

acid content of Hekla magma varies, being more acid the longer the period between eruptions. It is believed that the magma is differentiated in magma chambers between eruptions (Figure 8-7). The composition of the magma at the start of Hekla eruptions is also more acid than at the end.

It is generally believed that there are magma chambers underneath strato volcanoes (Figure 8-7). Seismic observations connected with volcanic activity in the Krafla area which began in the latter part of 1975, suggest that there is a magma chamber at 3–7 km depth under the area of the Leirhnjúkur mountain. Magma appeared to be filling the magma chamber from below and when it was almost full it caused the roof of the chamber to lift. The magma then moved underground every so often from the chamber along the fracture swarm accompanied by subsidence to the north or the south underground, a process involving *horizontal diking by magma surging from the magma chamber,* or it reached the surface in eruptions. Altogether there were 20 seismic events with 9 eruptions in the years 1975–1984. Eruptions and horizontal diking by magma surging from the magma chamber in the Krafla area were accompanied by considerable seismic activity. During and after intrusion and eruptions the area around Leirhnjúkur subsided by 1–2 m but rose between events due to magma filling from below (Figures 8-8, 8–10 and 8–11).

At the summit of many strato volcanoes are many subsidence features or *cal-*

71

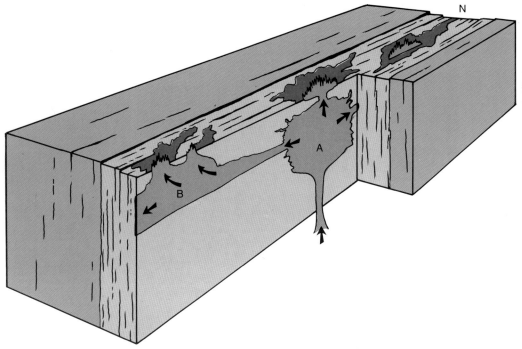

Figure 8-10. A) Magma chamber and B) lateral magma dike intrusion in the Krafla area. The fractures are ori-entated north-south. Magma from the magma chamber follows the fractures to the south and north reaching the subsurface in eruption fissures on the surface from which lava flows. The subsurface magma is shown in orange, the surface lava red. The arrows show the direction of flow. (Drawing Páll Imsland.)

deras. They are either caused by the top of the mountain exploding in phreatic or explosive eruptions (e.f. Vesuvius eruptions 79 AD), or the roof of the magma chamber gives way and collapses when the chamber empties in eruptions. The caldera in Dyngjufjöll was formed in this way following the Askja eruption on 29th March 1875. This caldera is now occupied by the deepest lake in Iceland, Öskjuvatn, which is 220 m deep and 11 km[2] in area (Figure 19-1). At the summit of Öræfajökull a large crater about 5 km in diameter is probably a caldera filled by glacial ice.

Ash and explosion craters. Explosive eruptions produce purely tephra and volcanic gases. The tephra is either composed of ash and pumice and occasionally only rock fragments which have ac-companied steam and volcanic gas explosions from feeder conduits.

Weak phreatic eruptions from circular vents produce *ash or tephra craters*, also called tuff rings which are almost entirely composed of bedded tephra, mostly ash and pumice. One of the best examples is Hverfjall at Mývatn. The crater here is about 1000 m in diameter and the crater rim stands 100–150 m above the surrounding land, the crater bowl being of a similar depth. Hverfjall can be shown to be about 2500 years old by tephrochronology.

Explosive eruptions on fissures produce *ash or tephra crater rows*. The Vatna-öldur craters in Tungnaáróræfi are an example and erupted during the settlement period, probably around the year 900.

If on the other hand the explosive eruption is violent then the products are

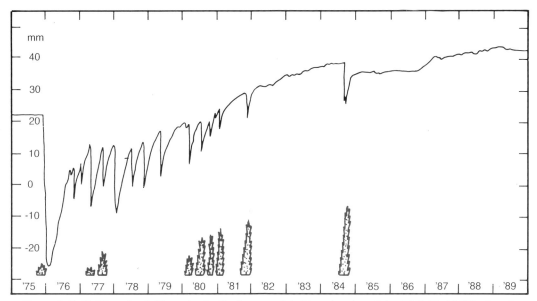

Figure 8-11. Uplift and subsidence in the Krafla area related to volcanic activity 1975–89. Uplift when the magma chamber is filling, subsidence when it empties with dike intrusions or eruptions, which are indicated on the diagram. Based on clinometer measurements in the power station. (Information from Eysteinn Tryggvason. Drawing G.H.I.)

thrown high into the air and practically no crater walls accumulate around the vent (cf. Víti in Askja, Figure 19-1).

In some explosive eruptions the main products are steam and volcanic gases. Little true tephra is produced but frequently deep crater depressions are formed. They are often filled with water and are so deep that they reach below the water table. The crater walls are low and usually of scoria and rock fragments which has been ripped from the feeder conduit. The latter fragments can be very large. The international term for volca-

Figure 8-12. The rhyolitic lava dome Mælifell at Búðir on the Snæfellsnes peninsula is probably of Holocene age since the landscape appears to have reached its present state when it was formed. Looking northwards from Búðir. The Búðahraun lava is in the foreground. (Photo Þ.E.)

73

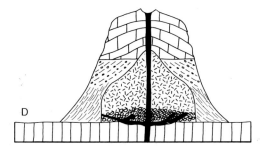

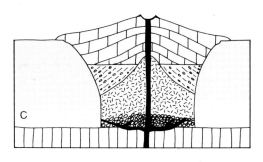

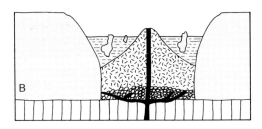

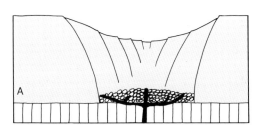

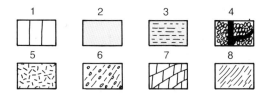

Figure 8-13. Diagram explaining the subglacial build-up of a móberg (hyaloclastite) mountain. Symbols: 1) bedrock, 2) glacial ice with crevasses, 3) meltwater, 4) pillow lava with dikes and sills, 5) móberg i.e. hyaloclastite, 6) foreset bedded pillow breccia, 7) lavas and 8) screes. Detailed explanation in text. (Drawing Þ.E. and G.H.I.)

noes of this type is maar. A good example of an *explosion crater* (circular vent) is Grænavatn in Krýsuvík which is about 300 m in diameter and 44 m deep. Other examples are Kerið in Grímsnes, 7–14 m deep (the lake surface is variable according to the water table level) and Ljótipollur in Landmannaafréttur (water depth 14 m).

Explosive eruptions on fissures leads either to the formation of *tephra crater rows*, such as Veiðivötn, or *explosion chasms* such as Valagjá east of Valafell to the northeast of Hekla.

Volcanic structures which are composed of tephra are usually bedded since the eruption usually takes place in continuous pulsating events with a frequency of tens of waves per minute or with individual explosions. The bedding dip from the vent varies being most in ash-and tephra craters, or 25–35°.

Rhyolitic dome extrusions

The foregoing classification only partly applies to volcanoes where rhyolite magma is produced mainly because it is much more viscous than basalt. Volcanoes which erupts rhyolite tephra on the other hand fall into the classification. Because of its viscosity, rhyolite magma often builds up over the feeder vent and there is little flow from the volcano. Such eruptions are termed *dome extrusions* and lead to the formation of *rhyolite domes* which can be extremely large, often several hundred metres in height. Even while extrusion is taking place the domes are covered by actively forming screes and it is therefore often difficult to assess their age

Figure 8-14. Three mountain types seen from Hagafell south of Langjökull. The table mountain (Icel. stapi) Hlöðufell (centre) and móberg ridges Þórólfsfell (right) and Skriðutindar (left). In background (right) Skjaldbreiður. In foreground (right) western Hagafellsjökull, Lambahraun and Hagavatn (left) (see Figure 24-14). (Drawing Guðmundur Kjartansson.)

by appearance. No domes of Holocene age are known with certainty in Iceland, although the dome of Mælifell near Búðir on Snæfellsnes is rather recent and probably of Holocene age (Figure 8-12). An example of a Pleistocene rhyolite dome is Hlíðarfjall at Mývatn. Rhyolite extrusions usually take place on short fissures or from circular vents so that their base is either circular or elongated.

Subglacial eruptions

The main *volcanic structures* resulting from eruptions on dry land have now been dealt with. It remains to examine those volcanoes which erupted underneath glaciers or in the sea.

In the last few centuries there have been at least four volcanoes active underneath glaciers: Öræfajökull (1362 and 1727), Eyjafjallajökull (1821–23), Katla (twice every century on average) and Grímsvötn (at 10 year intervals in the last few centuries, up until 1934). These eruptions are explosive or phreatic and are accompanied by *jökulhlaup* or catastrophic floods. The products are almost entirely tephra, especially pumice and ash. Nothing is known about the type of volcanic structure below the glacier ice but many have ice filled calderas. The móberg mountains, which were formed by sub-

glacial eruptions during the Pleistocene, give a good idea of their nature and their method of formation.

Móberg or palagonite tuff mountains: hyaloclastite ridges and table mountains. When magma reaches the surface through a fissure or circular vent underneath several hundred metres of glacier ice, it melts a cavity in it while on the glacier surface a depression forms accompanied by huge crevasses. In major eruptions a hollow is melted in the ice above the volcano, forming a depression on the glacier ice surface marked by crevasses. This then fills to about 9/10 with meltwater, being limited by the fact that the glacier floats upwards if the water depth is greater and the water can escape as a jökulhlaup (flood). As long as the water pressure above the volcano is sufficient pillow lavas accumulate in the hollow and if the eruption ceases at this stage a *pillow lava ridge* is formed (Figure 8-13). A good example is Sigalda on the Tungnaá river. If the eruption on the other hand continues, then the water depth decreases due to the accumulation of volcanic material in the depression and the pillow lavas can not form, the water pressue being insufficient to contain the steam and volcanic gases. The eruption then changes to being phreatic or explosive and tephra, either pumice, ash or

75

Figure 8-15. Surtsey seen from the southeast. The sea floods the crater causing explosive eruption. Ash laden explosive cloud about 250 m in height. Every "finger trail" corresponds to a lava bomb. (Photo Þ.E., 12ᵗʰ December 1963.)

breccia piles up on top of the pillow lavas. If the eruption stops at this stage the result is an hyaloclastite ridge *(móberg ridge)* of which good examples are Sveifluháls near Krýsuvík, Kálfstindar to the east of Þingvellir, Jarlhettur near Langjökull (Figure 24-14) and Möðrudalsfjallgarður, NE-Iceland. The equivalent formation in the case of a circular feeder vent is an hyaloclastite cone *(móberg cone)* of which Keilir is a good example. If the eruption continues still further, the crater walls build up above the water level thus preventing the water from reaching the magma and quenching it with the associated phreatic eruption. The formation of unconsolidated volcanic products then largely ceases and lava starts to flow from the crater, filling the depression to the top and even flowing out over the glacier surface. If the tephra crater walls are flooded by water the lava builds up to the surface with foreset bedded pillow breccia which is then overlain by lava sheets after which lava can flow like on land. Hyaloclastite mountains which have reached this stage are known as *table mountains (Icelandic stapi)* and they form some of the most spectacular mountains in Iceland, such as Eiríksjökull and Herðubreið. Other examples of table mountains are Bláfjall at Mývatn, Hlöðufell (Figure 8-14) and Hrafnabjörg east of lake Þingvallavatn, Geitafell and Brenni-

Figure 8-16. Pseudocraters in the Yngra-Laxárhraun lava at Skútustaðir, Mývatn. (Photo Sigurður Þórarinsson.)

steinsfjöll (Langahlíð and Geitahlíð) on the Reykjanes peninsula. Table mountains are usually elongate in keeping with the dominant tectonic orientation and the same probably applies to table mountains and shield volcanoes. The eruption has begun on a fissure and then become restricted to one place as it progressed. It could also be that the eruption began on a circular vent. The summit of the table mountains can all be regarded as shield volcanoes and in many cases there are still craters which closely resmble the summit craters on Holocene shield volcanoes.

Móberg or hyaloclastite mountains are always steep having had ice support on all sides while build up took place. Usually the tephra has been cemented together before the glacier melted, otherwise the unconsolidated materials would not have succeeded in building up such steep structures. Móberg i.e. hyaloclastite mountains occur mainly in the same areas as Holocene volcanoes. The best formed mountains provide evidence on the glacier thickness during their period of formation. The ridges give an indication of the minimum thickness while the table mountains suggest the maximum thickness.

All of the móberg hyaloclastite formations discussed are composed of basic rocks. As yet, less is known about how rhyolite magma behaves underneath glaciers. Some of the rhyolite masses of Kerlingarfjöll and the Torfajökull area, e.g. Bláhnúkur in Landmannalaugar (Figure 6-8), have probably been formed in subglacial eruptions. The pillows in them can reach 5–10 m in diameter while in between them is debris of obsidian, pitchstone and perlite.

Submarine eruptions

During historical time some tens of eruptions have occurred in the sea around Iceland's coast. Most of them have been off the Reykjanes peninsula. Others have occurred in the north, e.g. Mánáreyjar at the turn of the year 1867–68 around Vestmannaeyjar and most recently in the Surtsey area in 1963–67. During these eruptions at least 6 volcanic islands have emerged, three of them in the Surtsey area, but all have quickly succumbed to the forces of the sea with the exception of Surtsey.

The conditions for the build up of volcanic products in marine eruptions are in many ways similar to those underneath

77

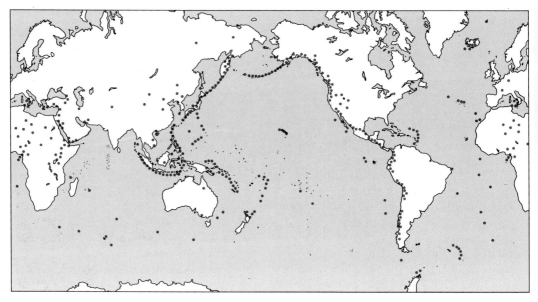

Figure 8-17. Map of the world's chief volcanoes and their distribution. (Drawing Þ.E. and G.H.I.)

glaciers. Admittedly there is no ice support and the effects of wave action are very evident in marine eruptions, especially when the volcanic structure builds up to sea level and above it. Eruption in deeper water leads to the accumulation of a pillow lava heap to a height of tens or hundreds of metres, when the eruption changes to the explosive phase. This results in tephra fall which continues until the crater walls have risen well above sea level and the sea can no longer flow into the volcanic vent to quench the magma. At this stage lava eruption takes over and closely resembles eruption on land. A lava cap then forms which gradually increases in size as the lava enters the sea and builds up foreset bedded "lava delta" of tephra and pillows. The transition from explosive to flood eruption is considerably later in marine than in subglacial eruptions since wave action ensures that the sea can flow into the crater for a longer time than the water in glacial reservoirs can (Figure 8-15).

Pseudocraters

When lava flows over shallow lakes, marshland or in river channels pseudocraters are formed. The lava absorbs water as steam, causing expansion and boiling, so that it explodes and produces *scoria*. This often leads to the formation of very regularly shaped *scoria* craters (Figure 8-16). Pseudocraters usually occur in irregular groups. Their distribution and form in depressions or valleys can often be used to distinguish pseudocraters from true volcanic craters. The *scoria* often contains diatomite which has been carried up from the lake bottom in the steam explosions.

The largest pseudocrater group in Iceland is the Landbrotshólar group in the Landbrot region, S-Iceland which have formed in the Eldgjárhraun lava. In Mývatn and surroundings there is a large number of pseudocraters. Geitey is the highest at 30 m, which is the highest pseudocrater in the country. All of these pseudocraters are in the 2000 years old Yngra-Laxárhraun lava. Also in this lava is the Rauðhólar group and the crater group in the Aðaldalur valley. Rauðhólar near Elliðavatn at Reykjavík is a pseudo-crater group formed in the Elliðaárhraun lava (Leitahraun lava).

World distribution of volcanoes

It is believed that about 1350 volcanoes have been active on the earth during the last 10.000 years and that eruptions in them have numbered about 5600 according to written sources and geological data. Most volcanoes lie on divergent plate margins (ocean ridges) and convergent plate boundaries (fold mountains) or on their edges (cf. chapter 12). Volcanoes are also associated with rift valleys on the continents e.g. the great fracture-or lake valleys in east Africa, e.g. Kilimanjaro and the Rhine valley in Europe. There are also active volcanoes within the continental plates, e.g. in Europe at Eifel in Germany and Massif Central in France, or on oceanic plates e.g. Hawaii, probably related to localised hot spots (cf. chapter 12).

Most of the volcanoes in the Cainozoic fold mountain chains, i.e. on convergent plate boundaries, e.g. in the Mediterranean (Etna, Vesuvius, Santorini in the Aegean Sea, Ararat in Turkey) and surrounding the Pacific (Erebus in Antarctica, Aconcagua and Cotopaxi in the Andes mountains, Mont Pelée in the West Indies, Popocatepett and Paricutin in Mexico, Mt. St. Helens in Washington state USA, Katmai and Pavlof in Alaska, Bogosloff on the Aleutian Islands, Bezymiannie on the Kamchatka peninsula, Fujiyama in Japan, Pinatuba and Taal on the Philippine Islands, Taravera and White Island on New Zealand, Krakatoa and Tambora in Indonesia where the largest eruption on earth in recent centuries took place in 1815. The amount of volcanic materials was 100–150 km^3 or ten times more than in the Laki eruption of 1783.

Although there is a lot of volcanic activity on ocean ridges, volcanoes are formed only where volcanic production is very great, i.e. on hot spots, e.g. in Iceland, Jan Mayen, the Azores and Tristan da Cunha.

Eruption forecasting

Eruptions always cause fear and with good reason since they have often destroyed entire settlements and towns and caused loss of life. In recent years attempts have been made to find ways of forecasting eruptions and thus reduce the damage they cause.

The period leading up to eruption is often marked by increased frequency of earthquakes, increased fumarole activity in the volcanic area and uplift. Other features include magnetic field variations and increased conductivity by groundwater due to the rising geothermal gradient. Exact surveying, especially surface dip measurements in the volcanic area have shown that the land "swells" due to pressure from the magma as it forces its way through the crust or fills magma chambers.

It will be clear from the above that eruption forecasts are based mainly on fumarole activity, conductivity and magnetic measurements, as well as exact surface-dip measurements. Direct measurements of these properties are usually difficult, however, because of the difficult conditions in volcanic areas. The accuracy of forecasts is also limited by the fact that there is often a long period between eruptions in the volcano. Also eruptions also occur where they are not expected. Eruption forecasts are therefore most applicable in areas where there are frequent eruptions in one volcano and the area is easily accessible. Among the most successful forecasts have been made in Hawaii and in Krafla in 1975–84, conditions in these areas being good and eruptions frequent.

Eruption forecasting in Iceland is difficult, however, because the active volcanic zones are long, or altogether 700 km and active volcanoes are numerous even though eruptions have only been frequent in a few of them in recent centuries. In such conditions it is easiest to monitor earthquake activity as a precursor to volcanic activity and then apply further techniques in the eruption area, both geophysical and geochemical. A seismographic network has been established in Iceland following the Heimaey eruption in 1973 and it is likely that the eruption could have been forecast with 30 hours warning, had there been more than two seismographs in southern Iceland at the time. In order to locate the foci of weak earthquakes a minimum of three seismographs is required, although it should be pointed out that eruption can begin without any measureable precursors. Thus the last three Hekla eruptions

in 1970, 1980 and 1991 began without any measureable indications and seismic activity did not start until the eruptions began. Furthermore seismic events can occur underneath volcanoes without any eruption taking place as has happened at Katla in past decades. The experience gained from eruption forecasting in Iceland during the last 20 years has been of three types. It is often possible to foresee an eruption from earthquake monitoring, surface dip measurements and geothermal activity, as was the case in Krafla from 1975–1984 and indeed in Askja in 1961. With hindsight it is sometimes possible to see the possibility of a forecast as for example in the case of Heimaey in 1973. Thirdly eruptions can take place without precursors, e.g. in recent Hekla eruptions. With improved technology, better techniques and increased manning it is likely that advances will be made in forecasting most eruptions, at least as regards where and perhaps when they will occur.

Geothermal activity

9

The upper layers of the earth's crust are subject to daily and even more so the seasonal temperature changes. Daily variations occur over depths of centimetres but seasonal variations occur from 10–30 metres downwards, though this varies according to the strata and climate in question. At the depth at which the seasonal effects die out the temperature is close to the mean annual temperature which in Iceland is 4–5°C near sea level. Below this level the temperature rises with depth. On continents where volcanism and folding have not occurred for a long period of geological time, the temperature at 1000 m depth is around 30°C. In Iceland the temperature at 1000 m depth outside geothermal areas is generally 50–100°C while in high temperature geothermal areas it can reach boiling point on the surface and increase by as much as 1°C/m where the increase is greatest (Figure 9-2).

Water which has percolated to only shallow depths thus varies in temperature according to season, but if it goes deeper the temperature will be the same all year, usually around the mean annual temperature of the area. Springs with water of a constant temperature are known in Iceland as *kaldavermsl*. On the other hand water which percolates downwards to considerable depth is heated in accordance with the temperature gradient in the area. When it rises again to the surface it carries heat from within the earth. The main characteristics of such water are that it is hotter than the ground water and contains more dissolved solids. For instance the amount of dissolved solids in Reykjavík's drinking water is around 60 mg/l while the domestic hot water in Reykjavík contains around 340 mg/l and in Hveragerði around 1200 mg/l. The outlet vents of hot water or steam are known as *hot springs* (Icel. hverir) and the area in which they occur a *geothermal area.*

For a long time it was believed that the hot water and steam in geothermal areas originated directly in cooling magma batholiths or intrusions deep within the crust. Research has now shown that most of the water is precipitation which has percolated downwards through the bedrock. Because of the high temperature gradient in geothermal areas the temperature of the water has already reached 100°C or more at a few hundred metres depth.

Geothermal areas have traditionally been divided into *low temperature areas* i.e. hot water areas and *high temperature areas* i.e. steam areas with solfataras and fumaroles. This division is based on the *temperature* of the geothermal area. The temperature is either measured in deep drill holes or calculated from the silica content of the hot water (silica temperature). The temperature in low temperature areas is usually around 100°C at 1000 m depth and increases slowly below that, e.g. a temperature of 142°C has been measured in a 2000 m deep drill hole in Reykjavík and 160°C at 3000 m depth. The division between low temperature and high temperature geothermal areas is internationally set at 150°C measured at a depth of 1000 m. The highest temperatures measured in high temperature areas in Iceland are 340°C at 2000 m depth in a drill hole at Krafla at Mývatn and 380°C at Nesjavellir, south of lake Þingvallavatn (Figure 9-2).

The water emerging in low temperature areas is always basic[6] and is usually accompanied by precipitation of geyserite around the hot spring.

At the surface in high temperature areas, on the other hand, are acid solution, e.g. sulphuric acid which dissolve the rock around the vent. Drilling in high temperature areas has shown, however, that beneath the water table the water is also basic. The difference between the water in low-and high temperature areas lies in there being much more dissolved material in the latter areas, the temperature being much higher (Figure 9-2). The steam in high temperature areas is formed by boiling at the water table level.

Accompanying the steam in geothermal areas are gases. In high temperature areas these are mainly hydrogen sulphide

(H_2S), carbon dioxide (CO_2), hydrogen (H_2) and a few others such as nitrogen (N_2). On mixing with the atmosphere in the solfatara fumarole vent the hydrogen sulphite combines with oxygen in the atmosphere to form sulphuric acid (H_2SO_4) which can be very strongly acid. At the high temperatures the rock dissolves and breaks down so that certain materials are washed away while the residual materials are a mixture of clay minerals, geyserite and gypsum. Some pure sulphur usually precipitates from fumaroles but this is largely washed away by rainfall. In earlier centuries a considerable amount of sulphur was worked in Iceland which, with Sicily, had a monopoly on sulphur for a long time. Most of the mines were at Krýsuvík, Námafjall and at Þeistareykir.

The gas in low temperature areas on the other hand is mainly nitrogen. There is also usually a little hydrogen sulphide and other gases as indicated by the smell. Around hot springs silicous material is deposited from the water as geyserite.

Hot springs generally emerge at dikes or fractures which prevent the water flow in porous beds in the bedrock while directing it upwards, for the fractures are frequently open and the rocks along the dikes disturbed.

In many geothermal areas the flow has been increased by deep drilling, which has several effects. Firstly, precipitates from the hot water fill cavities and cracks in the rock as it cools blocking the paths of flow. Impermeable sediment in the bedrock can also prevent the upward flow of hot water, for which drilling opens a pathway. Secondly, drilling can reach porous beds or fractures through which the water flows. Thirdly, the flow to the drill hole can be increased by pumping since this leads to the formation of a downdraw cone which causes greater inflow.

Before drilling for hot water is com-

---

6 Acidity (pH) is measured on a scale of 14. If greater than 7, the solution is said to be basic. Low temperature geothermal solutions have a pH of around 9. If lower than 7, the solution is acid, acidity increasing with decreasing values. Acidity in high temperature geothermal areas can be as high as pH 1 – 2.

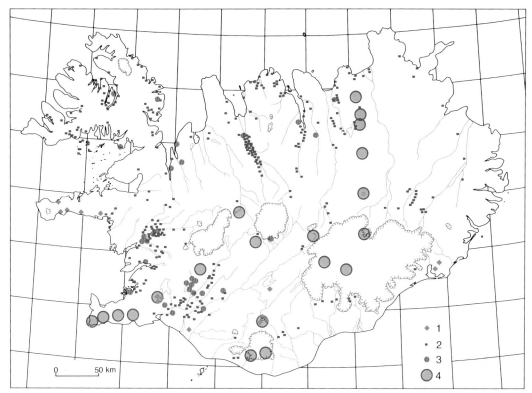

Figure 9-1. Distribution of geothermal localities in Iceland. Explanation: 1) mineral springs, 2) warm springs up to 70°C, 3) hot springs 70–100°C and 4) high temperature areas. (Drawing Þ.E. and G.H.I.)

menced in geothermal areas detailed geophysical, geochemical and geological research is carried out to determine the main area of upward flow and the amount of hot water or steam in the area.

High temperature or steam geothermal areas

High temperature areas occur only in active volcanic zones and probably mainly where there are shallow magma chambers or intrusions cooling underneath in active volcanic areas. Thus high temperature areas are localised areas of upward ground water flow in active volcanic areas.

There are 20–30 high temperature areas in Iceland of which the main ones are:

Reykjanes-Svartsengi, Krýsuvík, Hengill, Kerlingarfjöll, the Torfajökull area, Grímsvötn, Dyngjufjöll, Námaskarð, Krafla and Þeistareykir (Figure 9-1).

There are mainly two types of edifice in high temperature areas, *fumaroles and solfataras*. In fumaroles the temperature of the steam is sometimes more than 100°C, i.e. superheated steam, which emerges under considerable pressure. The water table is usually quite far below the surface so that very little water normally accompanies steam springs and what little there is forms by condensation of the steam on its way to the surface. Solfataras are common in high temperature areas. They contain blue-grey boiling clay, the colour being due to sulphur compounds of iron which form when sulphuric acid

83

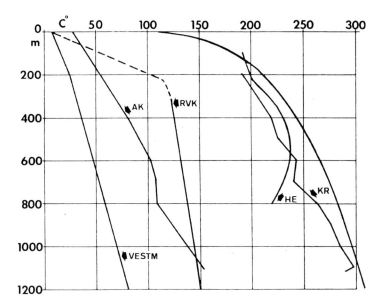

Figure 9-2. Temperature in deep drillholes in Iceland, i.e. in Vestmannaeyjar (Heimaey), Laugaland in Eyjafjörður (AK), Reykjavík, Hengill (HE), SW-Iceland and Krafla (KR), N-Iceland. Boiling point curve is shown on right.

dissolves the rock, the acid forming when hydrogen sulphide (H_2S) reacts with atmospheric oxygen. In the solfataras the clay splashes as gas bubbles burst and the clay builds up a rim around them. The rocks of high temperature areas are usually greatly altered as mentioned earlier.

Low temperature or hot water spring areas

There are believed to be about 250 low temperature areas in Iceland, in which there are 600–700 large or medium sized hot water springs. The natural discharge from them is estimated to be 1800 l/sec of 75°C hot water which can be increased by drilling and pumping, though this depletes the water supply so that care must be taken utilising the area that colder water is not drawn in. The flow is usually subject to little change except in geysers or erupting springs which shoot water or steam jets into the air every so often. The temperature of the springs seldom exceeds boiling point. In drill holes on the other hand the temperature is much higher while it should be borne in mind that boiling point increases with increased pressure, the temperature being for instance 121°C at a water depth of 10 metres (Figure 9-2).

Unlike the high temperature areas a minority of low temperature areas are connected to recent volcanic areas, since activity ceased in most of them during the Pleistocene or Tertiary. The hot water emerges in fractures or even along dikes in the bedrock. Deuterium isotope measurements suggest that the hot water in low temperature areas originated in inland mountain areas, such as in the active volcanic zones and has flowed from there as ground water and been heated at depth on its way to the geothermal areas over a long period. For example the hot water in the Borgarfjörður area, W-Iceland, is believed to have come from Langjökull. Water percolates downwards easily in the active volcanic belts because of the number of open fractures and the porosity of the rocks, i.e. the water sinks downwards rapidly. The low temperature

Figure 9-3. Solfataras at Hverarönd east of Námafjall east of Mývatn. The light-coloured mound on the right is composed of sulphur and gypsum. (Photo Sigurður Þórarinsson.)

areas are spread widely over almost the entire country except for the south-eastern and eastern parts where there is very little geothermal activity; the majority of thermal water spring areas are on the flanks of the volcanic belt in the south-west, e.g. in Borgarfjörður and Árnessýsla (Figure 9-1). Hot water springs are divided into several groups, mainly according to temperature.

Eruptive springs or geysers are the best known of all Icelandic hot springs especially since the international term for goshver, geyser, is coined from the largest of them, Geysir in Haukadalur. Geysir is first recorded following a great earthquake in southern Iceland in 1294.

Geysir eruptions usually start with rumbling accompanied by much boiling and frothing in the vent, which is then followed by water jets which erupt higher and higher until the eruption reaches its maximum. At its highest the eruption jet of Geysir reached 70–80 m. After a few minutes the eruption decreases and is replaced by steam which escapes with a loud whistling sound, until it gradually decreases. However the behaviour of "eruption" is very variable, even in the same *spring*.

Iceland has quite a number of erupting springs apart from Geysir, others being Grýta (Grýla) in Hveragerði, Strokkur in the Geysir area and Uxahver in the Reykjahverfi area in Þingeyjarsýsla. There are also goshverir in Kamchatka, New Zealand and in Yellowstone Park in the U.S.A., some of which erupt very regularly and to great heights.

85

Figure 9-4. Bláhver at Hveravellir, at Kjölur, central highlands. The water is 88°C. Around the hot spring an area of geyserite has formed. (Photo Hjálmar R. Bárðarson.)

Geysir consists of a 2 metre deep basin at the top which is about 15 m in diameter. Extending downwards from this is a 20 m deep pipe which is only 1–2 m in diameter. While Geysir existed as such, the temperature was 80–90°C on the surface with a discharge of 2–3 l/sec. The temperature at the base of the pipe was 128°C, which is below boiling point at this depth. At a depth of 10 m the temperature proved to be close to boiling point, or 120°C, boiling point being 121°C at this depth and in eruptions superheating has been measured.

Several theories have been put forward as to the cause of geyser "eruptions" which can be divided into the geothermal gas and boiling theories.

Figure 9-5. Erupting geyser Strokkur in the Geysir area, S-Iceland. The steam column is about 20 m high. (Photo Helgi Torfason.)

Geothermal gases escape in all hot springs, the force together with that of the steam sometimes being so great, that the hot spring appears to be boiling even though the water is below boiling point. The gas is believed to facilitate boiling in the feeder pipes to the main spring vent. When the total pressure of gas and steam is sufficient they erupt into the feeder pipe and cause eruption.

The boiling theory assumes that in the Geysir eruptions, 126°C hot water suddenly enters high up in the feeder vent, e.g. at 10 m depth, where it is in fact superheated, the boiling point at this depth being 121°C. This leads to flash boiling and the resulting sudden steam formation produces an eruption.

By definition *hot water springs* have varying water temperatures above 70°C. The largest hot water spring is Deildartunguhver in Borgarfjörður which has a discharge of 150 l/sec of 100°C hot water and as such is the largest thermal spring in the world. Water from it is used for domestic heating in the towns of Akranes, Borgarnes and surrounding areas. The largest hot water spring areas are Reykir in Mosfellssveit near Reykjavík, the Reykholt area in Borgarfjörður, W-Iceland,

Reykhólar in Reykhólasveit and Reykjanes in Ísafjarðardjúp, NW-Iceland, Skagafjörður and the Fljót-area and the Reykir-
area in S-Þingeyjarsýsla, N-Iceland.

In the upper Árnessýsla area, S-Iceland,
geothermal springs are widespread, e.g.
in Flúðir, at Laugarás, at Stóra-Fljót,
Syðri-Reykir and Laugarvatn. In addition
to these areas there are large hot water
springs in Hveravellir, at Geysir, in
Hveragerði, although the latter can be regarded as a high temperature area with
ground water at the surface.

Warm springs or laugar are closely related to hot springs but have only small
amounts of gas and no geyserite precipitation. Warm water springs or laugar
bridge the gap between hot water springs
(hverir) and kaldavermsl and are much
more common than hot water springs
(Figure 9-1). Many of them can be regarded as cooling hot springs since they
sometimes occur on geyserite fields, e.g.
at Leirá in Leirársveit, W-Iceland.

Warm mineral springs are closely related
to warm springs. The water in them is
warm but mixed with carbon dioxide
(CO_2) so that they appear to boil due to
rapid escape of the gas. There is usually
precipitation of calcium carbonate or travertine. The largest warm mineral spring
in Iceland is at Lýsuhóll on Snæfellsnes.

Cold mineral springs (ölkeldur) are cold
water springs mixed with carbon dioxide.
Most of them are on Snæfellsnes, e.g.
Rauðamelsölkelda. Ölkelduvatn is similar
to soda water in taste but with a slight
iron flavour.

At the close of the Hekla eruption in
1984 *carbon dioxide emission* was evident in
the Hekla lava above the farm Næfurholt,
while at the same time the water in the
area was carbonated and hard. Such
emissions are referred to outside of Iceland as mofettes and are common in ancient fold mountains and volcanic areas
throughout the world.

Economic use of geothermal heat

From ancient times geothermal water has
been used for bathing and washing. The
first drilling for hot water in Iceland was
at the Þvottalaugar in Reykjavík in 1928.
Drilling was started in Reykir in Mosfellssveit, 17 km east of Reykjavík in 1933
while the Reykjavík District Heating Authority was formed in 1943. Since then
many deep drill holes have been sunk in
Reykjavík which provide a large quantity
of water. The Reykjavík District Heating
network now also serves the neighbouring towns of Kópavogur, Garðabær, Mosfellsbær, Álftanes and Hafnarfjörður, in
all serving 140.000 people. The normal
consumption of hot water is about 1500 l/
sec which can be increased to 3000 l/sec
during cold spells. In addition the
Reykjavík District Heating Authority has
taken into use water from the geothermal
plant at Nesjavellir south of Þingvallavatn where cold water is heated by steam
from the high temperature geothermal area there. District heating authorities are
now widespread and serve about 85% of
the country. Many country schools have
also been built in geothermal areas.
Swimming pools which make use of geothermal heat number about 100. Geothermal heat is used for greenhouse heating,
particularly in southern Iceland and veg-
etables, fruit and flowers are produced in
considerable quantities. Electricity is generated from geothermal energy to a small
extent using steam turbines at Krafla,
Bjarnarflag at Mývatn, Svartsengi near
Keflavík and in the near future also at
Nesjavellir. Finally geothermal heat is
used in the production of diatomite at
Mývatn, algal meal at Reykhólar í Reykhólasveit and salt in Reykjanes.

Geothermal energy is of no less importance to Iceland's energy budget than hy-
dropower. It accounted for 31,3% of the
country's energy demand.

Tectonic movements and earthquakes

10

Slow but constant movement in the earth's crust results in stress in the rocks. When the stress is so high that the rock can not withstand it failure results. Movement causes the formation of fractures and displacement of the fracture edges. Such fractures are known as *faults* and are either vertical or dipping. Fracture lines can often be traced over long distances and are either straight or sinuous. Movement along them is often quite variable from one place to another. The fracture system often displays a preferred orientation over limited areas. In Iceland fractures and faults having a SW-NE orientation are common in the south while N-S trending fractures are dominant in the north of the country.

Fracture lines vary in type according to the nature of crustal movement. Sometimes divergent movement along the faults causes separation of the faces. Such open fractures are known as *fissures (Icel. gjár)* (Figure 10-2). They are for instance common in the Mývatn area (e.g. Gjástykki), in the Kelduhverfi area, at Þingvellir (e.g. Flosagjá, Figure 10-1) and on the Reykjanes peninsula. It is however much more common that one fault face is downthrown and beds common to both sides are thus at different heights. Faults of this type are known as *normal faults*

(Figure 10-2) and Almannagjá at Þingvellir is one of the best known (Figure 10-1). The fault faces expose the Skjaldbreiðarhraun lavas which are at least 9000 years old. Movement has not been continuous but rather in bursts and accompanied by earthquakes. Subsidence last occurred in the earthquake of 1789 when the Þingvellir plains subsided by at least 60 cm and the water flooded the land to its present extent. In youthful fracture areas faults are often dominant in the landscape. In places the crust has been fractured into long strips forming a series of step faults, one above the other. Examples of this can be found for instance in eastern Tjörnes, at Kárastaðir in the Þingvellir district and at Hjallar in the Heiðmörk area near Reykjavík.

The faults described occur mainly in areas where crustal drift or rifting occurs such as in the volcanic zones of Iceland. In fold mountains where the strata are being compressed, so-called *reverse or thrust faults* are formed in which one fault face moves over the other (Figure 10-2). Faults of this type are rare in Iceland. Sometimes there is lateral movement on the fault and in places horizontal striae can be seen on the fault faces. Such faults are known as *strike-slip faults* (Figure 10-2). They are rather rare in Iceland but can be seen for

Figure 10-1. Looking across Þingvellir from the northeast. Normal faults and open fissures (gjá) can be clearly seen and all occur in the Þingvellir lava Skjaldbreiðarhraun). Furthest west (right) is Almannagjá which is a normal fault whose eastern face has been downthrown by 30–40 m. At centre is the fissure Flosagjá. The crater island of Sandey can be seen in Þingvallavatn (left). The mainly móberg Hengill in background. Öxará and Öxarárfoss on right. (Photo Þ.E.)

instance in the Þjófagil gorge at Búrfell in the Þjórsárdalur valley in S-Iceland. The best known fault of this kind is the San Andreas fault in California. A sudden horizontal lateral movement of 6 m on it caused the great San Fransisco earthquake of 1906. The San Andreas fault is in fact a transform fault type plate margin. Such faults are also called transcurrent faults and are very common, cutting the mid-oceanic ridges at right angles. One such fault is the Húsavík fault off the north coast of Iceland.

Sometimes the land between two major faults sinks, resulting in a *rift valley or graben*. The Þingvellir plain between the faults of Almannagjá and Hrafnagjá is an example of such a graben (Figure 10-1, 10–2 and 10–3). Outside of Iceland two graben zones are well known, the Oslo fjord-Rhine valley-Rhone valley-graben which runs right across Europe and the Dead Sea-Red Sea-Africa-rift valley which extends from Lebanon to South Africa.

Sometimes the land between two faults is uplifted resulting in a *horst* (Figure 10-2). A good example of such is on the Tjörnes peninsula, N-Iceland where the crust has risen obliquely in the past few million years, by at least 600 m as for instance at Búrfell, Húsavík.

Gjár (fissures), normal faults and graben zones indicate drifting in the crust,

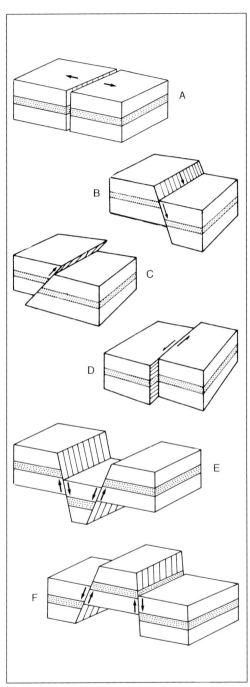

Figure 10-2. Faulting and landforms. A) fissure (gjá), B) normal fault, C) reverse fault, D) strike-slip fault, E) graben or rift valley and F) horst. (Drawing Þ.E. and G.H.I.)

while horsts and thrust faults indicate convergence.

Earthquakes

Earthquakes are shocks or series of shocks due to movements of crustal rocks. Most earthquakes originate on plate margins due to slow, constant rifting on diverging margins along spreading ocean ridges or subduction at trenches underneath continental plates on converging margins (Figure 10-8). Fold mountains form at the latter type of plate margin. Large earthquakes also occur on transform fault plate margins such as the San Andreas fault in California. Slow, constant movement results in stress in the rock which can be so high that it leads to failure of the rock. The rock then fails suddenly and the potential energy bound up in the rock due to build up of stress is released and transformed to kinetic energy which causes wave motion which spreads out in all directions from the point of origin. Faulting results and the fault faces usually separate or move, vertically (normal faults) or horizontally (gjár, (fissures)) or laterally (strike-slip faults, Figure 10-1 and 10-2).

Earthquakes have traditionally been classified into three groups according to origin. The most common are those which have been described and which are known as *fracture-related earthquakes*. All of the major earthquakes in Iceland such as the earthquake of 1896 in southern Iceland and the Dalvík earthquake of 1934 belong to this group.

The next most common recorded earthquakes are *volcanically-triggered earthquakes*. They occur when magma is forcing its way through the earth's crust. Earthquakes of this type are seldom large and usually at their maximum at the start of eruptions. At the start of the Hekla 1947, 1970, 1980 and 1991 eruptions and

91

Figure 10-3. Small rift valley 2 m wide and 30 cm deep formed in tephra on the eastern flank of Hekla two weeks after the start of eruption on 17th January 1991. The precipitation is sulphur and silica. (Photo Einar Ólafur Þorleifsson.)

the Heimaey 1973 eruption quite severe earthquakes occurred. The earthquakes which accompanied lateral magma intrusions and subsequent eruption in the Krafla fires of 1975–84 belong to volcanic earthquakes although rifting in the volcanic zone also plays a part.

The least common earthquakes are the so called *rock-fall triggered earthquakes*. They occur mainly when the roofs of caves in limestone areas collapse (Figure 14-1) or are due to large rock slides. As an example, the rockfall at Steinsholtsjökull in northern Eyjafjallajökull on 15th January 1967 produced an earthquake which was detected as a weak tremor on a seismograph at Kirkjubæjarklaustur. Earthquakes of this type are usually weak.

The point of origin of an earthquake is known as the *focus*, the point on the earth's surface directly above it the *epicentre*. Earthquakes are strongest close to the epicentre and decrease with distance from it.

Earthquakes are also classified according to depth of focus into *shallow* and *deep earthquakes*. Deep earthquakes have their focus at a depth of 50–700 km. They are rather rare, faulting not being very noticeable in the plastic mantle. Deep earthquakes occur almost entirely on convergent plate margins (subduction zones) where ocean plates slide underneath continental crust such as on the west coast of South America. The focus of shallow earthquakes is on the other hand within

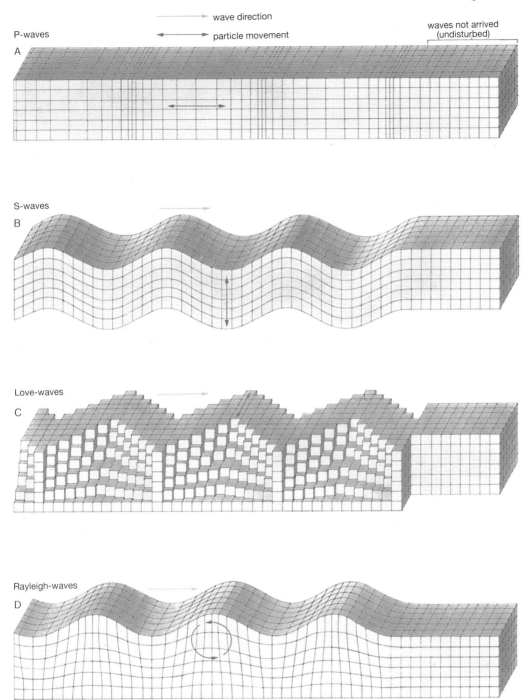

Figure 10-4. The course of seismic waves through the earth and on the surface: A) P-waves, high velocity long waves-compression and extension, B) S-waves, high velocity shear waves, C) Love-surface waves which are shear waves, D) Rayleigh-surface waves (which resemble ordinary water waves except particle movement is reversed.)

the earth's crust and most often at less than 20 km depth. The depth of focus of earthquakes in Iceland is usually shallow, often less than 5 km and seldom more than 15 km. High energy deep earthquakes are often felt over large areas but cause little damage. On the other hand small, shallow earthquakes can cause a lot of damage if they occur in built-up areas. An example is the earthquake in Agadir in Morocco in 1960 which was the same size (M=6) as the earthquake in Kópasker, NE-Iceland on 13th January 1976 (M=6–6.5). The earthquake focus in Agadir was at a depth of 5 km underneath the city and largely destroyed it causing 10,000 deaths, or about one third of the population. At Kópasker the nearest settlement was at least 10 km from the focus and the damage was relatively little.

Seismic waves

The tectonic movements which cause earthquakes in fact result in the formation of four wave types which spread outwards from the focus and epicentre at different velocities. The Primary or P-and Secondary or S-waves which are propagated in all directions outwards from the focus and equally through the earth and up to the surface where they are transformed into surface R-and L-waves which spread outwards in the earth's crust from the epicentre (Figure 1-4).

The P or compressional waves have the highest velocity. In them the particles vibrate backwards and forwards in the direction of spreading and thus resemble sound waves. The material is compressed and extended alternately. The wave length is on the other hand too large and the frequency therefore too low for them to be heard by the human ear. These high velocity compressional waves are known as *P-waves* or primary waves since they

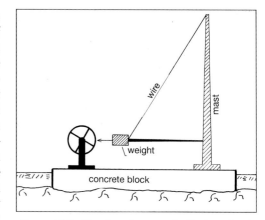

Figure 10-5. Simple seismograph. Explanation in text.

arrive first at the seismograph (Figure 10-6). Their velocity in the mantle is 8–13 km/sec. P-waves travel through solid, liquid and gaseous materials. P-waves thus travel through the earth including the liquid outer core.

Another type of seismic waves are *shear or transversal waves*. In them the particles vibrate at right angles to the direction of travel. They travel exclusively through solid material. Their velocity in the mantle is 4–7 km/sec and they therefore arrive later than the P-waves. As a result they are known as S-waves, or secondary waves, which arrive second in order at the seismograph. S-waves can not travel through the liquid outer core of the earth, nor travel through the liquid in magma chambers beneath volcanoes.

Surface waves occur when P-and S-waves reach the surface at the epicentre and travel outwards from it in a similar manner to waves formed when a stone is thrown into water. In large earthquakes the surface waves can travel right around the earth. Closest to the epicentre, they are steepest and strongest but decrease with distance. The surface waves travel at a lower velocity than the P-or S-waves and as a result arrive last at the seismo-

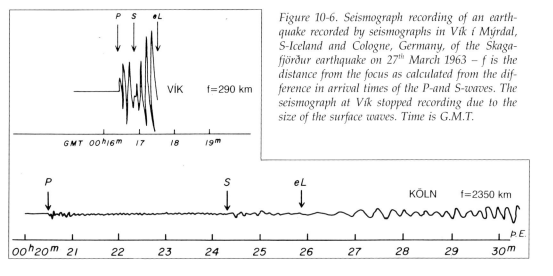

Figure 10-6. Seismograph recording of an earthquake recorded by seismographs in Vík í Mýrdal, S-Iceland and Cologne, Germany, of the Skagafjörður earthquake on 27th March 1963 – f is the distance from the focus as calculated from the difference in arrival times of the P-and S-waves. The seismograph at Vík stopped recording due to the size of the surface waves. Time is G.M.T.

graph. There are two types of surface waves. On the one hand are Rayleigh-waves which resemble a sea swell except for the fact that particle movement is opposite or against the wave direction. On the other hand are Love-waves in which particle vibration is normal to the direction of travel, in a horizontal plane. The damage in earthquakes is caused mainly by surface waves.

Seismic measurements

Detailed information about the focus and energy of earthquakes is obtained by *seismographs*. They are sensitive instruments which consist basically of a mast fixed in a solid base and to which an arm is attached on which rests a heavy weight. On the end of the arm is a pen which is in contact with a cylinder which turns and also serves as a clock (Figure 10-5). The weight is arranged so that it moves very little. During an earthquake the cylinder vibrates, the trace being recorded on paper attached to it. This produces the seismograph recording (Figure 10-6). The seismograph just described is rather old-fashioned but in modern seismograph

stations much more compact electronic seismographs are used in which a light beam replaces the pen and is reflected from mirrors to measure the movement on film.

The seismograph recording in figure 10-6 was recorded on a seismograph at Vík in Mýrdalur and in Cologne, Germany and is of an earthquake north of the Málmey bank off Skagafjörður in March 1963. On the trace the P-waves appear first and very suddenly. The wave movement then decreases until a new set starts marking the arrival of the S-waves. Movement then decreases again until new and rigorous wave movement appears on the trace. These are the surface waves. The difference between the arrival time of the P-and S-waves corresponds to the earthquake having been at a distance of 2350 km from Cologne. The time difference between the arrival of the P-and S-waves at Vík is equivalent to a distance of 290 km and a distance of 270 km at Reykjavík but 1980 km from Uppsala in Sweden. If circles are drawn using the distance to the focus as radius, then the focus is the point at which at least three such circles intersect (Figure 10-7).

95

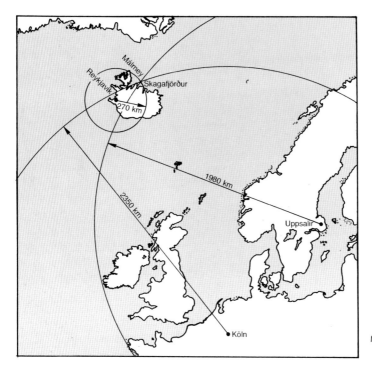

Figure 10-7. Distance circles based on difference in arrival times of P-and S-waves from the Skagafjörður earthquake in March 1963 at seismographs in Reykjavík, Uppsala and Cologne.

During the 1960's the world powers agreed on a ban on above-ground nuclear testing, although experimental testing continued underground. In order to ensure that the ban was honoured the number of seismographic stations was increased in the world and equipped with very sensitive instruments as a result of which information about the interior structure of the earth has greatly increased (cf. chapter 11).

Effects of earthquakes, size and energy

High energy earthquakes are usually severe over a large area close to the epicentre while around that is a still larger area where the earthquake is weaker. Weak earthquakes on the other hand are only noticeable over a small area closest to the epicentre. In weak earthquakes small effects are considered while in large severe earthquakes the damage they cause is taken into consideration. The effects are described on a scale of 12 on the *Mercalli-scale*. Earthquakes of strength 1–2 on the scale are so weak that they are hardly noticeable but those of 3–4 are felt clearly, especially indoors. At 5–6 on the scale objects move out of place and at 7, damage is caused to buildings. At 8–9 buildings are destroyed and loss of life can occur. If complete destruction occurs the earthquake is rated at 12 on the Mercalli-scale.

From observations on the effects of earthquakes in different localities isoseismic lines can be drawn. They join points where the effects of the earthquake were similar. Such lines are usually almost circular around the epicentre and can often be used to locate it.

The effects of an earthquake give little information on the energy released at the focus. When seismic recording began around the beginning of the century it quickly became apparent that many earthquakes which were clearly recorded on the seismograph were in fact hardly

96

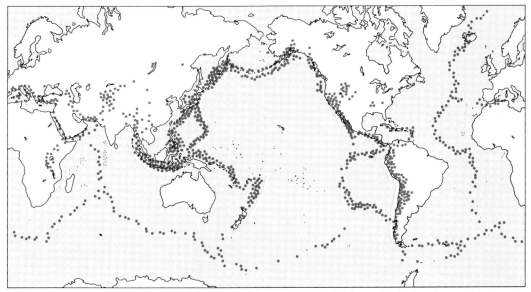

Figure 10-8. The map shows the focus of larger recorded earthquakes in the world during the past few decades. It clearly shows that the majority of earthquakes occur in the Alpine fold mountain belt, at plate margins surrounding the Pacific, or on ocean ridges. The majority of the world's active volcanoes also occur in the same areas. The light blue zones mark ocean trenches. (Drawing Þ.E. and G.H.I.)

noticeable. These were mainly earthquakes with their focus on the sea floor, especially on mid-ocean ridges and their transform fault zones. As a result the size of earthquakes was measured from the amplitude on the seismograph recording. The *earthquake magnitude* (M) is now defined as the logarithm of the measured amplitude, corrected for distance. The magnitude gives the maximum energy at the focus. According to this earthquakes are now classified on the *Richter-scale* which has no actual upper or lower limit. The largest earthquakes recorded in Chile in 1960 with a magnitude of 8.7 and in Alaska in 1964, 8.6. The earthquake in Armenia in 1988 was 6.9 on the Richter-scale but caused great damage. An increase of 1 on the Richter-scale corresponds to a 30-fold increase in the energy. Earthquakes of less than 3 on the Richter-scale are not noticeable. All the largest earthquakes outside Iceland occur on Cainozoic fold mountain ranges, or plate margins.

The largest earthquakes to occur in Iceland since the beginning of seismic recording in 1926 were on 23rd July 1929 on the Reykjanes peninsula (M=6.25), 2nd June 1934 at Dalvík (M=6.25), 27th March 1963 on the Málmey bank at the mouth of Skagafjörður (M=7), 5th December 1968 west of Krýsuvík (M=6), 13th January 1976 at Kópasker (M=6–6.5) and a few earthquakes of M=6 north of the Hvítá river in Borgarfjörður in the spring of 1974. The earthquakes of southern Iceland which occur on average once every century are even larger. The earthquakes on 26th August to 6th September 1896 were probably M=7.5. Earthquakes of a similar size could also occur in northern Iceland as for example on the Húsavík fault of 1872.

Earthquake regions of the world

All major earthquakes occur in particular zones or areas of the world (Figure 10-8) and earthquakes outside these areas are

97

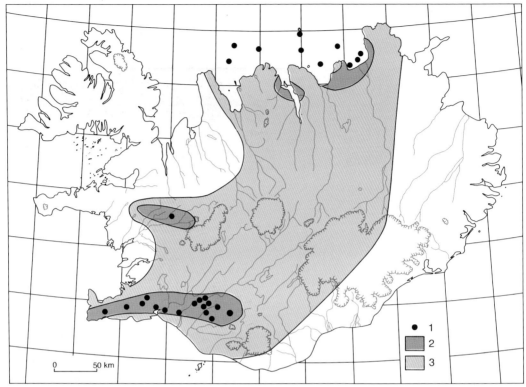

Figure 10-9. Earthquake areas in and around Iceland. Main earthquake areas in dark shading, weaker but clearly felt. Known or estimated focus of earthquakes of size M = 6 or more on the Richter-scale since 1700 (dots). The map is compiled from data based on Ragnar Stefánsson, (1976), Eysteinn Tryggvason, (1973) and Sveinbjörn Björnsson, (1976). In addition to the earthquake areas shown on the map, earthquakes are frequent in Mýrdalsjökull and in the west of Vatnajökull. Symbols: 1) Foci of large earthquakes, 2) strong, 3) weak. (Drawing Þ.E. and G.H.I.)

rare. The majority of earthquakes occur on plate margins, mainly in the fold mountain belt of the Alps in the Mediterranean and in Turkey, the Himalayas, Armenia, Georgia, Iran and where the strata are still being compressed, as well as on plate margins surrounding the Pacific where around 80% of all recorded earthquakes occur. Earthquakes are also frequent on ocean ridges which run through all the oceans such as the Mid Atlantic ridge, to which Iceland belongs.

Weak earthquakes are also common in a zone extending from Oslo fjord southwards through the Rhine and Rhone valleys to the Mediterranean and in a zone

from the Dead Sea southwards through the Red Sea to the great lakes of East Africa, both zones being delimited by rift valleys.

Earthquakes in Iceland occur on the one hand in the volcanic zones (spreading zones). Although they are frequent they are seldom more than 6 on the Richter-scale. The largest earthquakes in Iceland occur on the other hand in transform fault zones of which there are two. One zone extends across the southern lowlands from the Ölfus district and Selfoss to Hekla, the other is off the north coast and runs from the mouth of Skagafjörður and Eyjafjörður through Skjálfandi and Tjörnes. The size of earthquakes in the

Figure 10-10. Ruins of a farm at Selfoss on the Ölfusá river, S-Iceland, which collapsed in the earthquake of southern Iceland in 1896. (Þorvaldur Thoroddsen 1900.)

transform fault zones of the south and north can reach more than 7 on the Richter-scale and can therefore cause considerable damage. The main earthquake areas of Iceland are: 1) Reykjanes, Krýsuvík and Bláfjöll, 2) Hengill, Ölfus and Þingvellir, 3) the southern lowlands, 4) off the north coast from the mouth of Skagafjörður eastwards to the Melrakkaslétta area which includes Grímsey and Dalvík and finally 5) Borgarfjörður north of the Hvítá river. Earthquakes also occur in the volcanic zones such as around Hekla and in the Mývatn district, connected with volcanic events. Earthquakes are also frequent underneath Mýrdalsjökull and Bárðarbunga in NW. Vatnajökull (Figure 10-9).

Damage due to earthquakes

The effect of earthquakes on buildings and construction naturally depend on various external factors. Less damage is caused by deep earthquakes than by shallow earthquakes of the same size. Other important factors include method of construction, building materials and foundations. Damage is greatly dependent on the density of settlement as well as the time of day or year when the earthquake

occurs, which for instance affects whether people are outdoors or indoors. Less damage occurs to buildings which stand on bedrock or thick sediments than to those which stand on waterlogged sediment or artificial infill, the effect of an earthquake being similar to the blow of a hammer underneath a table (=bedrock). Objects fixed to the table move with it while loose objects are thrown about. Buildings which are close to the edge of marine gravel terraces or river banks are often at risk due to landslides. Buildings on uneven ground often suffer severe damage, the unevenness acting like wedges with the result that even strong concrete walls can fail in weak earthquakes.

According to written records around 50 earthquakes have occurred in Iceland during the past eight centuries strong enough to cause complete destruction of farms. Experience of the 1934 Dalvík earthquake and 1976 Kópasker earthquake suggest that these earthquakes were from 7 to 8 on the Mercalli-scale or 5.5 to 7.5 on the Richter-scale. Turf farms were rather poorly constructed as regards withstanding earthquakes, especially the roofs because of their weight (Figure 10-10). Loss of life has occurred due to earthquakes, several times in Iceland, altogether around 100 being killed in the earthquakes of southern Iceland as far as is known. On the earthquakes of southern Iceland in 1784, 69 farms were destroyed in Árnessýsla and 23 in Rangárvallasýsla, while three deaths resulted. At Skálholt most farm houses and the school were destroyed, as a result of which the school and bishop's seat were moved to Reykjavík. The cathedral survived, being of timber. In the 1896 earthquake in southern Iceland 161 farms were completely destroyed with the loss of 4 lives. The most severe shocks were felt throughout the entire country. Landslides and rock falls occurred in many mountain areas in the south and the soil was ruptured. The geothermal areas at Hveragerði and Haukadalur underwent great change, as has often been the case during earthquakes. In the present century the greatest damage has been in the earthquakes in 1934 at Dalvík and in 1976 at Kópasker. There was no loss of life, but there was considerable damage to property.

Although earthquakes are frequent in Iceland, large earthquakes are rather rare and because of the dispersed nature of the settlement, loss of life has been light. Outside of Iceland earthquakes have often caused severe loss of life. An example is the earthquake in the Messina straits in Italy in 1908 when 100,000 were killed and in japan in 1923 (M=8.2) when the cities of Tokyo and Yokohama were practically destroyed and 250,000 lost their lives. The greatest loss of life known was in Tangshan in China, 150 km west of Peking in an earthquake on 27th July 1976. It is thought that about 650,000 people were killed and a similar number injured. In the great Alaskan earthquake of 1964 (M=8.6) on the other hand only about 100 lost their lives, the country being sparsely populated.

Changes to the landscape have occasionally accompanied earthquakes in Iceland and been directly observed. For example in the earthquake of 1789 at Þingvellir the land between Amannagjá and Hrafnagjá subsided about 60 cm and the water flooded the land accordingly. As a result the Alþingi (the parliament) was no longer held there. In the seismic events in the Kelduhverfi district of January 1976 and January 1978 up to 3 m rifting took place on fractures and the land subsided the equivalent of 2–3 m at its maximum. A 5 km^2 lake was formed, known as Skjálftavatn (Earthquake lake). In large earthquakes outside Iceland there has sometimes been extraordinary large crustal movement. An example is the Alaskan earthquake of 1964 where a section of land larger than Iceland was affected. The maximum movement was 7 m east of the epicentre (Prince William Sound) while subsidence was similar to the west of it.

Landscape changes can also accompany earthquakes on the sea floor just as on land. They produce dangerous waves or tsunami (Japanese = ocean wave) which travel at a speed of 500–1000 km per hour over the oceans. They are low in the open sea but steeper in shallower water where they can reach 30 m in height in narrow fjords. In an earthquake off the Japanese coast in 1933 a 28 m high tidal wave flooded the coast and caused 3000 deaths. Such waves can travel right across the ocean and in the 1933 earthquake a tidal wave flooded the coast 10 hours later in California causing considerable damage. Such tidal waves are also caused by explosive eruptions in the sea. For example a large tidal wave flooded the coast in Indonesia when the volcanic island of Krakatau exploded in 1883. As a result 36,000 people lost their lives.

In the past few decades seismology has enabled advances to be made in knowledge of the internal structure of the earth (cf. chapter 11 and 12), as well as in various practical applications especially in petroleum geology. In Iceland it has aided geological research for power plant sites, harbour projects and in geothermal exploration. Small earth tremors are produced using explosives and the seismic waves produced are measured. From the refraction and reflection of the waves the position and dip of the beds can be determined and the general stratigraphy and tectonic picture of the area ascertained. The travel velocity of the waves also gives some information about the type of beds forming the bedrock. It is least in unconsolidated sand-and gravel beds but much greater in consolidated sediment and igneous rocks. The value of such research is however limited unless carried out in conjunction with geological observations and drilling.

Earthquake forecasting

Large earthquakes are the greatest natural disaster occurring in the world. Destruction and loss of life can be very great as discussed earlier and much more than in the most disastrous eruptions or storm waves. In past decades emphasis has been placed on forecasting earthquakes. The technology and methods are very similar to those used in forecasting eruptions. The frequency and behaviour of microearthquakes is monitored, changes in the land elevation, movement on faults, changes in the stress in the rock, water table level changes and escape of gases such as hydrogen and radon. The changed behaviour of domestic animals gives an indication of impending earthquake danger. Some advances have been achieved in this field making it possible to predict the location and even time of occurrence of earthquakes, mainly in U.S.A., China and the former Soviet Union. Unfortunately large earthquakes have occurred in the same areas without any warning signs. In Iceland research has been carried out in earthquake forecasting, mainly in the southern lowland area where a large earthquake occurs at intervals of about one hundred years.

Research on earthquake hazards is very similar to that carried out on eruption hazards, but unfortunately reliable forecasts of this type are still a long way off. With improved technology, more research and increased knowledge it is hoped to make accurate forecasts in the future and reduce loss of life and destruction to property. The necessary precautions against damage due to earthquakes also involve planning so that construction avoids active faults and that it is designed with earthquakes in mind.

Internal structure of the earth

Understandably, information about the internal structure and properties of the earth is scanty. Direct observations can only be made in the atmosphere, the oceans and in the upper part of the crust. The deepest mines reach about 3000 m beneath the surface and the deepest drill-holes about 12,000 m. The interior of the earth can best be studied at the roots of ancient fold mountains, or at around 10–20 km depth. As regards the structure and properties of the globe below this, only indirect measurements can provide information, i.e. various geophysical methods, mainly seismic, gravity and magnetic measurements.

Internal layers of the earth of the earth

Information on rock properties and the internal layers of the earth is obtained mainly by seismology, since P-and S-seismic waves spread in all directions from the focus including directly through the earth (Figure 11-1). If the arrival times of the P-and S-waves from the same earthquake are measured at several seismic stations at various distances and compared then their velocities at different depths can be calculated. Research of this kind has revealed that wave velocity increases downwards. At certain depths

Figure 11-1. Left: seismic wave velocity through the earth's interior. Depth in km. Right: P-and S-wave travel through the interior of the earth. S-waves die out at the boundary between mantle and core. Due to refraction and reflection there is a seismic "shadow" zone 110°-140° from the foci. Time in minutes.

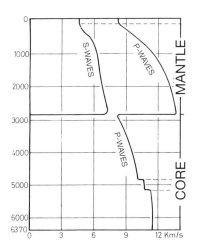

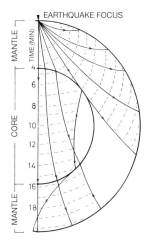

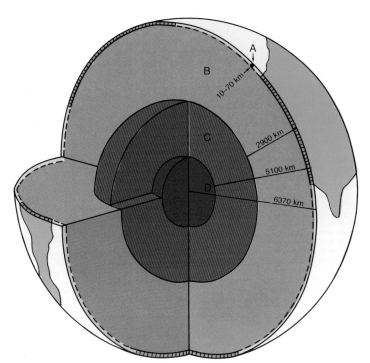

Figure 11-2. Cross section through the earth. Outermost A) crust 10–70 km thick, followed by B) mantle down to a depth of 2900 km, C) outer core down to 5100 km depth and finally D) inner core down to 6370 km depth. (Drawing G.H.I. et al.)

sudden velocity changes take place suggesting that the interior of the earth is "layered", i.e. that the rock properties change very suddenly. The first real velocity change occurs at a depth of 20–70 km underneath the continents and at 5–10 km depth underneath the oceans. Above the change the P-wave velocity is about 6 km/sec in continental crust and 7 km/sec in oceanic crust, while below it is 8 km/sec. This velocity charge is usually called the *Mohorovicic discontinuity* and is regarded as the base of the earth's crust.

The P-wave velocity then increases steadily down to a depth of 2900 km where it reaches 13.6 km/sec. At this depth the volocity decreases suddenly to 8 km/sec. The S-wave velocity below the Mohorovicic discontinuity is 4.35 km/sec but at 2900 km depth has reached 7.25 km/sec. At this depth S-waves die out and this, together with the P-wave velocity change suggests that there is a phase change at 2900 km depth, below which

the earth's core takes over. It appears to have liquid phases. At a depth of 5100 km the P-wave velocity changes quite suddenly again and below this depth the inner core begins to be a solid phase (Figure 11-1 and 11-2).

The crust and upper mantle-lithospheric plates. The lower limit of the crust or Mohorovicic discontinuity lies at about 10 km depth underneath the oceans and 20–40 km depth underneath the continental lowlands, while underneath the highest fold mountain ranges, e.g. Himalayan mountains it lies at a depth of up to 70 km. Extensive areas of continental crust lie outside fold mountain ranges so that the uppermost 2–3 km consist of unconsolidated or slightly consolidated sediment, which in places reaches 10 km thickness as in the North Sea. Underneath the sediment is a 20–40 km thick "layer of rock" whose properties resemble granite. This granitic layer is often called *sial*, the name being coined from the elemental symbol for silica (Si) and aluminium (Al). The lowest part of the continental crust resembles basic plutonic rocks however, rich in silica and magnesium (*sima*).

Underneath the ocean floors the earth's crust is considerably thinner or on average about 10 km. It is composed of basic igneous rocks; uppermost pillow lava then closely spaced dikes and toward the base, basic plutonic rocks which is gabbroic or rocks similar in composition (amphibolite) which have been formed by alteration of basic extrusive or plutonic rocks. The rock sequence of the oceanic crust is called ophiolite. The oceanic crust is formed at the mid-ocean ridges (spreading ridges) by eruption (pillow lava) or of intrusive rocks (basalt dikes and gabbro). It then drifts outwards from the ridge in both directions (ocean floor spreading) until destroyed at convergent plate margins in the subduction zones (cf. chapter 12). Sediment on the ocean floor is youngest and thinnest on the mid-ocean ridges and thickest at the trenches where it is oldest (cf. chapter 12 and 18).

The continental and oceanic crust as well as the uppermost mantle are of rigid and solid rocks, the *lithosphere*, and float on a "layer" of plastically deformable rock, the *asthenosphere*. The surface of the latter lies at about 20 km under the oceans but at about 100–150 km underneath the continents. The lower limit of the asthenosphere is supposed to reach 300–500 km. This "layer" is also often referred to as the low velocity layer since the seismic wave (P-wave) velocity through it is only about 8 km/sec, but 8.3 km/sec in the upper mantle. At the lower boundary the P-and S-velocities increase again. It could well be that the low velocity layer contains a small amount of melted rock, the temperature and pressure at this depth being sufficient to cause melting. The bulk of material in the asthenosphere must however have the proper-

ties of solid rock since S-waves pass through it (cf. chapter 10).

The crust and upper mantle, i.e. the lithosphere are called lithospheric *plates*, the most important being 7 in number. At their junction new oceanic crust is either formed, at divergent margins while destruction takes place at convergent margins (cf. chapter 12). The lithospheric plates "float" on the plastic material of the asthenosphere like ice in the sea and indeed the difference in density between ice and water is similar to that of the rock in lithospheric plates and the asthenosphere. Should the isostatic equilibrium of the plates be disturbed, e.g. due to erosion of mountain ranges the land rises. If downwarped, as for instance by the formation of a thick ice sheet, the land sinks, but rises again when the weight is lifted (cf. chapters 12 and 24). Below the asthenosphere the mantle is solid and the chief materials iron, silica and magnesium so that the term *fesima* is often used.

The core. As previously mentioned shear waves (S-waves) die out at a depth of 2900 km and since they travel only through solids it can be concluded that at this depth there is a transition to rock with liquid properties. The part of the earth's interior below 2900 km is called the core. It is believed to be divided so that at a depth of 5100 km there is a transition to the inner core which probably has the properties of solid material. The core is generally thought to be composed mainly of nickel-iron compounds and is therefore often referred to as *nife* (nickel, ferrous).

The density of the earth

The density of the whole earth is 5.52, but the rocks of the crust have a density of 2.7–3.0. From this it can be seen that rocks in the earth's interior are much heavier than can be observed in the surface layers. The average density of the mantle is 4.5, probably 3.3 at the top and 5.5 at the bottom. The density of the rocks in the core must therefore be 10–12.

As mentioned in chapter 2 the majority of meteorites are probably debris from planets which had orbits between Mars and Jupiter and disintegrated at some time in the distant past. Some meteorites have also been found which are believed to originate on the moon and Mars and have been thrown into space when a meteorite shower knocked them out of their gravity field. There are mainly three types: a) *iron meteorites* b) *stony meteorites* and c) *stony-iron meteorites*. Iron meteorites are 90% iron in composition and almost 10% nickel but other elements occur in small amounts. Stony meteorites, which represent 90% of all the meteorites are on the other hand composed of rocks which resemble basalt and very basic rocks, while stony-iron meteorites have a composition which resembles a mixture of both of the first two. Iron meteorites probably originate in the cores of planets while the other types are probably mainly from the mantle.

Temperature in the earth's interior

The uppermost layers in the earth's crust are subject to daily and in particular seasonal variations in temperature. At the depth at which seasonal temperature variations occur the temperature is near the average yearly temperature of the locality. Temperature observations in mines and drillholes indicate that below this the temperature increases with depth. On the continents the average temperature gradient is about 30°C for every 1000 m. In volcanic and fold mountain areas the increase is more, or 60–100°C or even more, for every 1000 m. The temperature gradient is believed to decrease as the centre of earth is approached. The temperature at a depth of 50–60 km is estimated to be 1000–1200°C or similar to molten lava in eruptions. At the earth's centre the temperature is estimated to be 6000°C or similar to that at the surface of the sun.

If it is assumed that the earth was glowing at the beginning, then the heat received at birth would long since have escaped into space by radiation if it had not been maintained by the decay of radioactive materials. The earth radiates heat equivalent to 75 cal/cm^2 per year and receives from the sun 1.9 cal/cm^2 per minute.

Pressure in the earth's interior

At a depth of 60–80 km all the rocks occurring at the earth's surface should be melted, i.e. occur in the liquid phase. however, pressure increases with depth due to the weight of the overlying rock and increased pressure counteracts the temperature increase so that the greater the pressure, the greater heat is required to cause a phase change. On the basis of the density of surface rocks, the pressure at 60 km depth would be 18,000 atmospheres, one atmosphere being equal to 1.033 kg/cm^2. The pressure at the centre of the earth is believed to be around one million atmospheres.

Crustal movement and plate tectonics

The earth's crust and lithosphere are constantly subject to the effects of internal processes which either cause sudden movements, e.g. earthquakes (cf. chapter 10), deformation in the crust and entire lithosphere, e.g. sea floor spreading and plate tectonic movements, fold mountain formation orogeny or slow epeirogenic and isostatic slow uplift or subsidence with accompanying marine transgression and regression.

Bedding, strike and dip

Strata which accumulate in the sea are normally horizontally bedded. The same applies to lava which flows and solidifies on flat ground. Crustal movements often upset the strata producing new dips from the original. The *dip* is usually measured with a clinometer attached to a compass. The maximum dip is then measured normal to an imaginary horizon. In addition the direction of the dip is measured. Horizontal beds have thus a dip of 0° and vertical beds 90°. A line drawn of the artificial horizon is termed the *strike* (Figure 12-1). Strata in the Icelandic Tertiary Basalt Formation for instance have a completely different dip now than at their time of formation. Dips in Iceland are generally 5–15° but reach 20–40° in a few

places (Figure 24-3). Observations on dip and strike are of great importance in geological research, for example in determining the age of strata and the movement of the bedrock.

Plate tectonics and sea floor spreading

With the advent of more exact global measurements in the 19th century it was noticed that the east coast of America and the west coast of Europe and Africa fitted particularly well together, as if the continents had been ripped apart. The idea was immediately raised that originally the continents had been together as one continent and have since become separated. The idea first got recognition however when the German Alfred Wegener pro-

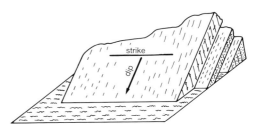

Figure 12-1. Explanation of dip and strike of strata (see text).

Figure 12-2. Results of measurements on geomagnetic field strength across the Reykjanes ridge, southwest of Iceland. The black bands represent a strong magnetic field, i.e. volcanic rock produced when the earth's field was normal. White represents weak field, i.e. volcanic rock produced in a reversed magnetic field. The ridge axis is clearly apparent, being of normally magnetized volcanic rock. The dotted line is at 1000 m depth.

posed his theory of continental drift in 1912. He considered that by the end of the Palaeozoic era all the continents had been one, Pangaea, which had broken up early in the Mesozoic era, probably 200–250 million years ago and drifted away from one another. In this way it became possible to explain for example the similarities of vegetation and animal life in all the continents of the southern hemisphere up until the Mesozoic, i.e. until 200–250 million years ago, and evidence

of widespread glaciation from this time are found on all the continents of the southern hemisphere and Wegener believed that they were all formed on one continuous continent, Gondwanaland which comprised S-America, Africa, Arabia, Madagascar, India, Australia and Antarctica. They were crowded together at the South Pole, South Africa being centred there as well as being the centre of the huge ice cap. The distribution of the flora and fauna from this time fitted the idea very well. Against the theory was the fact that no forces were known which were sufficiently large to move continents and in any case it was possible to explain the distribution of plants and animals by movement across land bridges which have since sunk beneath the sea. It is more difficult to find an alternative explanation for the distribution of glacial vestiges. The commonest was that changes had occurred affecting ocean currents and climate when the land bridges were formed or sank beneath the sea.

Strong evidence has emerged to support the theory of continental drift in the past thirty years. In the beginning the main evidence was based on measurements of magnetic stripes on the ocean floor parallel to the mid-ocean ridges. They have revealed that moving outwards from the ocean ridges are very extensive stripes having an alternately strong and weak magnetic field (Figure 12-2). This is explained by assuming that continuous drift occurs at mid-ocean ridges and that melted mantle material (basalt) constantly rises there adding to the plates as intrusions at depth and pillow lava on the sea floor. The plates then drift in association with the formation of igneous rock to both sides of the ridge. On solidifying the rock becomes magnetised according to the prevailing geomagnetic field, i.e. it becomes either normally or reversed magnetized. Over areas

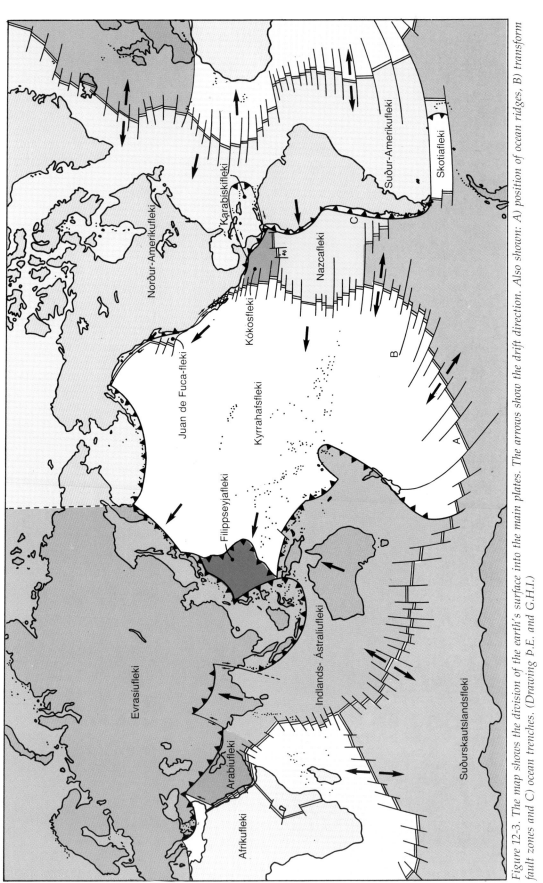

Figure 12-3. The map shows the division of the earth's surface into the main plates. The arrows show the drift direction. Also shown: A) position of ocean ridges, B) transform fault zones and C) ocean trenches. (Drawing Þ.E. and G.H.I.)

Norður-Ameríkufleki

Karabiskifleki

Suður-Ameríkufleki

Skotiafleki

Nazcafleki

Kókosfleki

Juan de Fuca-fleki

Kyrrahafsfleki

Filippseyjafleki

Evrasíufleki

Arabíufleki

Afríkufleki

Indlands- Ástralíufleki

Suðurskautslandsfleki

A

B

C

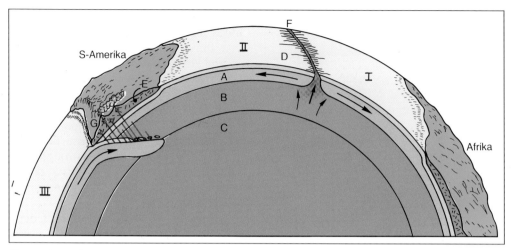

Figure 12-4. Schematic cross sectional diagram of the outermost part of the earth. A) lithosphere, B) asthenosphere, C) mantle, D) ocean crust, E) continental crust, F) volcanically active ocean ridge, G) volcanoes. The African plate (I) drifts eastwards and the South American plate (II) westwards from the Mid-Atlantic Ridge where new oceanic crust is constantly being formed. The eastern Pacific plate (III) drifts eastwards underneath the South American plate. The oceanic plate (III) sinks, partially melts and its remains are absorbed in the asthenosphere. (Drawing Þ.E. and G.H.I.)

where the rock is normally magnetised, i.e. has a similar magnetic field as today the magnetic field is very strong, but over areas which have reversed magnetised rocks, the magnetic field is weak. Since the length of recent magnetic periods is known, it is considered possible to measure the rate of drift. According to such measurements the drift on the Reykjanes ridge is about 1 cm per year, but in the South Atlantic it reaches as much as 5 cm per year and in the southern Pacific up to 20 cm per year in each direction from the ridge. This theory is called sea floor spreading. As a result it is now estimated that the entire ocean floor is younger than from the middle Mesozoic. This view is supported by age determinations on deep sea sediments which so far have not produced dates older than Jurassic, i.e. 150–200 million years old. Research on the sediment thickness also supports the theory of drift, since it is thin on the ridge itself but thickens outwards in both directions. One characteristic of spreading

ocean ridges is the rift valley which runs along them throughout the entire ocean and is similar to the rift valley at Þingvellir (Figure 10-1, 12–3 and 12–4).

Around 1970 a new theory emerged, the so-called *plate tectonics theory*, which combines the theory of continental drift and sea floor spreading and explains much which previously was unclear. It is assumed that the surface of the earth, both continents and the sea floor, is composed of several huge pates. It is believed by some that there are 7–8 major plates, Eurasian, African, Indian, Australian, Antarctic, North American, South American, Pacific and Nazca as well as tens of smaller plates (Figure 12-3).

The plates are formed of continents and ocean crust and the upper part of the mantle making up the lithosphere down to the junction with the asthenosphere which is at about 20 km depth under the ocean ridges and 100–150 km depth under the continents. All the plates are of both ocean and continental crust, except the

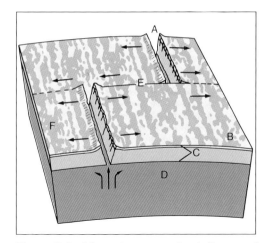

Figure 12-5. Schematic cross sectional diagram of divergent plate margin with transform fault zone on an ocean ridge. Both plates, which form on the plate margin, drift at the same speed out from the margin on both sides of the transform fault zone. A) axis of ocean ridge with rift valley, B) oceanic crust, B+C) lithosphere, D) asthenosphere, E) transform fault zone, F) magnetic stripes. (Drawing Þ.E. and G.H.I.)

Pacific plate which is entirely of ocean crust (Figure 12-3).

The plates move relative to each other. Almost all volcanism, seismic activity and fold mountain formation occur at the plate margins (Figure 8-17, 10–8, 12–3 and 12–4).

There are mainly three types of plate margins:

1) *Divergent plate margins* (spreading or rift zones) which occur on mid-ocean ridges where the plates drift away from each other (Figure 12-5 and 12-7). The ocean ridges run through the entire length of all the world's oceans, a total length of 70,000 km, while their height ranges from 2000–4000 m above the sea floor on either side (Figure 18-1). The ridges therefore lie at great depth, although they emerge from the sea in a few places. The largest section of ridge above sea level is in fact Iceland which is on the northernmost part of the Mid Atlantic

Ridge, i.e. the Reykjanes and Kolbeinsey ridges (Figure 24-4).

At the crest of the mid-oceanic ridges magma rises from below, i.e. from the asthenosphere, accompanied by spreading, to solidify as pillow lava on the plate margins or as intrusions within the crust thus adding to the plate margins in keeping with the drift rate (Figure 12-4, 12-5 and 12-6). The rock formed is roughly divided equally between the two plates. The crust is magnetised according to the prevailing magnetic field, normal or reversed, leading to the formation of magnetic stripes symmetrically outwards from the ridge axis as it drifts from it as already mentioned.

As previously mentioned, the Mid Atlantic Ridge (Reykjanes and Kolbeinsey ridges in Iceland) runs through Iceland. This means that volcanism and seismic activity take place due to the western drift of the American plate and the eastern drift of the Eurasian plate, the movement being estimated at 1 cm per year in either direction. The movement is not constant at the surface but occurs periodically in events at intervals of several hundred years in each area. The movement at depth is probably constant however and even. An example of such a spreading event on a divergent plate margin is afforded by the eruptions and lateral magma intrusion in the Krafla rifting area between 1975 and 1984. It is estimated that the spreading amounted to 7–8 m where it was most, at Leirhnjúkur. A 250 year period of volcanic and seismic quiescence had preceded the events in Krafla since the "Mývatn fires" of 1724–29.

Transverse fracture zones are common on ocean ridges and in these areas sections move laterally for tens or hundreds of kilometres. The cause of the transverse fracture zones has not yet been fully explained but they lie across the ocean ridges parallel to lines of latitude and the

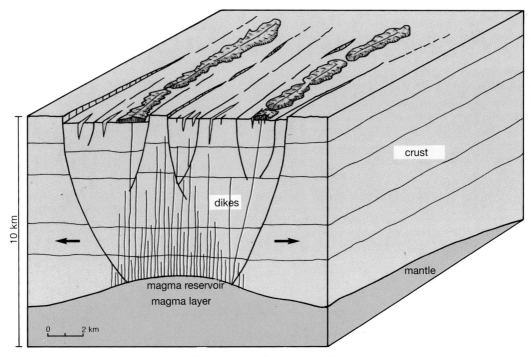

Figure 12-6. Cross sectional diagram of a widening rift valley with fissure swarm and eruption fissures. At the crust-mantle boundary is a magma reservoir or layer of partially melted rock and magma from which dikes extend up to the crust. (Trond Forslund and Ágúst Guðmundsson 1991.)

shape of the earth is probably an important factor. There are two such fracture zones in and near Iceland. On the one hand is an earthquake region running right across the south from the Ölfus district and Selfoss to Vatnafjöll south of Hekla and joining the volcanic belts of the mid south and Reykjanes, while on the other is the Tjörnes fracture zone which joins the northern end of the eastern volcanic zone and the Kolbeinsey ridge.

On the ridge axis earthquakes are frequent though seldom large being usually less than 5 on the Richter-scale. Earthquakes are quite common on the transverse fracture zones where they are considerably larger and can be more than 7 on the Richter-scale (cf. the earthquakes of southern Iceland).

2) *Converging plate margins* (subduction zones) refers to plate margins where ocean plates slide at an angle underneath the edge of continental plates. This forms ocean trenches which are often around 10 km deep. The ocean plates melt or are destroyed in the asthenosphere. The magma formed by melting is mainly intermediate in composition (andesite) and erupts within the continental plate, forming large central volcanoes. Convergent plate margins of this type occur for instance along the west coast of South America where the Nazca plate slides at an angle underneath the South American plate. Earthquakes and eruptions in Chile are a result of this movement and melting of the plates. The ocean plates are not completely destroyed before a depth of 700 km which is the depth at which the deep-

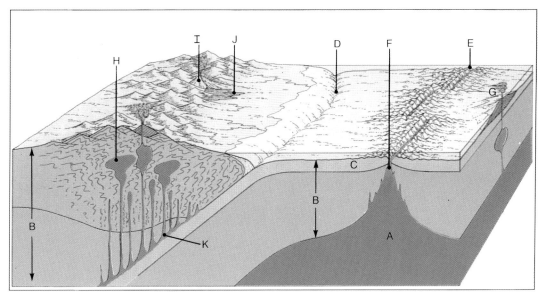

Figure 12-7. Converging plate margin. An ocean plate sinks and slides under continental plate. The ocean plate starts to melt at 100–150 km depth and magma forms, mainly andesite. It then rises into the continental crust where it solidifies as plutonic rock or to the surface in eruptions where it solidifies as lava or tephra. Collision of plates results in formation of fold mountains at the edge of the continental plate. Part of the oceanic plate is absorbed in the asthenosphere and mixes with it. A) asthenosphere, B) lithosphere, C) oceanic crust, D) ocean trench, E) ocean ridge, F) spreading and partial melting, G) island over mantle plume, H) magma intrusion, I) active volcano, J) lava, K) partial melting in the subduction zone. (Schematized by G.H.I.)

est earthquake foci are recorded (Benioff-zone (Figure 12-7)).

3) *Transform plate margins*, i.e. plate margin where neither spreading or subduction takes place. To this type belongs for instance the San Andreas fault in California where the land to the west of the fault, i.e. the Pacific plate, moves northwards compared with the land to the east of the fault, i.e. the N. American plate. There is no eruption on plate margins of this type but earthquakes are frequent and often large e.g. in the Los Angeles and San Fransisco areas.

From what has been said it is clear that the ocean plates are constantly being added to at the divergent margins as the plates drift outwards from the ridges, but destroyed at convergent plate margins where they slide under the continental plates and are destroyed. For instance the Nazca plate is formed at the Pacific ridge but is destroyed underneath the South American plate (Chile trench and Andes mountains). In this way the material in the mantle is constantly renewed.

Fold mountains are formed on the one hand at the junction of ocean plates and continental plates, e.g. the Andes mountains, or at the junction of two continental plates. It is believed for instance that the Alps and Himalayan mountains have been folded and thrusted between the Eurasian plate on the one hand and the African and Indian plates on the other, the latter having moved slowly northwards since they broke away from Gondwanaland during the early Mesozoic, probably about 200 million years ago. The fold mountain chains are constantly added to the edges of the continental core

113

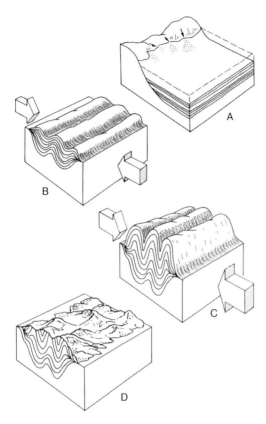

Figure 12-8. Formation of fold mountains by drift of two continental plates, e.g. the Alps between the African and the European plates. A) Strata accumulate in geosynclinal trough, B) drift of the plates pushes the strata and they become folded, C) fold mountains have formed and D) fold mountains fully formed and denudation has begun. (Drawing Þ.E. and G.H.I.)

with the result that the continents have been increasing in size throughout geological history (cf. chapter 23).

Fold mountain movements – orogeny

Every so often during the long life of the earth, extensive fold mountain chains have been formed. The most recent of these is the so-called Alpine chain which winds its way right around the earth. It was formed during the latter part of the

late Mesozoic and Cainozoic eras i.e. the past 150–200 million years and is still forming. The area where fold mountains form are originally an elongated trough (gosyncline) which lies on the sea floor along the junction of ocean and continental plates or between two ancient continental cores (Figure 23-2). The troughs can be considered to be of two types originally. One type is at a convergent plate margin where an oceanic plate is subducted under a continental plate as is now happening on the west coast of South America. The bulk of the material in the trough originates from the continent and the continental shelf; clay, sand, gravel and calcareous ooze while fairly thin deep-sea sediment is carried into the trench by the oceanic plate, as well as igneous rocks from the ocean crust and mud flow sediments (turbidites) which have flowed down the slopes. The ocean crust and sediment on it disappear partly into the crust underneath the continental plate while the sediment on the land side become compressed and form fold mountains (Figure 12-7). However sediment accumulation has occurred in the Cainozoic era between the Eurasian plate and the African-Indian plate. The bottom of the geosyncline slowly sinks while sedimentation commences and more or less keeps pace with the sinking. As a result the sediment is usually shallow water sediment, mainly mudstone (clay), sandstone and limestone, although deep sea sediment and fragments of ocean crust (ophiolite) are occasionally found in fold mountains. Such fragments are found e.g. Oman, Cyprus and the island of Storð in south-west Norway. The sediment thickness in geosynclines can reach 10,000 m or more while the equivalent sediment in nearby "quiet" areas is often only tens or hundreds of metres thick.

While the geosyncline is being filled the plates push the sediment from either

Figure 12-9. Drawing of folds which are overthrown due to movement from the right. See Figure 23-15. (Drawing by Cloos.)

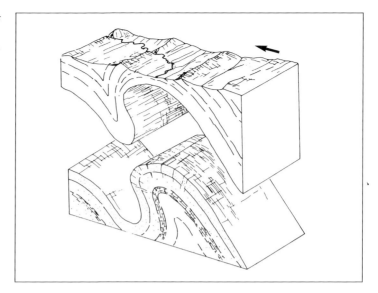

side, compressing the strata (cf. continental drift). At the same time volcanism becomes evident and lava erupts on the sea floor forming pillow lava or the magma builds up islands and island arcs, similar in type to Surtsey. The bottom of the geosyncline sinks still further while the pressure and temperature of the sediment infill rises. Under these conditions the rocks in the geosyncline and underlying crust weaken so that the strata are compressed and squashed still more and even become mixed with the crustal rocks below. As well, the strata in the geosyncline become metamorphosed and plutonic rocks, particularly granite intrude into the lower part of the of the sequence. It is now widely believed that granite is in fact formed by metamorphism deep within the geosyncline. The compressed and metamorphosed rock suite in the geosyncline is what we call fold mountains.

When the strata are compressed by folding, "waves" are produced similar to when a carpet is "compressed". The wave tops are known as *anticlines* in which the beds dip outwards from the wave crest. In the wave depressions the beds dip in-

wards towards each other forming what is known as *synclines* (Figure 12-8). When the fold mountains are uplifted above sea level erosion starts and valleys often form in the anticlines due to the tension of the beds while the synclines tend to form ridges due to their compression. The compressive forces in fold mountain ranges are often so great that their edges are thrust out over the continental masses on either side in so-called overfolds (overthrust or nappes). In such cases the oldest strata are at the top and the youngest further down in the succession (cf. Figures 12-9 and 23-14).

Folding leads to the crust thickening greatly so that lower density rocks extend much deeper than they normally would. This means that the crust is no longer in isostatic equilibrium with the result that the fold mountains rise, mostly in the central area, until equilibrium is reached. At this stage they really become true fold mountains for the first time, towering skywards.

Weathering and erosion begin to destroy the fold mountains as soon as they rise above sea level. Sediment (molasse)

115

Figure 12-10. Gneiss is a metamorphic rock formed from various both igneous and sedimentary rocks under great pressure and high temperature in fold mountains. The light bands are mainly formed of feldspar and quartz, the dark streaks of black mica and other dark minerals. The picture is taken on the island of Harris, in the Outer Hebrides, NW Scotland. The rock is about 2600 million years old. (Photo Sigurður Þórarinsson.)

accumulates in depressions which form, mainly on the flanks and such sediments often contain large amounts of coal and oil (cf. chapter 22). Finally the fold mountains are reduced to a peneplain, at which stage the internal structure and mountain roots are exposed. They are mainly of metamorphic and igneous rocks, especially plutonic rocks. Fold mountain earth movements are usually referred to as *orogenesis (Greek: oros=mountain and genesis = formation)* and almost all the highest mountains of the world have been formed in this way, as for instance Mont Blanc and Mount Everest. In the highest fold mountain peaks it is not uncommon to find marine sediments which bear witness to the immense pressure and uplift involved.

Metamorphic rocks

Deep within the geosyncline and at the plate margin (subduction zone) the temperature and pressure increase so that pre-existing sediment and igneous rocks are changed as regards texture and even chemical composition. Such rocks are known as *metamorphic rocks* A distinction is usually made with *altered rock* which is

the result of hydrothermal alteration caused by solution or movement of material by hot water or steam e.g. in geothermal areas (cf. chapter 9).

The uppermost beds of folded strata are always in their original form even though their position has changed. Deeper in the succession, the sediment has recrystallized. Newly formed crystals, usually mica, are oriented in accordance with the direction of pressure so that the rock is foliated or "layered". Such rocks are known as schist or slate, of which a typical example is mica-*schist*. They are usually easily split and used for instance as roofing tiles abroad. At greater depth in the folds or subduction zone there is much more radical recrystallization, forming for instance feldspar, quartz and mica. The minerals are usually aligned in differently coloured foliations according to mineral type producing beautifully banded rocks. Such rocks are termed *gneiss* (Figure 12-10 and 23-4). At still greater depth within the folding chemical change takes place, the rock either loosing or gaining materials often making it difficult to ascertain whether the original rock was sedimentary or igneous. It is a widely held view that metamorphism can eventually change the rock to granite and granite batholiths are indeed very common at the base of ancient fold mountains.

Metamorphic rocks are mainly found where weathering and erosion have removed the overlying strata of ancient fold mountains, e.g. Precambrian shields in Scandinavia, in mid and eastern Canada and in Greenland. Metamorphic rocks are not found in the bedrock of Iceland, although boulders of metamorphic rock occur along the coast which have been rafted there by icebergs or were used as ballast in ships in times past.

Vertical crustal movements

Gradual vertical crustal movements are termed *epeirogenesis* from the Greek *epeiros*=dry land or continent and *genesis*=formation. Such movements actually affect the sea floor as well as the land. Whether uplift or subsidence, the movement is very slow and often affects a large area. It usually involves very little disturbance of the strata so that the bedding is almost horizontal even though uplift has been of the order of tens or hundreds of metres. Uplift is accompanied by marine *regression* and increase in land area, while subsidence leads to marine *transgression* and the lowland continental areas become shallow seas. The causes of such slow crustal movements are not well understood.

Evidence for subsidence is seldom obvious since it is usually out of sight beneath sea level. However evidence of subsidence commonly found along Iceland's coast is submarine peat since peat is only formed above sea level. The marine peat at Seltjörn, Seltjarnarnes is a good example. The base of the peat is 5 m below the high water level and is 9000 years old while the surface is 3 m below the high water mark and is 3000 years old. From this it can be concluded that subsidence in the Reykjavík area is 3–5 m

Figure 12-11. Shoreline changes in Scandinavia since late in the Pleistocene and in the Holocene due to uplift after the glacier load decreased. Isohypses are relative to present day sea level. Heights in metres. Areas which were beneath the sea are shown in black. The highest shorelines are not necessarily of the same age, the ice sheet melting for instance very late in the Gulf of Bothnia.

in the past 3000 years (Figure 24-30). This type of subsidence is common on oceanic islands on mid ocean ridges. Long term subsidence can lead to the accumulation of thousands of metres of sediment as has happened in the North sea, where up to 10,000 m of various sediments have accumulated in 300 million years and the area is still sinking.

It is possible to find sediments containing fossils of marine animals far inland on the continents, showing that they accumulated on the sea floor which has since been uplifted and become dry land. Marine sediments from the early Pleistocene at Búlandshöfði on Snæfellsnes have been uplifted as much as 150 metres.

117

During the very long period of geological history there have continually been vertical crustal movements. Some areas have been both subject to subsidence and uplift and therefore been both sea floor and dry land. This was the case at Tjörnes NE-Iceland while the Tjörnes beds were forming. Beds of shells and lignite alternate, showing that the land was either below or above sea level. The conditions were similar in many coal forming areas during the Carboniferous period and beds of coal alternate with marine sediments in these rocks.

Equilibrium movements – isostatic movements

The crust or lithosphere "floats" on the soft mantle material in the uppermost asthenosphere like sea ice on the sea and indeed the difference in densities is similar in both cases. If extra weight is added to the crust it sinks, but rises when it is removed. Crustal movements of this type are known as *isostatic movements* and are the result of the earth's attempt to reach *isostatic equilibrium*.

The crust's search for equilibrium is most obvious in areas where ice sheets covered the land during the Pleistocene, their thickness up to 3000 m. An ice sheet from the last glacial period pressed the Scandinavian crust downwards by at least 300 m in the Gulf of Bothnia, where the ice was thickest. While the glaciers were melting and in particular after melting was completed the land rose again and in fact is still rising at the rate of 1 cm per year in the Gulf of Bothnia area. Because of the response of the crust the land rose more slowly than the rate at which ice thinned out and melted so that the sea flooded the low land. Later uplift got the upper hand a fact clearly borne out by the old strand lines and raised beaches which occur inland and high above present sea level. The highest strand line in the Gulf of Bothnia indicates that uplift there has amounted to 300 m in the 10,000 years since the last glacier melted (Figure 12-11).

Similar vertical crustal movements have affected Iceland as in Scandinavia due to the weight of glaciers. However the ice sheet in Iceland was never as thick as in Scandinavia. The highest raised beaches occur inland in the south of the country at a height of 110 m closest to the centre of the ice sheet, but generally at 40–50 m in other places, the ice sheet being thinner on headlands than inland (Figures 24-28, 24–29).

Research on the disruption of the crust's isostatic equilibrium due to glacier weight is much more complex than suggested here. The formation of huge ice sheets during glacial periods means that great quantities of water from the oceans have been stored there. It is estimated that this lead to as much as 100–150 m lowering of sea level during glacial periods and as a result large areas of continental shelf were dry land, e.g. the bottom of the North Sea and the English channel (Figure 23-23). On melting, the glaciers released the water again to the sea so that sea level rose and the sea flooded the continental shelves again as well as lowland areas which had been downwarped by ice. Changes in sea level due to the formation or melting of glaciers (eustatic sea level changes) occur everywhere in the world but isostatic movements due to changes in glacier load are more localised. If present day glaciers were to melt sea level in the world's ports would rise by 60 m and many of the densely populated areas would be flooded. Uplift due to the removal of glacier load would only occur however in Greenland and Antarctica, which would nevertheless have a severe climate.

The origin of magma

It is now generally agreed that magma forms by partial melting of rock in the asthenosphere or lithosphere. Various changes can affect the magma however on its way from its place of origin to its place of solidification. Certain minerals can crystallize out or the magma can melt the country rock or become mixed with other magma on its way, causing the composition to change before it solidifies (Figure 6-2 and 12-7).

There are mainly three places where magma can originate:

a) Basalt is believed to form in the asthenosphere high up in the mantle and reaches the surface mainly at divergent plate boundaries. This basalt is termed olivine-tholeiite and is the most primitive of all igneous rocks. It is very common on ocean ridges, while in Iceland it occurs mainly in shield volcanoes. Partial crystallization in magma chambers or at the junction between the crust and mantle leads to olivine crystallizing out and the formation of tholeiite (cf. Figure 6-2 and 12-7) which is the most common basalt type in the Icelandic volcanic zones.

b) Acid and intermediate magma is mainly formed by partial melting of sediment and igneous rock at fold mountain roots, or by partial melting of the ocean crust and hydrated sediments underneath continental crust at subduction zones (Figure 12-7). Such magma is usually rich in volcanic gases, especially steam and this results in explosive activity as in the volcanoes of the fold mountains which encircle the Pacific. In Iceland acid magma is formed mainly in magma chambers, by differentiation underneath central volcanoes or or strato volcanoes or by partial melting in the crust.

It is believed that underneath the crust or in the uppermost lithosphere in volcanic areas such as in Iceland magma oc-curs everywhere and that eruption can take place if deep fractures are formed which reach the partially melted rock (Figure 12-6). Because magma has a lower density than the solid rock, it either rises towards the surface where it solidifies either as eruptive rock or in the upper crust as dikes or plutonic rock. Seismic measurements suggest that melted rock occurs at shallow depth, 10–15 km or less, underneath ocean ridges and the Icelandic volcanic zones. It occurs at still shallower depth in magma chambers underneath strato volcanoes (central volcanoes), as the magma chamber which has been located, with seismic measurements and from surface deformation, at a depth of 3–7 km underneath Krafla. Outside the volcanic zone or the rift belts the layer in which partial melting occurs lies at greater depth and also thins out until it disappears at either side. During the Heimaey eruption of 1973 magma movements were detected by seismic measurements at a depth of 15–25 km underneath Eldfell. On Hawaii magma movement is believed to take place down to 60 km depth where it starts to rise and collects in magma chambers at a depth of 2–3 km underneath volcanoes.

Roughly speaking there are three types of volcanic zones in Iceland, each being typified by certain volcanic rock series.

In the rift belt itself the volcanic zones from Reykjanes to Langjökull and from Veiðivötn northwards to Axarfjörður are typified by so-called *dike swarms* which are evident on the surface as fracture swarms often more than 40 km long and 10 km wide (Figure 12-6). At the base of each swarm is a magma chamber, supplied by magma from below, which mixes with the magma already in the magma reservoir (Figure 6-2). Higher up in the crust acid magma is more common and strato volcanoes (*central volcanoes*) form in the centre of the swarm. The acid magma

119

forms by differentiation and partial melting of the roof of the magma chamber or the surrounding country rock. When the magma chamber has grown high enough in the crust it sometimes happens that during eruption the roof collapses to form a caldera with the explosive production of large amounts of rhyolite tephra. Such an eruption occurred in Dyngjufjöll (Askja) in 1875. When spreading events occur in rift zones or central volcanoes of this type, magma flows laterally from the magma chamber at depth into the fracture swarm and often to emerge as a fissure eruption (cf. Krafla fires 1975–84).

The volcanic zone from Surtsey to the Torfajökull area differs from the volcanic zones just mentioned and is believed to be geologically young and still forming. It is thought that the crust here is rifting from the north. In the Vestmannaeyjar furthest south in the zone the rocks are alkali basalt. North of this is the Veiðivötn area where there is tholeiitic basalt. The volcanic zone on the Snæfellsnes peninsula does not fit well into the plate tectonics picture but the eruptive rocks there are alkaline.

The cause of magma production is due to the presence of radioactive material in the mantle and crust. The mantle heats up so that the rock partially melts forming basalt magma. This magma then either solidifies as basalt i.e. rocks of various types, or melts its way through the crust changing the chemical composition along the way until it solidifies as some kind of evolved rock. On the other hand thick piles of sediment and igneous rocks in geosynclinal infill materials heat up spontaneously due to radioactivity, high temperature and pressure, causing partial melting. The magma produced then rises to solidify as for example granite batholiths in fold mountains or reaches the surface in explosive eruptions to solidify as andesite or rhyolite lava.

When the distribution of volcanoes in the world is examined (Figure 8-17) it is clear that many of them are located on or near spreading ocean ridges where basalt is the dominant rock type, e.g. Iceland, the Azores and Tristan da Cunha. Many more volcanoes are associated with subduction zones and fold mountains as for instance the volcanoes surrounding the Pacific and Mediterranean such as Etna, Vesuvius and Santorini, most of which erupt andesite or rhyolite although some produce basalt. There are also volcanoes outside these areas which can not be connected with either divergent or convergent plate margins. Examples are Hawaii in the centre of the Pacific plate, volcanic areas in central France and Germany (Eifel) on the Eurasian plate, Cameroon, the Canary Islands and Tibesti mountains on the African plate. These areas, probably 20–30 in all, are believed to be associated with so-called *hot spots*. The magma in these areas comes from great depth within the mantle from so-called mantle plumes, probably from a greater depth than the lower limit of the asthenosphere i.e. from a depth greater than 200 km. Hot spots are also believed to occur at places where magma production is greatest on ocean ridges, e.g. in Iceland. Mantle plumes are stationary relative to the spreading of the plates. Thus the mantle plume under Hawaii is thought to have been in the same place for at least 50 million years and the islands have moved with the westward drift of the Pacific plate. The westernmost islands are the oldest and inactive. However the mantle plumes can "jump" to new localities. Thus the present Icelandic plume is believed to have been underneath the Ægir ridge mid way between Iceland and Norway from between 25 and 60 million years ago.

Geomorphology, weathering and denudation

13

The events and forces of plate tectonics, such as volcanism and earthquakes are, together with other crustal movements, due to *internal or endogenic forces*. The fundamental cause of internal forces is not completely understood since they originate deep within the earth where direct observations are not possible. The same is not true of *external or exogenic forces,* which along with gravity shape the surface of the earth i.e. by breakdown of the surface rocks and transport of the debris. The basic cause of external forces is solar energy. The processes of differential heating, frost, precipitation, rain, running water, glaciers, wind and wave action are of external origin.

Weathering and denudation

The breakdown and disintegration of rocks in situ is called *weathering*. Usually though the debris and dissolved materials do not remain for long in the same place, but are transported away by wind, water, glaciers or downslope by gravity. The debris is ground down in transport and at the same time erodes the rocks over which it is carried. The removal of rock debris and dissolved materials by whatever processes is termed *denudation* which works towards smoothing the

earth's surface and is usually most in mountains and areas of relief, as well as along the coast.

If internal forces did not also play a part, the earth's surface would have become completely flat long ago. However, because of constant build up due to volcanism, thrusting of strata during folding, slow crustal and plate movements and isostatic equilibrium movements of the crust denudation is far from ever reaching its ultimate goal. It is estimated that denudation is equal to 1 metre thickness every 15,000 years on the surface of the earth above sea level. In Iceland denudation is thought to be ten times more or around 1 m every 1000 years, while underneath Vatnajökull it could even be 3–5 m every 1000 years.

Denudation in one locality involves the formation of sediment elsewhere, though mainly on lowland and in the sea.

Weathering and denudation are dependent on various outside factors. The type of strata is for example very important. In areas with porous rocks, precipitation sinks downwards and drains away as ground water thus resulting only in chemical weathering. If the bedrock is impermeable on the other hand the water runs off the surface directly, leading to the formation of gorges, canyons and val-

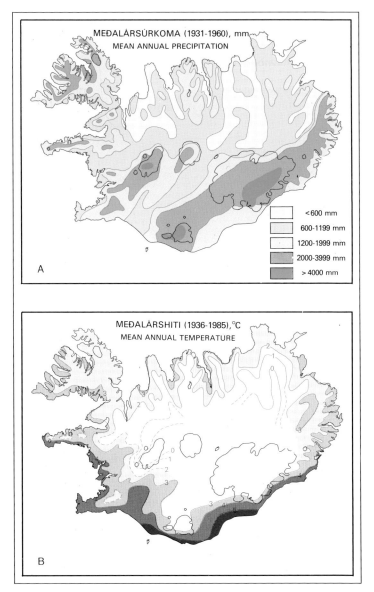

MEÐALÁRSÚRKOMA (1931-1960), mm
MEAN ANNUAL PRECIPITATION

<600 mm
600-1199 mm
1200-1999 mm
2000-3999 mm
> 4000 mm

A

MEÐALÁRSHITI (1936-1985),°C
MEAN ANNUAL TEMPERATURE

B

Figure 13-1 A and B. Mean annual precipitation and mean annual temperature for Iceland for the period 1931–1960. The mean annual temperature for 1961–90 is for most weather stations 0.7° lower and the precipitation somewhat less. (Map: Landmælingar Íslands – Iceland Geodetic Survey.)

leys. The most important factor in geomorphology is, however, the climate. In the rain forests of the tropics chemical weathering is rapid since precipitation amounts and temperatures are high. In desert areas weathering due to temperature changes is important, however, and transport of the debris is almost entirely by wind, although water erosion is great in downpours which are though rare. In the temperate belt the climate varies according to locality. In the hotter parts chemical weathering and fluvial erosion dominate while in colder parts frost weathering and fluvial erosion are most significant though glacial erosion also occurs to some extent. In Iceland frost weathering is important because of fre-

Table of mean temperature and mean precipitation at selected weather stations 1961–1990.

	Mean temperature			Mean precipitation		
	annual	Jan.	July	annual	Jan.	July
Reykjavík	4.3	−0.5	10.6	799	76	52
Akureyri	3.2	−2.2	10.5	490	55	33
Reykjahlíð	1.4	−4.8	9.9	435	33	47
Dalatangi	3.5	−0.3	8.0	1410	135	97
Kirkjubæjarklaustur	4.5	−0.4	11.2	1645	145	121

quent change between freezing and thawing. In polar areas and in cold mountainous areas frost processes and glacial erosion are the main geomorphological processes.

The time available to external forces is of great importance to shaping the land by weathering and denudation.

Climate in Iceland

The following chapters frequently refer to various climatic factors in Iceland and for this reason a brief summary is included at this stage.

Iceland lies at the junction of two climatic zones i.e. the temperate zone and the arctic zone. The climate is cool temperate and maritime, the weather constantly changing and with high precipitation. The summers are cool and the winters mild. There is, however, a considerable difference in climate in different parts of the country as the table of mean temperature and precipitation values for 1961–90 at various localities shows.

The mean temperature is higher in the south and this difference is mainly due to higher winter temperatures. The highest temperature recorded in Iceland is just over 30°C and the lowest −38°C. In Reykjavík the absolute warmest day recorded is 24.3°C and the coldest −24.5°C. The precipitation is, however, very much less in the north due to the fact that the prevailing winds producing precipitation are southerly or south-easterly. They lose their moisture over the southern highlands and are mild and dry by the time they reach the north. The highest mean precipitation to be recorded at Kvísker in Öræfi was 3500 mm, while at Reykjahlíð, Mývatn it was only 435 mm. Such climatic differences are without doubt reflected in denudation amounts for the surface runoff per square kilometre is for instance much higher in the south. For the same reason glaciers are larger in the south and glacial erosion therefore more intensive. The temperature is considerably lower in the highlands than on the coast and frost intensity is also more so that frost processes are of greater significance. Because of the lack of vegetation in the highland areas wind erosion and denudation by wind is much more than on the lowland.

Weathering – chemical and mechanical

14

Chemical weathering

The term chemical weathering is used when rock breaks down due to the effects of material in solution in rainwater or ground water. This can either mean that the rock simply dissolves on reaction, or that there are reactions between the rock and solution.

Rainwater always contains some atmospheric gases but mainly two of them are chemically active, i.e. oxygen (O_2) and carbon dioxide (CO_2). The atmosphere contains 21% oxygen and 0.03% carbon dioxide, but the gases in rainwater contain 34% oxygen and 2.5% carbon dioxide. On sinking downwards through the rock various other substances are added to a small extent in particular from rotting plant and animal remains. These are mainly ammonia, nitric acid, chlorine compounds, sulphuric acid and humus acids and it is mainly these as well as the gases mentioned which cause weathering.

One of best examples of chemical weathering is the solution of chalk in carbonated water (water in which CO_2 is dissolved). Pure water has practically no effect on chalk but carbonated ground water dissolves it quite rapidly. In chalk areas this leads to the development of large caves and sink holes or *karst* scenery, the name being coined from a chalk area of that name in Yugoslavia (Figure 14-1). Where the water emerges again on the surface, carbon dioxide escapes from it while the chalk precipitates out as spring chalk (travertine). If chalk water is boiled it loses carbon dioxide and chalk precipitates to form kettle stone. Chalk is actually unusual in that it dissolves better in cold water than in hot.

Oxygen and hydrogen ions which are carried downwards with the water are very reactive and combine with metals an example being the rusting of iron compounds. *Oxygen weathering* occurs mainly above the water table.

Chemical weathering is very dependent upon climatic factors, especially temperature and moisture, as well as upon vegetation. In poorly vegetated polar areas and in desert areas where there is practically no water, almost no chemical weathering takes place. In hot temperate climates and rain forest areas of the tropics it is on the other hand very rapid and can be effective to depths of tens or hundreds of metres. In cold temperate climates chemical weathering is slow since the air temperature is low. Chemical weathering is also dependent on the rock types which make up the bedrock since they vary in strength.

Normally when rocks break down not

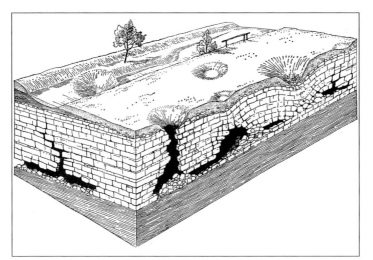

Figure 14-1. Undulating landscape formed when carbon dioxide rich ground water dissolves chalk bedrock is known as karst. Most of the world's caves are in such areas. (Wagner 1950.)

all of them goes into solution to be washed away but rather various amounts of residual material is left behind. In southern latitudes these materials can form thick strata. Thus chemical weathering frequently involves the formation of new rock types and minerals, e.g. clays, bauxite and bog iron ore.

Chemical weathering is of great importance to soil formation since it releases nutritional materials for plants while the clays which form retain them, absorb moisture and prevent them being leached out too quickly.

In Iceland chemical weathering is not very significant because of the low air temperature. The chief type is the solution of iron from the volcanic rocks by bog waters. This then accumulates in bogs as bog iron ore. During the Tertiary period chemical weathering was much more important in Iceland, the temperature at that time being much higher than now. The red beds which occur interstratified with the basaltic lavas bear witness to this warm climate. They contain large amounts of clays and bog iron ore (colour!) (Figure 24-8). The alteration of rocks in geothermal areas can be regarded to some extent as chemical weathering.

Biogenic weathering

Animals and plants cause chemical weathering an example being that lichens dissolve the rock with carbon dioxide which they produce to the advantage of higher plants. Certain shells, sea urchins and sponges bore their way through the rock with the help of acids which they produce, thus preparing the way for further weathering processes.

Plant roots often force their way into openings and fractures in rocks thus loosening or shattering them. This is known as *root shattering*. Plant roots also break down the soil. Earthworms which eat their way through the soil also perform a weathering role. It should also be mentioned that livestock loosen the soil by tramping thus accelerating soil erosion.

Mechanical weathering

Mechanical weathering is the weathering of solid rock or unconsolidated material without any change to the chemical composition. It is the result of temperature changes, frost weathering, as well as disintegration due to salt crystallization and plants and animals.

Figure 14-2. Frost weathering on the Icelandic Parliament building which is constructed of grey basalt in 1881. The cement between the blocks weathers more slowly than the basalt and can be used for comparative purposes. At least 5 cm of the block on the right have flaked off. A "crust" which is flaking off can be seen on the left block. (Photo Þ.E.)

Differential thermal weathering

In hot and dry climates as in deserts, there is a great difference between temperatures at midday and at night, the daily variation reaching up to 35–45°C. The temperature differences in rocks exposed to sunlight are, however, even greater, or 50–60°C. In most cases materials expand on heating and contract on cooling and this also applies to rocks and minerals. Because of the diurnal temperature variations the rock expands and contracts with temperature change but the changes do not affect the rock at depth since most rocks are poor conductors of heat. As a result the outer crust of the rock is constantly expanding and contracting and therefore gradually flakes off.

Sometimes this occurs suddenly accompanied by a loud report and is called *sun bursting*. Not only does the outer crust exfoliate in this way, but individual minerals have their own coefficient of expansion with the result that mineral grains press against each other and gradually break down the rock. Desert sand has usually formed as a result of breakdown due to differential temperature changes. In Iceland such processes are of little importance since the diurnal temperature changes are small, but they can

Figure 14-3. Frost weathering on an erratic on the Breiðamerkursandur, SE-Iceland, which was deposited by the Breiðamerkurjökull glacier around 1945. Breiðamerkurjökull and Öræfajökull in the background. (Photo Þ.E. 1977.)

be significant on east-facing cliffs where the morning sun can suddenly heat precariously positioned boulders after a cold night.

Frost weathering

Water has the unique property of expanding when cooled below freezing point. The volume increase is around 9% as is illustrated by the fact that 1/10 of an iceberg floating on water is above the water level. If water freezes in cavities filled to more than 91% the ice exerts enormous pressure on the walls of the cavity causing them to give way and disintegrate.

Frost can therefore only break down rock if it is fractured or porous. In Iceland rocks are usually of this kind and in addi-

tion flow-banding is common. Secondly, the rock must be moist. The more porous and fractured the rock is, the more rapid frost weathering will be. It is greatest in conditions where freezing and thawing is frequent.

Icelandic rocks withstand frost weathering to various degrees. Pleistocene basalt lavas disintegrate and break down rather quickly since they contain numerous small cavities. A good example of frost weathering in the rock can be seen in the Parliament building (Alþingishús). Since its construction in 1881 several centimetres have flaked off the walls (Figure 14-2). Móberg (palagonite tuff) weathers in a similar way to the Pleistocene basalt lavas. In the Tertiary basalt lavas frost is active mainly in fractures between co-

Figure 14-4. Þúfur forms due to frost heaving in grass-covered land. The picture is taken at the edge of a peat bog at Laxnes in Mos-fellsdalur, SW-Iceland. (Photo Þ.E.)

lumns, dislodging them. On the other hand frost breaks down rhyolite mainly along the flow banding and rhyolite mountain slopes are usually covered by screes of large and small slabs. Frost shattering is more active in the highlands than on the lowland and can very quickly break down huge boulders (Figure 14-3).

Frost weathering is very important for the formation of soil in Iceland for much of the inorganic part of it is the result of rock breakdown due to frost. The rest is largely composed of volcanic ash or aeolian dust. Practically all the scree material on mountain slopes in Iceland is the result of frost weathering. Where the process is rapid the screes are usually bare of vegetation (Figure 7-12).

Frost activity (Sorted ground)

Needle ice. During the winter the soil gradually freezes and ice forms in it. Needle ice crystals are first to form but they coalesce to form ice lenses. The soil also lifts upwards due to the volume increase involved when the water freezes and forms *needle ice.*

Ice expansion lifts small stones and pebbles but with the next thaw these do not return to their original position but the hollows are replaced by fine grained material when the ice melts. In this way stones are gradually lifted so that in time a gravel bed covers the ground. It should also be borne in mind that the wind removes the finest material and plays some part in the production of the deposit. On the other hand frost can not lift the large stones due to their weight or because they lie so deep that they reach below the ice. As a result hollows form above them as the surrounding soil is heaved upwards. For the same reason fence posts lift upwards and slope if they have not been driven far enough into the ground.

Solifluction. When ice melts in the spring it does so from above and also from below due to the heat flow from the earth. The water formed on melting can not move downwards since the ice frozen layer beneath is impermeable. The thawed soil becomes saturated, remaining so until all the ice goes, when it dries up in a few days. On sloping ground the waterlogged soil creeps slowly downslope over the frozen layer underneath. This is known as *solifluction*, a process which can be classified as denudation

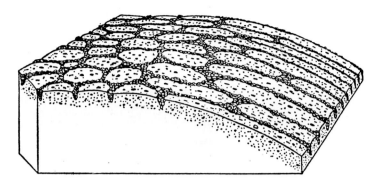

Figure 14-5. Frost heaving and solifluction on unvegetated land result in stone polygons on flat ground, stone stripes on sloping land.

rather than weathering since it results in debris transport.

Ice melt often causes difficulties in the spring. On roads the mud squirts up though the ridges between wheel tracks and out to the side of the road, while furthermore the roadfill sinks. In a few places the ice remains in small patches into the summer and leads to the formation of potholes in the road. In order to prevent frost activity affecting structures such as roads so called "frost free" materials are used such as sand, gravel or crushed pillow lava. Water drains easily through such materials thus preventing ice formation.

Þúfur (vegetated hummocks) and stone polygons. Ice expansion not only causes lifting of the soil but also results in pressure laterally which causes the soil to push upwards in a hummocky pattern. Repetition of this movement results in *þúfur* on grass covered ground (Figure 14-4) and *stone polygons* on unvegetated ground (Figure 14-5 and 14-6). Stone polygons are usually 4–6 sided and 25–100 cm in diameter. They are delimited by some garlands which form when small pebbles creep due to frost expansion or slide in the mud of the first thaw out from the soil hummocks. The stone garlands therefore form the depressions between the hummocks. Where there is little slope a network of stone polygons forms while on sloping ground the garlands are drawn out due to more active creep and *stone stripes* are

Figure 14-6. Stone polygons on Axarfjarðarheiði, NE-Iceland. The shovel is 1 m in length. (Photo Þ.E.)

Figure 14-7. Palsa bog with palsa hillocks Þúfuver in Þjórsárver, central highlands. The palsas are about 1 m in height. The peat has been dug away from the palsa in the foreground. In July 1984 the ice core was at a depth of 50 cm. (Photo Þóra Ellen Þórhallsdóttir.)

formed (Figure 14-5). On steeper slopes a series of rising steps is formed rather resembling sheep tracks, the steps themselves being unvegetated. In milder conditions, the mildest areas of Iceland such as in the lowlands on the southern slopes of the Eyjafjöll mountains and in Mýrdalur the steps are well vegetated and form due to downslope creep rather than due to frost activity. This could be termed soil creep. Where the slope is steep solifluction lobes can form.

Frost polygons and wedges. In persistent and severe frost the ice starts to contract, its behaviour resembling any other solid. This causes the soil to crack, often with considerable noise , the cracks being termed *frost polygons*. In Iceland they only form on lowland in severe frost winters when the ground is snow-free. On highland quite a lot of frost polygons occur, however, often as large polygons resembling stone polygons but with a much greater diameter of 10–30 m. Frost polygons get gradually wider with repeated frosts as ice forms in them (ice wedges). When the ice melts in the summer sediment or soil occupies the fractures so that they can be used as evidence of a colder climate during the Pleistocene in warmer countries. Whole systems of *ice wedges* are widespread in the highlands as for instance at Hvítárvatn and in the Mývatn area.

Permafrost. In polar areas and in mountainous areas where the mean annual

131

temperature is below 0°C and precipitation rather low, the ice remains in the ground all year. The thickness of the ice layer is furthermore dependent on the ground temperature, which is most in Alaska and Siberia where it reaches up to 1000 m. In the summer the soil thaws to a depth of 0.8–1 m but because of the underlying ice the water can not sink downwards. For this reason permafrost areas are also very water logged and difficult to cross. Vegetated permafrost areas are either wooded (taiga) or covered in stunted growth, mainly grass and shrubs (tundra).

In a few areas above 500–600 m in central Iceland there is permafrost, the mean annual temperature being under 0°C and precipitation low. It occurs mainly in topogenic depressions and hollows as well as along rivers. These areas are also very boggy and closely resemble the topogenic bogs (flóamýri) in the lowlands. They are known as *palsa bogs* and are interspersed by low dome shaped hills or *palsas* while in between are small lakes and areas of bog cotton (Figure 14-7). The palsas are usually 1–2 m in height and 5–15 m in diameter. In the late summer the ice core is at a depth of just under a metre. Palsa bogs are common in the Þjórsárver area and north of Langjökull and Hofsjökull for instance.

Sediments and sedimentary rocks

15

Due to weathering and erosion the solid rocks of the earth become gradually broken down as explained in the preceding chapters. Rock debris and dissolved materials are, however, seldom long in the place where they weathered, but are transported away by water, wind or glaciers and settle out in the short term on dry land, in river channels and lakes, or in the long term in the sea to form new beds known as *sediment* or *sedimentary beds*.

Through time the beds are compressed by overburden load and become consolidated and cemented and bonded to form new *sedimentary rock*. The hardening of the sediment is either due to the effects of outside materials such as chalk, silica or bog ore which seep through it in the ground water, or due to the coalescing of the sediment grains. The speed of coalescing is very dependent on temperature and pressure the rate of chemical reaction being greater if one or both increase. The amount of time available and type of rock are also of great importance e.g. the coalescing of sand composed of quartz grains is much slower than of volcanic ash and pumice. For this reason Icelandic sediments are usually hard and consolidated even though they are young, e.g. from the late Pleistocene because they are

mixed with fine volcanic materials. In other countries sediment of a similar age is usually unconsolidated. The consolidation of sediments changes for instance sand to sandstone and calcareous ooze to limestone.

Classification of sedimentary rocks

Sediment is classified according to weathering mechanism, transport and how it accumulates into three main groups:

1) *Chemical sediment* is formed by the precipitation of dissolved materials in the sea, lakes or soil. Among chemical sediments are bog ore, which is deposited from iron rich waters in bogs, rock salt which is precipitated in the sea by rapid evaporation in hot dry climates on coastal lagoons or salt lakes and calcareous ooze (limestone) which is a widespread bottom deposit in warm or tropical oceans. In Iceland at present there is little formation of chemical sediment apart from bog ore although beds of geyserite form at hot springs (e.g. at Geysir), calcareous travertine at warm mineral springs (e.g. Lýsuhóll on Snæfellsnes) and clay, sulphur and gypsum at solfataras and fumaroles. Thick deposits of bauxite and other clay-rich sediments which are widespread in hot wet countries are residual deposits

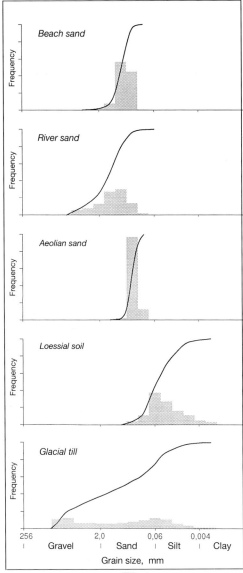

Figure 15-1. The graphs show the grain size distribution of selected sediments. The curves are cumulative from 0 to 100%. They are steep when the sediment is well sorted, but gentle and span many grain sizes when the sediment is poorly sorted. The bar graphs also show the grain size distribution, the height of the columns indicating the amount of material in each size group. The vertical scale for the bar graphs is twice that of the cumulative graphs. Note that grain size decreases from left to right. (Drawing Jón Eiríksson.)

formed when the soluble materials of weathered rocks were washed away.

2) *Organic sediment* is formed from plant and animal remains. Certain organisms absorb calcium carbonate or silicic acid making use of it as shell for protection or as tissue for strength. Amongst animals which absorb calcium are for example shells, corals, sponges and foraminifera while among plants examples are algae. In addition the spine of vertebrates is mainly composed of calcium carbonate. Similarly siliceous diatoms, radiolaria and siliceous sponges make use of silica. When the organisms die their remains survive, often accumulating as thick beds, especially in the sea and in lakes where conditions are more favourable for their preservation than on dry land. Thick beds of shelly sand (e.g. in Faxaflói), calcareous ooze and coral reefs on the sea floor are formed in this way and in time form limestone. In northern regions thick beds of siliceous diatoms accumulate on lake bottoms forming diatomite (e.g. in Mývatn). On land, plant remains accumulate to form widespread thick beds, especially where water protects them from rotting. This occurs mainly in lakes and bogs forming for instance layers of peat which through time become coal. It should also be pointed out that on the sea floor where there is little current and a lack of oxygen the soft tissues of organisms only rot to a very small extent and this results in the formation of oil (chapter 22).

3) *Clastic sediments* refer to rock composed of rock fragments. Clastic sediments are classified in various ways. Firstly they are classified by grain size, i.e. the diameter of the grains of which they are composed and in particular the largest grains although usually there are fine grains in between. Clastic sediments are furthermore classified according to means of transport, e.g. æolian sand, or

134

Sediment classification by grain size
(Udden-Wentworth scale)

grain diameter	sediment	sedimentary rock
> 256 mm	boulders	conglomerate
64–256 mm	stones	stony breccia
2–64 mm	gravel	breccia
0.063–2 mm	sand	sandstone
0.004–0.063 mm	silt	siltstone
< 0.004 mm	clay	mudstone

according to the location of the sedimentation, e.g. fluvial, lake or marine sediment. Sometimes they are classified according to the mineral content, e.g. quartz sandstone or moberg or tephra sandstone. On transportation the rock debris is sorted by grain size according to the current velocity. Thus boulders are the first to be deposited followed by gravel, sand and clay.

Glacial till, scree deposits and rockslide or landslide deposits are given special treatment in the classification of clastic sediments. In *glacial till* there is very little sorting according to grain size as in other sediments, but rather all the grain sizes are completely mixed together and include all sizes from clay up to subrounded boulders and erratics, which are often striated. Hardened glacial till is called *tillite*. The same applies to screes on mountain slopes and to rockslides with the difference that the debris and boulders are not smoothed but angular. Such sediment is known as *breccia.*

The composition of sediment grain is to some extent dependent on the properties of the rock grains from which it was formed, since the debris is ground down during transport. When igneous rock such as granite breaks down, all its rock forming minerals occur in the debris at the weathering location. On transportation the debris by for instance running

water mica (hardness 2) is the first mineral to break down and be destroyed followed by feldspar (H6). Finally only quartz grains (H7) remain since they are both hardest and are also resistant to chemical weathering. For this reason beach sand in most places is mainly composed of quartz grains. In Iceland on the other hand sand is not classified according to the properties of the grains to the same extent since the transport distance is usually short and mineral composition different (basalt).

In fluvial and marine sediments resistant and heavy mineral or metal ores, e.g. gold and platinum sometimes accumulate because they settle out in strong currents due to their weight where lighter grains are in suspension or resist weathering because they are chemically stable. Valuable mineral resources have accumulated to such an extent in some places that they can be mined although it would not be economical to extract them from the rock of origin. This is true of platinum in the Ural mountains and gold in South Africa, Alaska and elsewhere as well as of diamonds in for instance the Vaal river in South Africa.

Sediment bedding

Through time thick sedimentary formations accumulate in which there is usually bedding. The bedding is usually the result of variations in the sediment supply or of changes in the current or depth while the effect is that the grain and chemical composition of individual beds varies. Thus beds of clay alternate with sandstone, conglomerate or limestone and so on. Sometimes the bedding varies according to the time of year, e.g. wave deposits in proglacial lakes. The division between individual beds is known as a *bedding plane*.

Sediments are often thin layered or laminated except where there has been current or wave action, in which case there are inclined foreset beds (Figure 16-15). Delta deposits are for instance always dipping because they settle out in the sea or lakes where the current ceases, suddenly releasing its load. This results in steep slopes down which coarse sediment slides (Figure 16-14). Sediment in river channels e.g. floodplain deposits or glacial sandur deposits, is usually inclined or with pockets of beds dipping in various directions (cross bedding). The current velocity and direction in such cases is constantly changing and for this reason individual pockets dip in various directions. Aeolian sand also consists of groups of variably dipping beds which can be observed during sand dune formation, erosion being on the weather side and sedimentation on the lee side. Fluvial, lake or marine sediment is usually transported in waves as wave marks in the sediment show and miniature cross bedded sets are often produced in this way.

Soil

The uppermost layer in the earth is called soil (earth, peat). From an economical point of view the unconsolidated layers in which plants grow or can be grown can be regarded as soil, as demonstrated by the planting of Icelandic sand areas in recent years. It would be more accurate to define soil as *sediment composed of fresh or weathered rock debris mixed with rotting or rotted animal and plant remains*. The proportion of organic to inorganic material varies considerably, e.g. the mineral content of Icelandic peat formed before the settlement is 10–30% after subtracting layers of volcanic ash, while in aeolian soil, the tephra loess on dry land (peat soil), it is 85–90%.

Icelandic soil can be divided into two main groups, on dry ground the *aeolian soils or tephra loess* (chapter 20) and *waterlogged soils* or peat bogs (chapter 22). This classification depends mainly on the ground water conditions rather than the rock permeability e.g. the loessial soils are more widespread on móberg and lava areas than on the Tertiary basalt areas. From a sedimentological point of view the mineral soil in Iceland should belong to clastic sediments, being mainly composed of wind blown material and volcanic tephra. The peat soil is classified as organic sediment being formed mainly of plant remains.

Due to the low air temperature chemical weathering is very slow in Iceland. Subaerial formation of clay is for instance practically non existent in the soil, which is to be regretted, for clay delays the leaching out of plant nutrients from the soil and retains fertilizer. For the same reason various nutritional salts are released only slowly from the rock debris, a fact which accounts for the phosphor scarcity of Icelandic soils.

Rivers, fluvial erosion and sedimentation

16

Due to the sun's heat, water is constantly evaporating from the oceans and indeed also from the land. The water vapour is carried by the wind, condenses as cloud and then falls as precipitation. Precipitation on land runs off as rivers and streams or sinks down into the soil and bedrock to flow slowly underground as groundwater. Part of the precipitation which falls on land evaporates again due to the sun or plants. The relative importance of each of these factors depends on the permeability of the bedrock, the climate and the vegetation cover in the area concerned (Figure 16-1). The permeability of the rock depends mainly on its porosity, i.e. how many pores it contains. For instance sand and gravel beds are porous while clay is non porous and impermeable.

Of the water resources of the world, 97.2% is in the sea, 2.1% in glaciers, 0.6% in groundwater, 0.009% in lakes and rivers and 0.001% is in the form of water vapour in the atmosphere.

Groundwater

Below a certain level all the pores and fractures of the rock are occupied by water. This is known as *groundwater* and its surface the *water table*. The area between the water table and the earth's surface is always moist even though the pores are full of air. This area is known as the *vadose zone* and its moisture content is fairly constant since precipitation percolates through it during wet periods while during drought or frost capillary forces draw moisture from the groundwater. The groundwater level is thus variable according to weather conditions and season. In wet periods such as following autumn rains or spring thaws, the level is high but low following extended frost or drought.

Groundwater flows slowly but constantly downslope, the fractures, cracks and pores in the rock producing considerable resistance to the flow. The smaller the pores, the slower the flow will be. On the other hand groundwater rarely flows in any preferred channels or direction except in fractures and along dikes.

The water table follows the surface landscape but lies proportionally deeper under hills than under hollows (Figure 16-2). In wetlands the water table coincides with the ground surface, while in drill holes and wells it is at the water table level. Where the water table intersects the surface, particularly on valley sides and floors *springs* are formed. The water table usually corresponds to the water

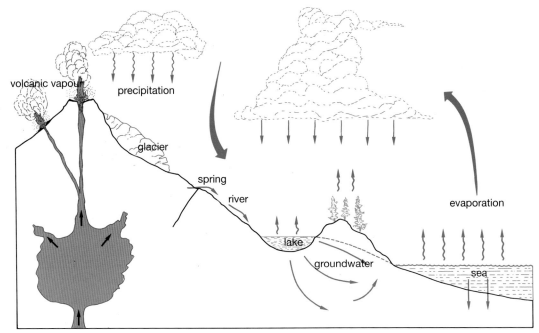

Figure 16-1. The water cycle. Evaporation, cloud formation, precipitation, volcanic vapour, surface runoff and groundwater flow. (Drawing G.H.I.)

level in lakes and also to sea level. In lakes from which there is no surface outlet such as Öskjuvatn, Kleifarvatn and Kerið in Grímsnes, the water level is the same as the water table level and is therefore subject to the same variations.

Non porous and impermeable beds such as clay have a strong effect on groundwater flow. In Iceland it is most conspicuous where sand and gravel beds overlie clay beds as for instance in river banks. Here there are often spring or groundwater seepage at the junction of the beds and they keep the clay moist. In bedded formations where permeable and impermeable beds alternate such as the Tertiary basalts which are intercalated with fine grained sediments the groundwater can often occur on several "levels". In such cases the bedding dip controls the groundwater flow so that it emerges downslope in mountain sides as a spring line. Such springs are common in the Tertiary Plateau Basalt areas where the spring line is often coloured light green by moss and plant vegetation because of the water supply.

Basalt dikes and fractures which cut across the bedrock also affect the groundwater and control its flow. Springs are common where dikes and fractures intersect the surface in hollows or on sloping ground. Reykjavík's water supply at Gvendarbrunnar and Hafnarfjörður's supply at Kaldárbotnar are examples of productive fracture springs. The water production of such springs is very much dependent on the size of the groundwater catchment area and the porosity of the rocks. If the catchment area is large the flow is fairly constant but if it is small, the springs have a high flow in wet periods but dry up during drought.

On islands, peninsulas and along the

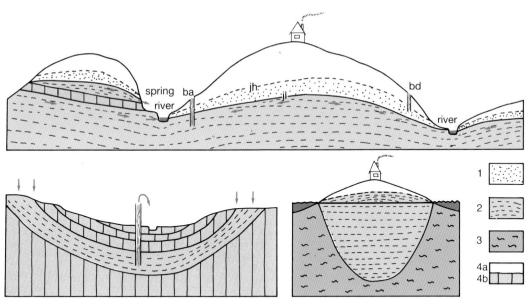

Figure 16-2. Groundwater. Top: Normal groundwater conditions. On the left is an impervious bed which controls the groundwater flow so that a spring forms where it cuts the hill side. Below, left: Groundwater under pressure between impervious beds (artesian water). The arrows to left and right represent precipitation, that in the middle the height to which the water rises. Bottom right: A groundwater lense floats on sea water on an island or peninsula of porous rock. Symbols: 1) rock occupied by groundwater during wet periods, but dry during drought, 2) rock occupied by groundwater, 3) sea water occupying bedrock, 4a) vadose zone, 4b) impermeable beds, jl = lowest groundwater situation, jh = highest groundwater situation, ba = well which supplies water all year and bd = well which dries up during drought. (Drawing Þ.E. and G.H.I.)

coast where the rock is porous, the groundwater often floats on top of the sea water and does not mix because of the difference in density and due to the flow resistance in the rocks. The thickness of the groundwater lens is 40 times the height of the water table above sea level (Figure 16-2). This situation occurs in Iceland at Keflavík on the Garðskagi peninsula for instance. Care must be taken in utilizing the water in areas like this since downdraw of the water table due to pumping causes a 40 fold rise in sea water from below.

Where clay or other impermeable beds cover porous rock in bowl-shaped formations, the water from precipitation flows from the edges in towards the centre of the bowl. The groundwater is then under pressure (artesian water, Figure 16-2). Drilling through the impermeable layer into the centre of the depression causes the groundwater to erupt under pressure. If a pipe is positioned at the drill hole, the water rises in it to the level of the lowest scarp at the edges of the clay layer. This is the only situation where groundwater will flow of its own accord from drill holes or wells. The most famous examples of this are in the Paris and London depressions, where groundwater flows from the highland surrounding bowl shaped depressions in Cretaceous chalk beds which are overlain by early Tertiary clays.

As mentioned earlier, the flow and

139

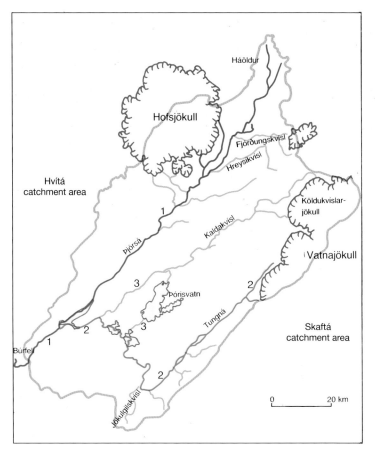

Figure 16-3. Catchment area of the Þjórsá river above Búrfell in Þjórsárdalur, S-Iceland. Þjórsá (1) is the main river, Tungná (2) a first order tributary and Kaldakvísl (3) a second order tributary.

amount of ground water depends largely on the porosity of the bedrock. In Iceland there are mainly three types of groundwater area (cf. Figure 24-1).

1) *Tertiary basalts and early Pleistocene basalt lavas.* The bedrock in areas having these rocks is fairly impermeable since the clay beds between the lavas are very impermeable and in the Tertiary lavas most of the pores and fractures are filled by clay or amygdales with the result that the precipitation largely runs off on the surface. Thus the groundwater is very limited and can be observed mainly as water seepage at the downslope intersection with bedding planes or at fractures and dikes. Even in the Tertiary areas there

can be considerable water flow along dikes and faults as was discovered during tunnelling at Strákar in Siglufjörður in 1965–67, at Ólafsfjarðarmúli in 1988–1991 and in the Ísafjörður tunnel 1993 (cf. also chapter 9 on geothermal energy).

2) *Móberg, late Pleistocene basalt lavas and hyaloclastites and Holocene lava areas.* In these areas the bedrock is very porous. The precipitation sinks rapidly so that there is practically no surface run off but productive springs occur in depressions and valleys. The water flow and temperature in these springs are very constant throughout the year since the water has been in the ground for a long time and is almost immune to changes of air temperature.

3) *Unconsolidated strata*. In alluvial deposits outwash deposits and sandy Pleistocene and Holocene sediments there is usually plentiful groundwater. The amount depends mainly on the size of the area and the thickness of the sediments.

Groundwater is always superior to river or stream water because impurities are filtered out as it flows through the rock. Groundwater is usually exploited by well digging or by drilling. Pumping causes a depression to form in the water table around the well or drill hole and the inflow increases as a result. However, shallow wells and drill holes often dry up due to seasonal changes in the water table level, especially in dry periods during the summer or in frost during the winter (Figure 16-2).

Water is one of the most important necessities in daily life. Population increase in the past few centuries and the concentration of people in the cities causes ever increasing problems in obtaining domestic water supplies. Because of overuse the depth to the water table steadily increases so that the purification of river water or even sea water has been resorted to in many places. This has become increasingly difficult because of widespread pollution caused by industrial waste disposal and sewage. In rural areas in Iceland drinking water has been fairly easily obtained, but with urban growth water consumption has greatly increased and will soon cause problems in acquiring domestic water supplies.

The acidity (pH) of domestic water in Iceland generally, is not well known, but in Reykjavík for instance it is around 9, i.e. too basic by international standards (6.5–8, maximum permitted 8.5). Little is known about the amount of dissolved solids and harmful products in domestic water in Iceland.

An increase in industrial activity and in the number of motor vehicles has resulted in acid rain in many areas abroad, especially due to sulphur and poisonous materials in smoke so that soil, river water and lakes have become dangerously acidic. This acid rain has killed aquatic organisms, plants and forest areas where the soil is naturally acid such as in Scandinavia, central and eastern Europe as well as Canada and United States. The only way to reduce the pollution is by using less oil and coal and by preventive methods such as smoke purification. Neutralizing the acid soil with lime is of little use due to the size of the polluted areas.

Rivers

Rivers and streams can originate as surface run off from impermeable bedrock, as groundwater from porous rock or as meltwater from snow or glaciers. The area from which the river receives its run off is known as the *catchment area* and the division between catchment areas is known as the *water shed,* which runs along highland ranges or ridges, the catchment areas sloping outwards from it in both directions (Figure 16-3). In Iceland Jökulsá á Fjöllum has the largest catchment area at 7750 km^2 with Þjórsá being the next largest at 7530 km^2 . The highest mean discharge is at the estuaries of Þjórsá, 383 m^3/sec, Ölfusá, 440 m^3/sec and Jökulsá á Fjöllum, 212 m^3/sec. By comparison the mean discharge of Elliða-ár at Reykjavík is 5.5 m^3/sec. The mean velocity in rivers is around 5 km/hr or similar to a man's mean walking speed. Although the catchment area of Jökulsá is much bigger than that of Þjórsá, its mean discharge is only about half of that of Þjórsá. This clearly illustrates the difference in precipitation in the north and south of the country. The longest rivers in the country are Þjórsá, 230 km and Jökulsá á Fjöllum, 206 km.

141

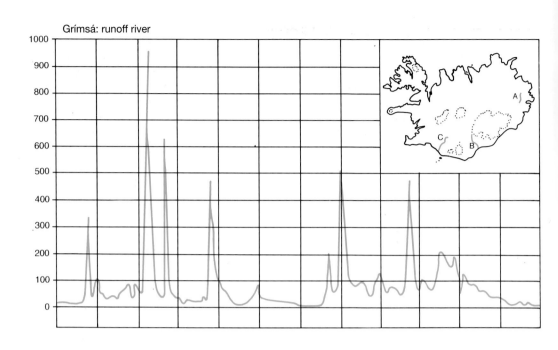

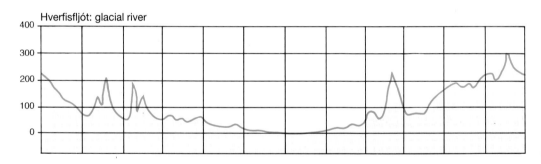

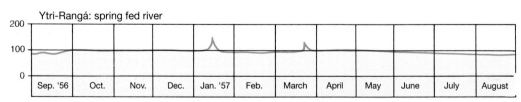

Figure 16-4. Runoff patterns of Icelandic rivers. Grímsá in the Fljótsdalur district, E-Iceland, is a direct run off river. Hverfisfljót in the Vestur Skaftafellssýsla district eastern S-Iceland is a glacial river and Ytri-Rangá, S-Iceland, is a spring fed river. The average discharge is represented by 100 and variations calculated as a percentage. Measurements are for September 1956-August 1957. (Sigurjón Rist 1956.)

Classification of rivers

Icelandic rivers are classified by source and character into three groups: direct run off rivers (dragá), spring fed rivers (lindá) and glacial rivers (jökulá).

Direct run off rivers are restricted to areas with rather impermeable bedrock and are therefore mainly found in the Tertiary Plateau Baslat areas in the west, east and north. Such rivers frequently have no clear source but originate in seepage from hollows and valley networks, gradually increasing in size down channel. Similar to most rivers abroad, their discharge is very dependent on the water conditions. In rains they increase rapidly but dry up in dry periods or in frost. The vegetation in the catchment area also greatly affects the discharge pattern of direct runoff rivers, well covered soil retaining moisture and evening out run off. The water temperature in these rivers closely follows air temperature, being warm in the summer and cold in the winter. During frost ice quickly forms so that they frequently swell during freezing. Their discharge thus falls in frost or they even dry up completely. During thaws their discharge increases rapidly, they burst through the ice and clear themselves. This is sometimes accompanied by the formation of ice ridges or dams so that they flood their banks or change their courses. During floods direct run off rivers are sometimes strongly coloured by peaty water. A good example of a direct run off river is Grímsá in Skriðdalur, E-Iceland, (Figure 16-4). It has a mean discharge of 27 m^3/sec but in flood a record discharge of 645 m^3/sec which is about 24 times more. During frost the river has almost completely dried up. Other large rivers of this type are for example Stóra-Laxá in Hreppar, S-Iceland, Norðurá in Borgarfjörður, W-Iceland, Eyjafjarðará and Fnjóská, N-Iceland, which is the longest, 117 km.

Spring fed rivers have their source in springs in Holocene lava, móberg (pyroclastic rock) and Pleistocene doleritic lava areas. As opposed to direct runoff rivers they have a very clear source, often in gushing springs and sometimes attain their full size a short distance from the source. Their discharge is even throughout the year and the water temperature is also constant. As a result they are not sensitive to changes in precipitation or temperature or the changes are delayed for a long time. Floods are rare in spring fed rivers and occur mainly during thaws in winter or spring when there is frost in the ground and the melt water can not sink downwards. Rivers of this type do not freeze near their source but in severe frosts they can freeze further downstream. The main spring areas are Ódáðahraun (Svartá) south of Mývatn, the Hekla area (Ytri- and Eystri-Rangá), inland in Árnessýsla in the west (Brúará) and the Reykjanes peninsula (Kaldá). Spring streams also have their source in large rockslides or landslides. A good example of a spring fed river is Ytri-Rangá (Figure 16-4) in which the mean discharge is 50 m^3/sec, the least discharge recorded 24 m^3/sec and the greatest flood, 364 m^3/sec in February 1968 was unusual, or 7 times the mean discharge.

Rivers such as Sog draining Lake Þingvallavatn and Laxá in Þingeyjarsýsla in N-Iceland also belong to this group of rivers even though their source is in lakes, because the lake water originates as spring water. For instance only about 5 m^3/sec surface runoff enters Þingvallavatn while the mean discharge of the Sog river is about 106 m^3/sec. This large discrepancy between the inflow and discharge can be explained by groundwater which constantly flows into the lake from the surrounding lava and móberg rocks.

Glacial rivers have their source in glaciers and are the result of ice melt. Their

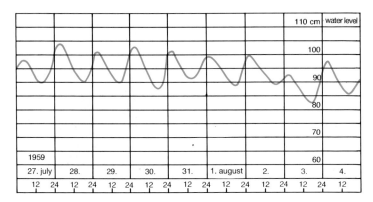

Figure 16-5. Daily variations in the glacial river Kaldakvísl, southern highlands. Illugaver about 50 km from its source in the Köldukvíslarjökull. (Sigurjón Rist 1956.)

discharge is very dependent on air temperature and is several times more during the summer than in the winter. They are at their highest in summer rains when the rain water adds to the meltwater. They increase greatly during mild spells and in sunshine regular daily variations in their discharge occur (Figure 16-5). At the glacier snout they reach a maximum discharge between midday and three o'clock and are at their minimum in the morning around sunrise. The temperature of glacial rivers is just over 0°C at the snout, but on calm sunny days it can reach 15–20°C further downstream. Ice piles up quickly during frost so that normally they freeze over during the first frosts. They are grey in colour due to the rock flour and sediment which the glaciers have ground down from the bed rock. However during frost they can be almost clear blue in colour. Hverfisfljót in Vestur-Skaftafellssýsla in S-Iceland, near Kirkjubæjarklaustur can be taken as an example of a glacial river. It has a mean discharge of 38 m^3/sec, a minimum discharge of 2.5 m^3/sec and a maximum flood of 282 m^3/sec. The discharge during floods is thus 7.5 times more than the mean. The catchment area of Hverfisfljót is only 330 km^2 and the figures show that the mean discharge per square kilometre is thus very high.

Jökulhlaup. In certain rivers which have their source in Vatnajökull and Mýrdalsjökull there are occasionally catastrophic floods or jökulhlaup, for which there are two main causes.

Firstly, valley glaciers in the main valley can sometimes block ice-free tributary valleys damming the flow from them and leading to the formation of glacial lakes. In this way Skeiðarárjökull blocks a tributary at Grænafjall and forms a 15 km^2 lake, Grænalón, which is 200 m deep. When the water depth in the lake reaches 9/10 of the glacier thickness the glacier lifts up and the water bursts out. Glacial lakes often burst at regular intervals so that Grænalón has for instance a burst almost yearly, the flood water emerging on the western part of the Skeiðarársandur in the rivers Súla and Núpsvötn. At its maximum the discharge is about 2000 m^3/sec.

Secondly, jökulhlaup floods accompany subglacial eruptions such as occur in Katla and Grímsvötn. The maximum discharge in Katla floods is between 100,000 m^3/sec and 200,000 m^3/sec and 50,000 m^3/sec in the Grímsvötn or the Skeiðará floods of 1934 and 1938. The flood water has different origins, but both volcanoes are in depressions or calderas which fill with meltwater between eruptions. At the beginning of the eruption the depression empties, while in addition water accompanies the eruption which is probably

Figure 16-6. Skeiðará is a glacial river which spreads out over its plain, Skeiðarársandur. In the background the glaciers Svínafellsjökull, Skaftafellsjökull and Skeiðarárjökull farthest left, SE-Iceland. Looking towards the NE. (Photo Sigurður Þórarinsson.)

mainly heated groundwater and this melts the glacier ice. When the eruption commences the water bursts out on top of, underneath or within the glacier which it breaks up and fractures. In past centuries the Skeiðará-jökulhlaup have often caused great damage. Grímsvötn has flooded at 4–5 year intervals in past decades without any visible signs of eruption and the floods have been smaller with a maximum discharge of 2000–10,000 m^3/sec or similar to the Grænalón floods.

The main types of Icelandic rivers and their typical features have now been described. Close to their source their features are well developed but further downstream these become less well de-

fined as the rivers tend to become a mixture of several types. For instance the Ölfusá river in S-Iceland is a glacial river at its source (Hvítá), a direct run off river (Stóra-Laxá) and a springfed river (Brúará and Sog). Rivers in neighbouring countries are almost all direct runoff rivers. The channels of rivers will be described more fully by a description of their sediment load

Denudation by rivers

Running water is very effective in shaping the land and is in fact the most effective of the external processes in this respect. If the velocity is low the water flow is layered, but usually it is so high that

145

Figure 16-7. Gullfoss, looking northwards. The lower waterfall threshold is 20 m high and the upper 11 m. At the bottom is conglomerate (Sa), followed by the lower threshold bed which is coarsely columnar grey basalt (B_1) which forms the ledge at left foreground. The sedimentary layer Sb comes between B_1 and the upper threshold bed, the grey basalt B_2, which can be seen at the top of the section to the right. At the top of the gorge face on the left is a basalt flow unit which overlies foreset bedded pillow breccia. For notation of the beds see Figure 16-8. (Photo Þ.E.)

the flow is irregular and typified by eddies and whirlpools.

Sediment load of rivers

Rivers transport debris which has been removed from the rock by weathering or by current and use it as a tool to deepen and widen the channel. The sediment load is transported mainly in two ways. Firstly the smallest grains are borne upwards and float in the current as *suspended sediment*. The grey sediment of glacial rivers belong to this category.

Secondly, coarser debris rolls or slides along the bottom with the current as *bedload*. It is mainly bedload which erodes the river bed, but at the same time the debris itself is broken down and gradually becomes sand and rounded gravel. The finer sand travels downstream as sand waves called ripple marks.

River water always contains some *dissolved solids* which are the result of chemical weathering and erosion. The amount of dissolved material depends on the type of rock and soil in the catchment area. In Iceland the amount is on the average about 70 mg/litre or similar to the amount in Reykjavík's domestic water. In tropical rainforests chemical weathering and erosion are so active that the rivers are dark in colour as for example the name Rio Negro suggests.

Figure 16-8. Cross section of Gullfoss. Symbols: 1) grey basalt beds, 2) fine grained sandstone ("mudstone"), 3) sandstone, 4) conglomerate, 5) tillite. The dotted lines show the beds as they were before erosion. B_1 = lower threshold layer, B_2 = upper threshold layer. (Drawing Þ.E.)

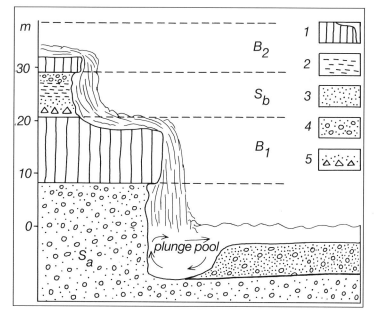

The transport capacity of rivers depends on their discharge and stream velocity. If the velocity doubles, as for instance during a flood, then the transport capacity increases greatly or by about 2^6 (two to the power of 6). If the river can move gravel of 20 g weight at this mean discharge then a doubling of velocity during a flood will enable it to transport 1280 g boulders. This explains the huge rounded boulders which are often found in stream and river beds and which could not be transported in normal discharge conditions. The bedload also doubles in these conditions so that twice as much sand and gravel is transported per unit area and with twice the energy which means that the erosive capacity of the river is many times greater. It should also be borne in mind that objects immersed in water are lighter by the amount of water which they displace so that for example a 2.5 g basalt fragment is 1 gram lighter in water. Furthermore river ice can lift large and small boulders and carry them over long distances.

As can be seen, denudation by rivers is very dependent on their discharge patterns. Direct runoff or glacial rivers which have irregular flow cut downwards much more than spring-fed rivers for their discharge in floods is often 5 to 15 times more than in average conditions. In addition the source of spring-fed rivers is usually not far above sea level so that their beds slope little.

During floods direct runoff rivers carry a heavy load and cut rapidly downwards, so that they often flow in gorges where the slope is steep. On reaching flat land their velocity and transport capacity falls and gravel and boulder beds are formed. The erosive ability is at its most in direct runoff rivers during rapid thaws in the winter or spring when they break up the ice cover . The broken ice pushes large boulders, cutting and tearing the banks. As a result these rivers usually flow over extensive flood plains where vegetation is sparse due to disturbance in floods.

The same applies to glacial rivers. However, the sediment load is much more and

147

Figure 16-9. The Hvítá canyon below Gullfoss was formed due to erosion by Hvítá since the end of the Pleistocene or in the past 10,000 years. The canyon is about 3 km in length. Looking from the air to the southwest. The figures show channels of various ages (canyon sections). 1. channel older than 6600 years (H_5), 2. channel older than 4000 years (H_4), 3. channel younger than 1300 AD and older than 1693 and 4. channel younger than 1766. The age is based on the age of tephra layers from Hekla in soil profiles, cf. Figure 16-10. (Photo Hjálmar R. Bárðarson.)

more constant since glaciers provide an almost unlimited quantity of debris. Erosion is therefore much more than in direct run-off rivers and their gorges are the largest in the country. Where the slope decreases they spread out so that their velocity and transport capacity decreases. They release their sediment load and become braided. Their channels rapidly fill with sediment and the branching streams wander over the gravel plains but can not cut any permanent channel. This is mainly because the bed load contains more coarse material than it can transport. However, the main stream often flows for long periods in more or less the same place or until the sediment has filled up the channels to such an extent that the flow shifts (Figure 16-6 and 16-14).

Spring-fed rivers are quite different due to their constant discharge. Their sediment load is fine grained, usually sand and their banks are vegetated right to the water level.

During the past years the sediment load amount of several Icelandic rivers has been measured. Þjórsá at the Urriðafoss waterfalls transports 5 million tons of and 0.8 million tons of bed load yearly, though the coming of hydroelectric schemes in the area has changed this. It is believed that Icelandic rivers have a higher amount of suspended sediment than bed load, opposite to rivers in other coun-

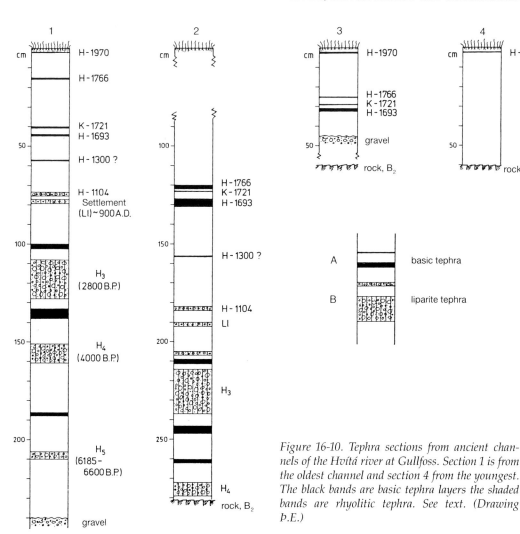

Figure 16-10. Tephra sections from ancient channels of the Hvítá river at Gullfoss. Section 1 is from the oldest channel and section 4 from the youngest. The black bands are basic tephra layers the shaded bands are rhyolitic tephra. See text. (Drawing Þ.E.)

tries. On the whole Icelandic rivers transport about 50 million tons every year as suspended sediment while bed load barely amounts to half this.

It is quite easy to measure the amount of suspended sediment and dissolved solids in river water but very difficult to measure bed load. This is changing however, with the advent of man-made lakes at hydroelectric plants. The filling up of reservoirs by suspended sediment and bed load (sand and gravel) is a wide-spread problem in the world since such infill gradually reduce their storage capacity. The acidity (pH) of precipitation in Iceland is around 5.6 but due to chemical weathering and erosion of the rock and soil it is 7–7.5 in glacial and direct runoff rivers and 8.5–9.5 in spring-fed rivers.

Bed erosion by rivers

When debris slides or rolls with the current it wears down and erodes and at the

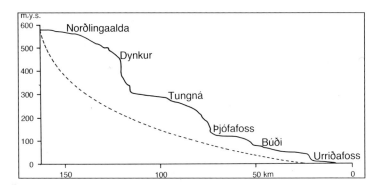

Figure 16-11. Section of the channel of the Þjórsá river from the coast and inland to Þjórsárver, central highlands. This represents the channel of a youthful river, but in time when the falls and irregularities are smoothed and the river attains a graded profile, the channel will resemble that shown by the dotted line. See Figure 16-3.

same time the rock in the river bed. The rate of erosion depends to a large extent on the velocity and is usually greatest where there is a considerable slope in the channel. An example of bed erosion is provided by Gullfoss where the basalt layer which forms the threshold of the waterfall is only 1–4 m thick, but 10 m in the canyon wall east of the waterfall (see Figure 16-7). Bed load in the Hvítá river has thus eroded a deep channel into the basalt.

Potholes. In streams and rivers which flow over a rough bed there are frequently eddies, so that the gravel and boulders revolve in the current cutting steep-walled circular potholes in the bed. They are often 1–2 m in diameter and several metres deep. If they form side by side in the riverbed the partitions are gradually worn away and the channel is deepened considerable. Well-formed potholes occur at the waterfall edge in the western branch of the Elliðaár river in Reykjavík and at Brúarfoss falls in the Hítará, W-Iceland river.

Waterfalls are common in rivers which cut downwards through layered strata where the beds vary in hardness. Hard beds form the *threshold* of the falls and protect the softer bed underneath. The soft bed is then undercut so that the overlaying rocks overhang and become unstable and gradually collapse. The falls are most impressive where the softer beds are thickest and most of the largest falls in the country have formed in this way.

A *pool* always forms beneath the waterfall due to the force of the falling water and the formation of the pool often plays a major part in undercutting.

The geological setting and history of one of Iceland's largest and most beautiful waterfalls, Gullfoss in the Hvítá river (Figure 16-7, 16-8, 16–9) will now be described and in particular how its development has been traced through tephrochronology (Figure 16-10). There are two steps to the waterfall which has an overall height of 31 m. The upper step is 11 m and the lower 20 m. Late Pleistocene ba-

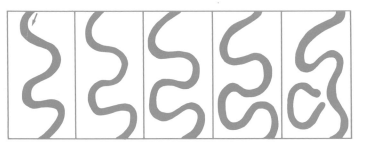

Figure 16-12. Meanders are features of a "mature" river which has attained a graded profile. They migrate slowly as the current erodes the banks in sharp meanders. (Holmes 1965.)

Figure 16-13. Currents in a meandering river. The stream current cuts the banks outermost in the meander, but deposits the load on the inside curve.

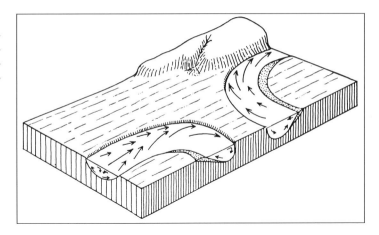

salt lavas forms the threshold of both stages of the waterfall, while underneath are thick sediments. The thickness of the upper and lower lavas is 10 m and 12.5 m respectively as observed in the canyon downstream of the falls. Between them is an almost 10 m thick sedimentary bed consisting of boulder beds, siltstone and uppermost conglomerate, while underneath the lower lava is a layer of conglomerate, which is visible in the waterfall as being 8 m thick. The sediments are all well cemented except for the conglomerate. It contains pockets of loose gravel which is easily washed out and they play the main part in undercutting the waterfall. Due to undercutting in the sediment, large columns frequently fall from the lava layers causing the threshold to move upstream, while slowly lengthening the canyon at the same time. The Hvítá canyon below the Gullfoss fall is 40–70 m deep and about 3 km in length (Figure 16-9). It was eroded in the bedrock after the ice sheet disappeared from the area 10,000 years ago. Denudation has therefore been about 30 cm per year on average, but was probably strongest while the ice sheet was melting probably in catastrophic floods with a discharge of tens or thousands of cubic metres/sec. The greatest floods in the Hvítá river at Gullfoss in

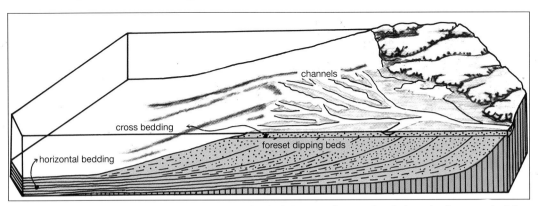

Figure 16-14. Deltas are formed from the sediment load of rivers at the mouths of rivers in the sea or in lakes. They extend gradually outwards as sediment is constantly added. The sediment is coarsest at the mouths of the channels but becomes finer with distance. (Drawing G.H.I.)

151

Figure 16-15. Section through a delta. Leirvogstunga gravels in Mosfellsbær, SW-Iceland. Two series of foreset beds.

this century as for instance in March 1930 are around 2000 m³/sec or almost 20 times the mean discharge. Visible changes to Gullfoss are slow.

Among other large canyons which have formed in a similar manner are those of the rivers Jökulsá á Brú and Jökulsá á Fjöllum although their history is more complicated. The horseshoe formation of Ásbyrgi in the lower part of the Jökulsá á Fjöllum valley should be regarded as part of the latter canyon since it formed as the result of fluvial erosion at least partly in catastrophic floods from the Vatnajökull glacier. The river Jökulsá á Fjöllum last flowed there 2000 years ago.

The thresholds which lead to the formation of waterfalls originate in various ways, such as being due to glacial erosion (Fjallfoss in Dynjandi, NW-Iceland), ma-rine erosion (Skógarfoss, S-Iceland), rock slides (Skeiðfoss in Fljót, N-Iceland), lava flow (Goðafoss, N-Iceland) and due to faulted strata (Öxarárfoss at Þingvellir, Figure 10-1).

Geomorphology of rivers and fluvial landforms

Canyons and gorges are typical features of *youthful rivers*. They are deepened through time when falls and obstructions are worn away while the canyon walls become gradually sloped due to weathering and form *V-shaped* valley profiles. The river continues to cut downwards, deepening the valley until the river bed is at sea level at which point the limit of erosion is reached, the *base level* (Figure 16-11). Some direct runoff rivers in Iceland,

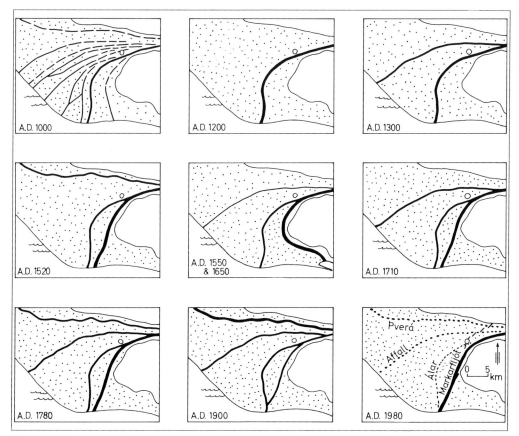

Figure 16-16. Changes to Markarfljót, S-Iceland, during historical time. The river has migrated over its plain and its mouth has been at several locations, from Holtsós off Eyjafjöll and westwards as far as Hólsá, or over a distance of 50 km. (Hreinn Haraldsson 1981.)

such as Eyjafjarðará, have reached this stable of development.

There are few V-shaped valleys in Iceland, the time since the last deglaciation being too short for them to have been re-established. Exceptions are to be found in extensive rhyolite areas such as the Torfa-jökull and Kerlingarfjöll areas as the rocks are easily eroded.

As the development of the valley approaches the base level the river meanders and widens the valley. The V-shaped valley profile eventually becomes flat bottomed or U-shaped in profile. The *meanders* which typify the *mature river* are, however, far from stable as the force of

the current constantly cuts into the outer banks of the meanders so that they gradually move down the channel until the river cuts through into the neighbouring meander (Figure 16-12). As a result water ceases to flow in the old meander and so called oxbow lake forms in it. Good examples of meander rivers are Víðidalsá, N-Iceland, Reykjadalsá in Borgarfjörður, W-Iceland and Laxá in Kjósarsýsla, SW-Iceland. The channel length in meandering rivers is often double that of a direct line through the valley (Figure 16-13).

Provided there are no crustal movements in the catchment area at this stage in the river's development then the valley

153

broadens until all the irregularities of relief are worn down and a completely smooth *peneplain* has formed.

Faults in the bedrock often control fluvial erosion. For instance most rivers in Southern Iceland run from north-east to south-west while in northern Iceland they run from *south to north*. This orientation follows the dominant tectonic fracture system. Where the river channel lies across a fracture system the gorges or canyons often follow a zigzag path (Figure 16-9).

Deltas and alluvial fans

Fluvial erosion occurs mainly in the upper reaches of the channel where there is a considerable slope. The lower part of the channel on the other hand usually slopes gently so that the current velocity drops and the sediment load is deposited. This is most obvious where rivers or streams emerge on to plains from canyons or gorges. As a result *alluvial fans* often form which slope outwards in all directions from the gorge mouth and which are criss-crossed by streams and rivers during floods.

Of similar origin and formation are the *sand and gravel banks* of direct runoff rivers and the *sandur* of braided glacial rivers (Figure 16-6 and 16-16) although much greater in extent. Boulders and gravel are deposited first to form gravel *flood plain deposits*, then sand to form sandy plains and finally, where the land is very flat or at the coast, silt or clay where mudflats form. Fluvial sediment is always *bedded*, either composed of *sets of inclined beds* of sand and gravel or almost horizontal lens-like cross bedded deposits (Figure 16-15).

The part of the sediment load which is not deposited as *outwash plains* or flood plains is carried on by the current as far as the river mouth at the sea or in a lake.

Here the current decreases suddenly so that the sediment is deposited to form *deltas* or *coastal plains*. Characteristic of delta deposits are *dipping foreset beds*. A delta bed which is deposited at the same time, such as during a flood, is usually well sorted by grain size. Gravel and then sand from the bed load are deposited closest to the river mouth while further out at greater depth silt and clay are deposited from the suspended load (Figure 16-14). Through time new beds are constantly added to the slope (foreset beds) so that the river mouth and delta formation extends further seawards. During floods the river changes channel and erodes the foreset beds but forms cross-bedded lens-like beds instead.

Deltas are common at the mouths of all rivers, both in the sea and in lakes. They are very extensive indeed at the mouths of major rivers such as the Mississippi and Nile and they really represent the cradles of civilization being ideal for cultivation and irrigation. In Iceland the delta of the Markarfljót river in S-Iceland is one of the largest and belongs to the flourishing but marshy region of Landeyjar. In the past 1000 years the Markarfljót river has wandered over the outwash plains between Fljótshlíð and Eyjafjöll its mouth reaching furtherst east at Holtsós south of Eyjafjöll and furthest west at Þverá which enters the sea together with the rivers of Eystri-Rangá and Ytri-Rangá at Hólsá. Altogether this area amounts to some 40–50 km along the coast (Figure 16-16). In past decades the Markarfljót river has been controlled by protective dikes which restrict its flow to a particular channel.

In many valleys in Iceland there are *gravel terraces* and deltas which formed at a higher shoreline at the close of the Pleistocene i.e. in late glacial time some 10,000 years ago (Figure 24-29). They are usually old delta deposits in origin.

Glaciers and glacial erosion

17

Glaciers form where more snow accumulates yearly than rain and evaporation and summer temperatures can melt. The snow remaining from each year is known as *firn*. The division between the firn area and the ablation area of the glacier is called the *snowline* and is often clearly delimited on glaciers in the late summer. The altitude of the snowline depends on air temperature and precipitation. In polar regions it generally lies at sea level. It is highest at the tropics at 5000–6000 m, but somwhat lower at the equator where the precipitation is greater. Outside of the polar regions therefore glaciers are almost entirely on mountains, which is understandable bearing in mind that air temperature falls by 0.5–1°C for every 100 metres increase in height. Nowhere is the height of the snowline more dependent on precipitation than in Iceland, its height being very variable in different parts of the country. Along the southern edge of Vatnajökull it lies at a height of 1000–1100 m, while along the northern edge it is at 1300–1400 m. In the Ódáðahraun area north of Vatnajökull it lies at 1700 m (Herðubreið at a height of 1682 m is ice-free). This difference corresponds to the difference in precipitation between the northern and southern parts of Iceland (cf. chapter 13).

Glacier formation and movement

New fallen snow is soft and light being formed of feathery, hexagonal snowflakes. Through direct evaporation, compression or initial melting of the snow, the branches disappear and coalesce as grains. The snow changes to *firn or névé* and then to *crystalline glacial* ice as more is added from above, i.e. as new snow. Normally the transformation of firn to glacial ice is complete at 20–30 m depth and the crystals are about 1 cm in size.

When the firn and ice thickness in the firn area has reached 30–50 m thickness it is so plastic that it starts to creep under its own weight outwards from the ice divide. Usually the glacier flow follows the landscape so that glaciers flow from the firn area down valleys and depressions to below the snowline as valley glaciers or outlet glaciers. The firn area does not increase to any significant extent however even though snow is added to annually, because the flow of ice more or less keeps pace. Glaciers are therefore sensitive to climatic changes and advance or retreat according to how the seasons have been. Several snow-heavy years in a row produce more snow than normal in the firn area which shortly afterwards results in flow of the glaciers which originate there.

Figure 17-1. Breiðamerkurjökull and Jökulsárlón on the Breiðamerkursandur, SE-Iceland. Looking towards the NW. The nunataks in the background are Mávabyggðir on the left and Esjufjöll on the right. From them extend the medial moraines of Mávabyggðarönd and Esjufjallarönd. The black bands are tephra layers. (Photo Þ.E. 1977.)

It is believed that a change in the mean annual temperature of 1°C causes the snowline to move upwards by about 200 m if warmer, and downwards by 200 m if cooler. Not only do the glacier snouts advance but the glaciers also thicken at the same time. If the climate gets warmer again the glacier snouts retreat and thin out (Figure 17-3). Melting of glaciers involves both the retreat and thinning of their snouts due to a warming climate and an advance in a cooling climate. These changes are largely independent of glacier flow itself which is constant throughout the year.

It is relatively easy to measure glacier flow by for instance setting up a reference line of markers across it. At the end of a year the markers have moved, the greatest movement being by the markers in the middle part of the glacier, where the thickness is greatest and the resistance to flow least. The rate of flow of most larger valley and outlet glaciers in Iceland is about 1 m per day although it depends on glacier thickness, the slope of the land and the size of the accumulation area.

Certain valley and outlet glaciers *surge,*

Figure 17-2. Vatnajökull. Firn and snow above the snowline appear rather dark while glacier ice below the snowline is blue-white. Unvegetated land is dark red or grey, vegetated land yellow-brown. Rivers, lakes and sea are blue, glacial water green. Satellite picture taken on 22ⁿᵈ Sept. 1973. (Iceland Geodetic Survey.)

their snout advancing by hundreds of metres or several kilometres in a short time. Brúarjökull, NE-Vatnajökull, surged in this way by 8 km during the winter of 1963–64, the peak flow rate at the snout being 25 m in 24 hours. Altogether an area of 1400 km² was affected which was severely fractured and disrupted. Brúarjökull also surged in 1750, 1810 and 1890,

in the latter year huge end moraines being pushed up at its snout at Kringilsárrani and known as Hraukar (Figure 17-13). Such surges are known both here and abroad, examples being in Dyngjujökull in 1934 and 1951, Tungnárjökull in 1945, Hagafellsjökull, Langjökull, 1971–80 and Síðujökull in 1994, all outlet glaciers of Vatnajökull. The reasons for such surges

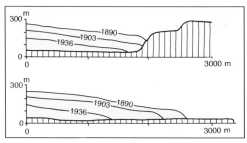

Figure 17-3. Cross section (above) and longitudinal section (below) of Hoffellsjökull. Scale in metres. The years show the glacier surface in 1890, 1903 and 1936. It can be clearly seen that glaciers become thinner as they retreat. (Ahlmann and Sigurður Þórarinsson 1937.)

in glaciers are not known for certain but they occur mainly in glaciers which rest on a fairly flat surface. Between surges the crevasses close and heal and the glaciers retreat until the next surge takes place.

The upper layers of the glacier are fairly brittle since the ice there has not become plastic. *Crevasses* form on the surface when the glacier flows over variable relief or if the valley width changes. If the glacier flows over a threshold or cliff a *transverse crevasse* forms. When the glacier is thin and the slope steep it breaks up into ice slabs which coalesce and form continuous glacier ice again below the step. Glaciers of this type are called glacier falls good examples being Falljökull on the west of Öræfajökull and Kvíárjökull on the south of Öræfajökull (Figure 17-11). Widening of the glacier (channel) results in *longitudinal crevasses* forming on the surface. At the edge or snout of a glacier there are often small *radial crevasses* which are orientated at an angle against the direction of flow. Crevasses are seldom more than 30–50 m deep, the ice being so plastic at this depth that fractures heal again (Figure 17-7).

In glaciers outside of polar regions the *ice temperature* is at freezing point. Thus it

follows that melting can occur anywhere within the glacier in such areas (temperate glaciers). However, melting occurs mainly below the snowline and is more rapid the further below this the glacier reaches. The temperature of Antarctic glaciers is on the other hand always below freezing point (*cold glaciers*). Glaciers in these regions get smaller mainly by direct evaporation, removal of snow by wind or by calving *icebergs* when they enter the sea. These are carried by ocean currents into warmer waters where they melt. Melting due to the sun is rather slow if the glacier is composed of pure ice, but if covered by 1–2 cm thick dirt layer it is much faster. If the dirt layer is more than 3–4 cm thick, melting is slower since the

Figure 17-4. The Greenland ice sheet. The glacier has been "lifted" to show that the centre of Greenland is below sea level. The glacier is 2000–3000 m thick. (Geological Museum, Copenhagen.)

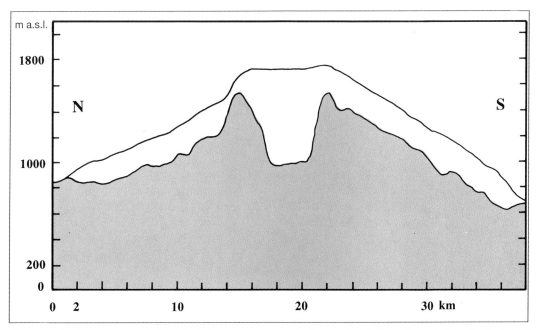

Figure 17-5. Cross section of Hofsjökull from north to south, from Sátujökull to Blautukvíslarjökull. (Helgi Björnsson 1988.)

ice will be insulated. This is particularly clear where dirt has collected in depressions in the glacier. On melting *ice cones* are formed which are covered by dirt. The most rapid melting is due to sunshine and warm winds.

Classification of glaciers

Glaciers are divided into three main groups ice sheets, ice caps and outlet or valley glaciers.

Ice sheets and ice caps are characteristic of polar regions and cold mountainous regions. Their *firn* area is usually much more extensive than their ablation area. They are usually very thick with a rather flat surface which slopes gradually outwards to the edges. This group includes the largest glaciers in the world such as the Antarctic ice cap which is 13 million km² and about 4000 m thick and the Greenland ice cap which is 1.8 million km² and 3000 m thick in central Green-

land. The underlying surface of the Greenland ice sheet is a basin shaped depression the bottom of which is below sea level in the centre while the edges are the coastal mountain ranges which rise above the ice cover in many places as knife edged ridges (Figure 17-6).

Most major glaciers in Iceland are ice caps. They differ in many respects however, from polar glaciers, not least in that the ice temperature is at freezing point and not below it. The largest is Vatnajökull, 8300 km², followed by Langjökull, 950 km², Hofsjökull 923 km², Mýrdalsjökull, 600 km², Drangajökull 160 km² and Eyjafjallajökull, 80 km². Several other glaciers in Iceland should be included in this group such as Tungnafellsjökull, N-Iceland 50 km² and Snæfellsjökull which was 22 km² at the turn of the century. During the past few decades it has decreased in size due to milder weather conditions and is now only 11 km².

The thickness of Vatnajökull has been

159

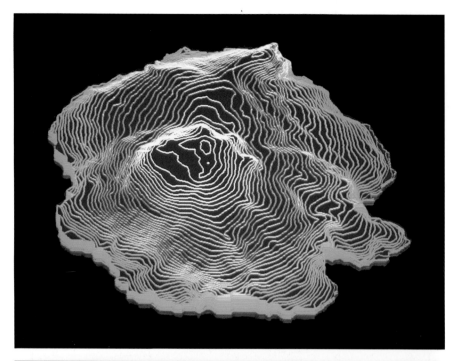

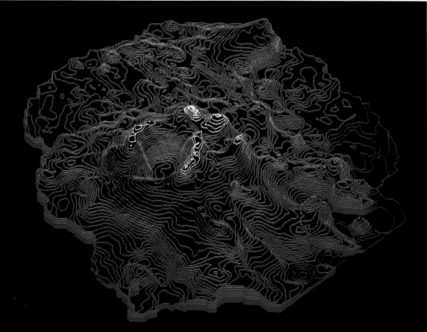

Figure 17-6. Hofsjökull. Computer generated map based on measurements using radar. The upper picture shows the glacier surface, the lower picture the underlying surface. See text and Figure 17-5. (Helgi Björnsson 1988.)

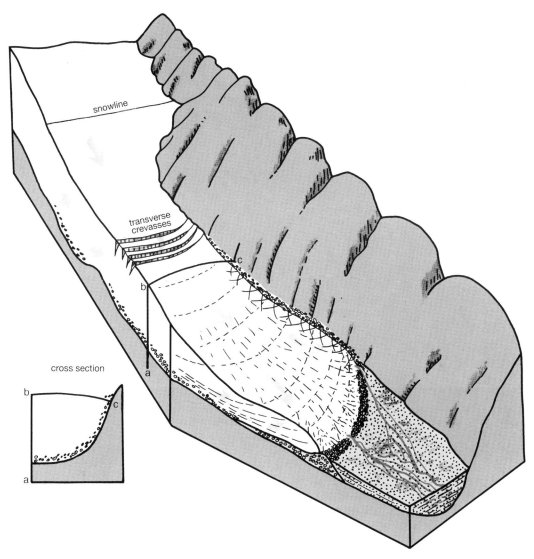

Figure 17-7. Diagram showing valley glacier with accumulation area and ablation area. Transverse crevasses occur where the glacier slides over irregularities. Chevron crevasses occur at the edges and "finger" crevasses at the snout. In front of the glacier are meltwater deposits. The arrows show the direction of glacier movement. (Drawing G.H.I.)

investigated using radar and seismology. It is generally 600–800 m thick and at the most 900–1000 m thick in the valley of Skeiðarárjökull just south of Grímsvötn. The land surface underneath is generally 600–1000 m above sea level, being highest in Bárðarbunga, Háabunga and Breiða-

bunga where it reaches 1200–1800 m. The outlet glaciers flow in huge valleys underneath the ice sheet.

Extensive research was carried out from 1980–90 on Hofsjökull which included thickness measurements using radar. The glacier is 923 km^2 with a maximum

161

height of 1800 m. About 2/3 of the under-lying land surface is higher than 1000 m, while the base of Múlajökull, which flows out of the southeast corner is at 550 m above sea level, i.e. about 50 m below the land surface bounding the glacier at Þjórs-árver. The average thickness of Hofsjökull is about 215 m and its volume 200 km^3. A large volcano, probably a central volcano, is situated underneath the summit of the glacier. It has a 650 m deep caldera which is overfilled with ice for the total thick-ness is over 800 m at this point. The nu-nataks Hásteinar are part of the eastern rim of the caldera and are composed of rhyolite. (Figure 17-4 and 17-5).

Valley or outlet glaciers. From ice sheets and ice caps usually flow large tongues known as outlet glaciers and which are in a sense their discharge. Their flow rate depends mainly on the amount of snow accumulation in the firn area, the glacier thickness and the slope of the ground. The rate of flow is often considerable, be-ing about 1 m a day in Iceland while in Greenland it can reach 30 m a day since the glaciers represent the discharge from a very extensive and thick ice sheet. The largest and most active outlet glaciers in Iceland are on the south of Vatnajökull. Valley and outlet glaciers reach far below the snowline (Figure 17-1).

The *valley glaciers* occur in high moun-tains outside the polar regions. They usu-ally originate in small firn areas in the val-ley bottom above the snowline. They are thin and their flow rate low, while their sur-face usually closely resembles the under-lying land surface and valley shape through which they flow. The rate of flow of valley glaciers in the Alps is for example only about 50–100 m a year. Some glaciers in the mountain ranges between Eyjafjörður and Skagafjörður, N-Iceland, resemble valley glaciers to some extent. The longest valley glacier in the world is the Hubbart glacier in Alaska, which is about 120 km in length.

Where many valley or outlet glaciers reach low ground over a limited area they coalesce on the lowland forming a glacier expanse which often displays a striped pattern of central moraines and seasonal dirt bands. Such glaciers are known as *piedmont glaciers* (or lowland glaciers). The best known example is the Malaspina glacier in Alaska which is formed by coa-lescing of several valley glaciers and spreads out over a 2500 km^2 lowland ar-ea. In Iceland Breiðamerkurjökull resem-bles a piedmont glacier, or at least it did, to some extent at the beginning of this century, when it extended further than at present and Hrútárjökull and Fjallsjökull extending to the southeast from Öræfa-jökull, joined it. The *outlet glaciers* in the southeast of Hofsjökull are also of this type (Múlajökull and Blautukvíslarjökull).

Finally there is a group of small gla-ciers which form near the snowline in hollows or depressions in the mountain-side. They form when snow from nearby mountains or mountainsides drifts into the valley heads. The snow layer then be-comes so thick in the winter that it does not melt in the summer. The thickness of *corrie or cirque glaciers* is sometimes so lit-tle that they barely flow. They usually separate from the backwall during the summer, releasing scree material to the crevasse or bergschrund which the gla-cier later transports. Cirque glaciers are fairly common in Iceland, mainly on high north-facing mountain slopes in NW-, N- and E-Iceland.

Glacial erosion

Glaciers transport debris which lies in their path and use it as an erosion tool. It is mainly the debris which is frozen into the base and sides of the glacier which cuts and erodes into the bedrock like a serrated plane. At the same time the de-bris is worn down and becomes rounded.

Figure 17-8. Striated bedrock with a scattering of erratics. The picture is taken west of the Hvítá canyon below Gullfoss. (Photo Þ.E.)

Striated rock surfaces are one of the main characteristics of glaciated areas while boulder clay or till is characterised by striated boulders. *Striae* vary in coarseness and length while their orientation indicates the direction of flow of the most recent glacier to cover the area. Glacially eroded rock hills often have a unique shape. On the side facing the direction of ice flow where the pressure is most they are quite smooth and sloped and often beautifully striated. The lee side is on the other hand steep and craggy where the glacier has plucked blocks from the bedrock. Glacially eroded hillocks of this type are known as *whaleback forms or roches moutonnées* (Figure 17-8). They are very common in Iceland, even characterising the landscape in some cases as in Borgarfjörður, W-Iceland, Eyjafjörður, N-Iceland

and in the Fljótsdalshérað region of E-Iceland. Together with striae they enable the direction of ice flow to be determined accurately and also provide information on the thickness and direction of flow of Pleistocene ice sheets.

The landscape formed by glacial processes differs in many ways to that formed by fluvial processes. Glaciers occupy the full width of the valley and therefore erode a much wider surface than rivers. Also glaciers cut into the mountain side as a whole, whereas rivers only erode where the force of the current is directed at the bank or mountain side, although in time rivers widen the valley. It should also be borne in mind that a thick glacier presses down heavily on the rock tools adding further to their erosive power. A glacier which is 1000 m thick for instance

Figure 17-9. Looking eastwards across Skutulsfjörður, NW-Iceland. The part of the town of Ísafjörður which can be seen stands on a gravel spit which has been formed by currents and wave action. The Tertiary basalt mountain face opposite is formed of almost horizontal lava layers. The cirque in the mountain is Naustahvilft formed by corrie glacier erosion. (Photo Hörður Kristjánsson.)

exerts a pressure of 900 kg/cm^3 on the rock surface. Glaciers which flow in ancient V-shaped river valleys widen them greatly and steepen their sides so that they become *U-shaped* in cross section. This is the main characteristic of the glacially eroded valley (Figure 17-7).

Glaciers do not have as strict a limit of erosion as rivers, their effectiveness being mainly dependent on the thickness of the glacier and rate of flow. Their erosive power decreases at sea level as they float when the water depth is 9/10 of their thickness and calve. This really represents their base lavel of erosion. Glaciers can thus erode deep troughs in solid bedrock

far below sea level. Thus the rock threshold responsible for the lake Lagarfljót in the Fljótsdalshérað, district, E-Iceland is 20 m above sea level and the maximum lake depth is 112 m so that it reaches 92 m below sea level. A similar situation applies to some fjords in Iceland such as Arnarfjörður, NW-Iceland and Hvalfjörður, SW-Iceland and some Norwegian fjords such as the Sognefjord which is about 1250 m deep, but only 100 m at its mouth. This discrepancy between the depth within the fjord and at its mouth is mainly because valley or outlet glaciers thicken landwards but are thinner towards the coast and as a result their erosive power is less at the snout.

Figure 17-10. Landscape shaped by rivers and glaciers. At the top is a landscape formed by rivers. V-shaped valleys are characteristic. Centre: valley and corrie glaciers shape the landscape. Bottom: rivers begin to modify the landscape anew. (Geological Museum, Copenhagen.)

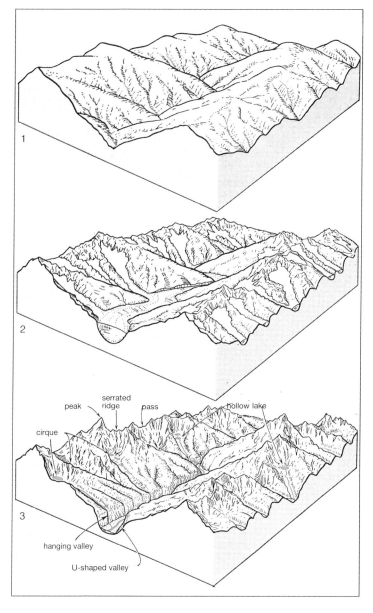

For the reasons outlined above, the landscape in glaciated valleys is completely different from that of fluvially eroded valleys. Glaciated valleys usually have an irreular relief because of difference in the strength of the bedrock and therefore resistance to erosion and plucking. In broad valleys and on lowland, whaleback forms are noticeable with hollows occupied by tarns or lakes between them. The heads of glaciated valleys are also much steeper than of river valleys, especially in cases where valley glaciers and cirque glaciers have been active. They separate from the backwall in the summer forming a gap between the gla-

165

Figure 17-11. Kvíárjökull in the south of Öræfajökull, SE-Iceland, extends from a summit ice cap. In front of the glacier is a very high end moraine, Kvíármýrarkambur, about 100 m in height. The glacier extended this far at the begining of the century and ice cascaded over the moraine. A medial moraine can be seen in the middle of the glacier. The nunatak on the left is Hnappar 1851 m. Debris from a rockslide covers part of the glacier snout. (Photo Þ.E. 1977.)

cier and rockwall. In the winter this fills with snow again so that the ice constantly freezes to fresh rock protrusions which it loosens the following summer (Figure 17-9). Cirque glaciers which form on either side of mountains therefore erode the mountain ridge between them and in time produce a serrated ridge. Most high mountain ridges in the Tertiary basalt areas have been formed in this way such as Breiðadalsheiði, NW-Iceland. Siglufjarðarskarð, N-Iceland and Oddsskarð, E-Iceland. Thin knife edged ridges now divided the valleys on either side. This together with lateral erosion by valley glaciers produces steep peaks and sometimes only isolated pinnacles remain. examples are Kirkjufell near Grundarfjörður on the Snæfellsnes peninsula (Figure 24-19),

Hestur in Ísafjarðardjúp, NW-Iceland, Súlur above the town of Akureyri and the Matterhorn in the Alps.

One important difference remains between glaciated areas and areas where only fluvial processes have been active. If the river in the main valley cuts rapidly downwards the tributary rivers cut downwards in accordance with the changed base level. This is not the case where the valley has been glaciated.

The glacier in the main valley is often many hundreds of metres thick and thus cuts downwards much more rapidly than the valley glaciers in the tributary valleys which are much thinner. Thus they can not keep pace with the main glacier in downwards erosion, their surface determining the erosion limit. The mouths of

Figure 17-12. The snout of a retreating glacier. A) End moraine formed by its maximum advance. An end moraine is formed as well as a proglacial lake. A glacial river runs along the moraine. B) The glacier has retreated and is practically at a standstill, a new end moraine forming. Rivers flow along the end moraine forming meltwater deposits. Between the outermost end moraine and the glacier are drumlins, either of till or kettle meltwater deposits. (Wagner 1950.)

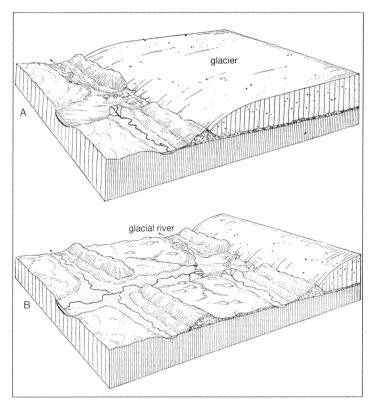

tributary valleys and cirque glaciers therefore often hang high above the main valley floor when the glacier melts. Because of the decreasing ice thickness down valley the bottoms of the tributary valleys inland lie higher up the main valley sides than they do further out the main valley (Figure 17-10). Good examples of *hanging valleys* can be seen at Skarðsheiði in southwest Iceland, in the Northwest fjord area, in Eyjafjörður, and E-Iceland.

Moraines and glacial till

Close to the ice divide erosion dominates and striated rock surfaces and whaleback forms are common. In the ablation area *glaciers* deposit till. This occurs mainly at the glacier snout where the glacier thins out and its transporting ability is gradually reduced until it is zero at the glacier snout. On the Breiðadalsheiði pass, NW-Iceland, for instance glacially polished outcrops covered by erratics occur while lower down towards Skutulsfjörður and Önundarfjörður the bedrock is generally covered by till.

Usually a large quantity of debris is carried along in the basal layers of the glacier as *ground moraine*. A considerable amount of debris is also distributed throughout the glacier as supraglacial till while debris which falls on to a glacier from the mountain slopes is transported as *lateral moraine*. Where two valley glaciers emerge from two valleys and coalesce or divide around a nunatak and coalesce on the lee side, the lateral moraines combine to form *medial moraines* such as occur at Esjufjöll and Mávabyggðarönd on Breiðamerkurjökull. The median moraines appear at the surface of the glacier

167

Figure 17-13. Esker at the edge of Brúarjökull, Kringilsárrani, which was uncovered with the retreat of the glacier in the past few decades. On the horizon an end moraine from the glacier surge of 1890 can be seen. (Photo Þ.E. 1955.)

and separate individual glacier streams (Figure 17-1).

In front of glaciers stand curved *end moraines*, which have either been pushed up when the glacier was advancing or have been deposited from ground moraine, lateral moraine, medial moraine and fluvioglacial deposits. End or terminal moraines are largest when the glacier front is at a standstill for long periods, all the load being deposited at the same place for a long time. Amongst the largest in Iceland are the end moraines at Kvíárjökull and Gígjökull. In Iceland there are, for instance, large end moraines at considerable distance in front of the outlet glaciers which were formed at their maximum advance over the past centuries (Figure 17-11).

Till which glaciers deposit on melting and disappearing is called *boulder clay or drift*. It is usually unsorted and composed of well mixed debris of all grain sizes, from clay particles up to large boulders. Boulders in till are often striated and usually fairly rounded. They are known as *erratics*. (Figure 14-3 and 17-8).

When a stationary or retreating glacier melts, individual slabs of ice often remain in till or fluvioglacial deposits. When the ice melts depressions are formed which become filled with water to form lakes called *kettle holes*. These have formed in till in many areas such as for example

168

Figure 17-14. Varve deposits at Krókslón above Sigalda, at the Tungná river, southern highlands. (Photo Þ.E.)

north of the Blanda river at Blönduós, at Ljósavatnsskarð near Tjarnir and at Laugar in Reykjadalur in the Suður-Þingeyjarsýsla district, N-Iceland. Kettle holes are common in the sandur areas of southern Iceland where icebergs have pressed or ploughed into the sandur deposit during jökulhlaup catastrophic floods. On the Skeiðarársandur there is still ice in kettle holes from the jökulhlaup of Skeiðará in 1903.

Fluvioglacial and glaciolacustrine sediments

As mentioned in the chapter on fluvial processes, fluvioglacial deposits or sandur areas (Figure 16-6) are formed from sediment of glacial rivers, mainly bed load. The sediment is usually bedded, either with foreset or cross bedded deposits. Old *sandur deposits* are widespread in areas which were covered by glaciers during the Pleistocene and along with striated rock surfaces and till deposits are clear evidence of the extent of former glaciers. Fluvioglacial deposits are known as sandur internationally, the name being coined from the Icelandic sandur of southern Iceland. A good example of old deposits of this kind are the lowlands of Rangárvellir, S-Iceland, which formed in late glacial and early Holocene time, which were formed at the glacier margins at the maximum of the last glaciation about 18,000 years ago. Also famous are the heaths of west Jutland in Denmark.

Meltwater which flows in channels on top of the glacier, but in particular in or underneath it, deposits its sediment load

169

in the same way as other rivers. On melting the glaciers unveil long sinuous ridges of sand and gravel, called *eskers* (Figure 17-13). Eskers also form where meltwater sediment is deposited in proglacial lakes at the edge of retreating glaciers. Eskers from the end of the Pleistocene are common in Scandinavia and North America but rather rare in Iceland. They do occur for instance on the south of Þjórsárver, and Reykjadalur in Suður-Þingeyjarsýsla, NE-Iceland, where the main road runs along a sinuous esker for several kilometres. Sediment in eskers is usually cross bedded or foreset bedded and is one of the best concrete aggregates occurring in Iceland, the finest grains having been washed out.

In some cases the meltwater flows between the glacier and the valley side, depositing sand and gravel which form terraces or deltas when the glacier melts. The erosive power of such meltwater can cut channels known as *meltwater channels,* clear examples of which can be seen at Másvatn west of lake Mývatn. Terraces or meltwater channels sometimes occur as a series of steps down the valley side making it possible to see how rapidly melting occurred, each step representing the yearly position of the retreating glacier.

In the summer glacial rivers are milky or dirty grey from their suspended sediment while in the winter they are almost clear. For this reason sediment deposited from glacial rivers, in still water or in the sea, is very sharply and regularly bedded, the suspended sediment being coarser in summer than in winter. Such laminated sediment consists of thick coarser summer beds which alternate with thin fine grained winter beds. The division between the beds is usually clearly defined. The thickness of individual layers varies according to season but is from several millimetres up to several centimetres (Figure 17-14). The yearly deposit, summer and winter layers, are known as *varves* and the sediment as a whole *varve deposits*. By counting the varves they can be used as a dating tool. Observations on varve deposits in Sweden have helped work out the history of the retreat of the last ice sheet and climatic changes in the past 14,000 years. Varve deposits are quite common in Iceland in for instance former proglacial lakes such as the Skáldabúða-lón in the Hreppir district, S-Iceland, in silt deposits belonging to the higher marine limit from the close of the Pleistocene such as at the Elliðaár river, at Reykjavík, the Borgarfjörður lowlands in the west and in the Fnjóskadalur (valley), east of Akureyri. in the latter case the varves were deposited in an ice dammed lake at the close of the Pleistocene. Icelandic varve deposits are generally composed of silt rather than clay.

Marine processes and landforms, the oceans and marine denudation

18

The sea covers about 71% of the earth's surface. In a similar way that the land is divided into lowlands and highlands the oceans are divided into the *deep oceans* which form 81% of the sea floor and the *shallow seas* or continental shelves which form 8% of the sea floor. The continental shelves are often regarded as reaching to a depth of 200 m where the *continental slope* commences. It is generally steep and comprises over 11% of the sea floor. The greatest ocean depth measured is just over 11,000 m in the Mariana trench in the western Pacific while the average depth of the oceans is about 3,800 m.

The floor of the deep ocean is rather smooth though ocean ridges stand up from it which run right around all the oceans of the world. The mid oceanic ridges are mountainous often having high peaks and deep valleys (Figure 18-1). One of the largest is the Mid Atlantic Ridge which runs the entire length of the Atlantic from Jan Mayen in the north through Iceland, the Azores and Tristan da Cunha to Bouvet island in the South Atlantic ocean. Volcanism and earthquakes are frequent on mid oceanic ridges. The entire deep ocean floor is composed of basalt, especially pillow lavas which erupt on the spreading ridges and moves slowly outwards, but beds of

deep-sea sediments are thinnest on the ridge where new crust is formed but increase in thickness outwards, the crust being oldest where it is subducted under continental plates (cf. chapter 12 on plate tectonics).

The continental shelves vary in width and are often of variable relief. The shelf around Iceland is only a few kilometres wide off Dyrhólaey but off the northwest, the north and east coasts it is tens of kilometres over a wide area. The Icelandic continental shelf (platform) has either formed due to deposition of sediments as is the case off the south coast and around the island of Flatey in the Skjálfandi bay, or due to fluvial, glacial or marine erosion as is the case off the west, northwest, north and east coasts. Here the shelf is formed of bedrock with islands and skerries sometimes quite far out such as Kolbeinsey, Grímsey and Hvalbakur. Submarine valleys or canyons of various depths cut the continental shelf in several places. They are usually a continuation of fjords or valleys on land. Little is known of their origin but it is generally believed that they are the result of erosion by strong bottom currents and turbidity currents, or fluvial or even glacial erosion at a lower marine limit of 100–150 m during glacial periods in the Pleistocene. In some ma-

171

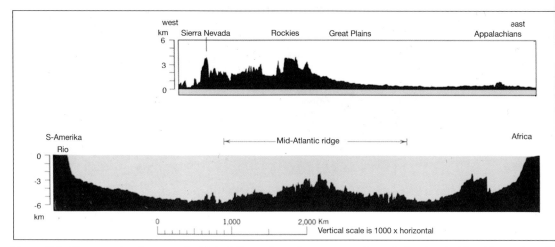

Figure 18-1. Upper section is across the United States from the east coast through the Appalachian Mountains, the Great plains, Rockies and Sierra Nevada Mountains to the west coast. For comparison the lower section is of the floor of the Atlantic Ocean from Namibia in west Africa, through the Mid-Atlantic Ridge westwards to Rio de Janeiro in Brazil. Vertical exaggeration 1000X. The sections clearly show that there is as great relief on the sea floor as on the continents. (Skinner and Porter 1987.)

rine sediments from earlier geological periods there are rich oil deposits such as in the North Sea and N.-Alaska.

An important characteristic of the sea water is the *salt*. The sea contains almost all the known elements in dissolved form. The total amount being 3.5%. About 78% is common salt (NaCl), followed by magnesium, calcium and potassium salts. Other materials occur in only small amounts although many of them are extremely important to marine life. Almost all the salt in the sea originates on land and has been carried there by rivers to accumulate during geological time. The salt content of the sea means that it does not freeze until the temperature falls to −2°C.

Movement of the sea

There are mainly two types of movement, currents and wave movement.

Ocean currents originate mainly in the trade wind belts where the wind blows constantly from the same direction causing the surface of the sea to move down-wind. In addition temperature and salinity cause ocean currents though mainly at depth, as well as vertical currents. The velocity of ocean currents is usually low, being for example only about 8.5 km per 24 hour period around Iceland. They have practically no erosive power but transport suspended sediment which surf has disturbed along the coast, or which has been carried to the sea by rivers or wind and distribute it through the oceans where it settles gradually to form sediment. A lot of animal and plant plankton is also carried by ocean currents. This settles to the bottom when the organisms die and mixes with the sediment to various degrees. Ocean currents assist in distributing fine grained sediment evenly over the extensive area of the sea floor.

Tides depend on the relative position of the moon and sun, being the result of their gravity force. The tides are unlike other movements of the sea in being regular. There are on average 12 hours and 25 minutes between tides. The tides are most obvious in shallow seas and espe-

Figure 18-2. Explosive activity on Jólnir, which appeared in December 1965 and disappeared in December 1966. Surtsey in centre of picture. The lava shield in the foreground and the crater walls of Surtur I (right) and Surtur II (left) stand up behind. Surtsey reached a maximum height of 171 m but is now just under 150 m. Vestmannaeyjar in background. Geirfuglasker nearest, Heimaey behind. Looking from the southwest. (Photo Sigurjón Einarsson 20th June 1966.)

cially in bays where the current velocity can be considerable as at Hornafjarðarós, SE-Iceland, for example where it reaches 20 km/hr. The difference in height between high water and low water varies. In Iceland it is greatest in the Southwest where it is 4–5 m at spring tide and least in the north and east where it is about 1.5 m. The erosive powers of tidal currents can therefore be considerable and they are thought to be effective for depths of up to 200 m. Where sea level changes due to tides are significantly large the breakers affect a much broader stretch along the coast than otherwise would be the case.

Wave motion is the result of wind on sea's surface. Wave size is mainly dependent on wind velocity, how constant the winds are and their reach over the surface uninterrupted by any restrictions. Wind produced waves are generally fairly irregular. On moving outwards from the storm area they gradually lose energy and the wave motion becomes more regular swell. The horizontal distance between two wave tops is the wavelength and the difference in height between the wave top and wave trough is the wave height. The ratio between height and length in large storm waves is usually 1:30 to 1:50. The greatest recorded wave height around Iceland was about 23 m on 9th January 1990 on the Selvogsbanki, west of Surtsey.

In wave motion the sea itself barely moves forwards, but rather the wave form. A bird sitting on the sea's surface rises and sinks with the waves but its position only shifts slightly. The water particles follow an almost circular path which is equal to the wave height in diameter. Wave movement is however effective to a depth equal to the wavelength. On reaching shallow water where the depth is less than half the wavelength the velocity

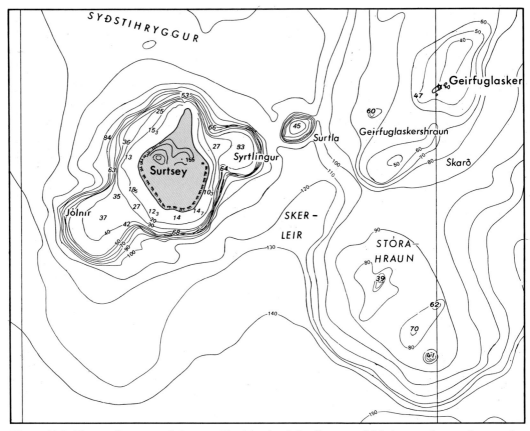

Figure 18-3. The sea floor around Surtsey. The islands of Syrtlingur and Jólnir were destroyed soon after eruptions on them ended, although they reached a height of 70 m. The sea is now 35–40 m deep there. (Sjó-mælingar Íslands – Icelandic Hydrographic Survey.)

decreases and the wave becomes steeper and higher the shallower the water becomes. The circular motion of the water particles is replaced by water flow similar to that in currents. Because of friction at the bottom the current velocity is more at the surface so that the wave becomes oversteepened, collapses and breaks. In shallows the wave tops bend in accordance with relief and often surround skerries and small islands with a fringe of surf. If the wave top approaches the shore at an angle the section nearest the shore slows down and breaks first, while the outer section continues at the same velocity bending gradually towards the shore until it finally breaks when almost parallel to it. As a result the waves break with greater energy on headlands than in bays and fjords.

Marine erosion and abrasion

As pointed out earlier ocean currents are generally to slow to erode solid rock. The same applies to tidal currents, although in narrow straits and on the continental shelf they can be strong enough to cause some erosion. A good example of bottom transport by currents are the shelly sand sediments on the bottom of Faxaflói bay in southwest Iceland, which occur over a limited area and are probably due to density sorting by bottom currents. The sediments of the bottom of Faxaflói form the main raw material (calcium carbonate) of the cement factory at Akranes.

Wave motion is the most effective of marine processes in erosion. Its effects are almost entirely in shallow water, particularly along the coast. The upper limit of marine erosion is high water level at spring tides and the lower limit is probably at a depth of 5–10 m except in surf when waves break on rocks at depth of 20–30 m. Amongst the greatest destruction and damage to property is caused when deep depressions coincide with spring tides, the seas surface rising by 1 cm for every millibar which the air pressure falls. In the south of Iceland the wind direction becomes southerly as the depressions cross the country, causing a build-up of the sea at the coast. Under such conditions the sea is much higher than normal and reaches further inland causing great damage such as occurred at the villages of Eyrarbakki and Stokkseyri in the early hours of 9th January 1990. The greatest coastal flooding recorded in Iceland occurred on the night of 8–9th January 1799 when high winds from the southwest crossed the southwest of the country at spring tide and destroyed property including the village of Básendi on the peninsula of Garðskagi.

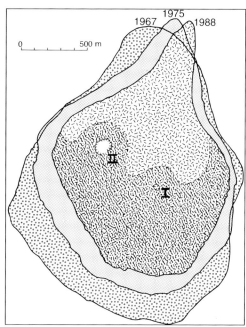

Figure 18-4. Marine erosion on Surtsey. At the close of the eruption in May 1967 the island was 2.8 km², in 1975 it was about 2 km² and it is now about 1.6 km². Surtsey is composed of móberg (tephra, hyaloclastite) in the north, while in the south it is composed of lava layers which are eroded more rapidly. (Drawing G.H.I. based on aerial photographs from Iceland Geodetic Survey.)

A good example of deep erosion by wave action and rapid breakdown is the destruction of the island Syrtlingur and Jólnir near Surtsey. In the summer of 1965

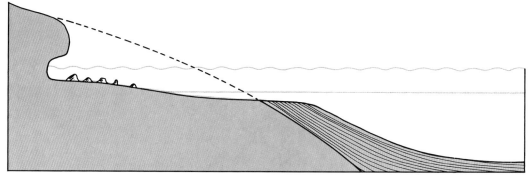

Figure 18-5. Wave eroded coast. The dotted line shows the original coastline. Wave cut cliff at left and horizontal wave cut platform. Offshore the debris forms foreset beds. (Drawing Þ.E. and G.H.I.)

Figure 18-6. The crater Lóndrangar (78 m), Snæfellsnes, W-Iceland. The picture is taken from Svalþúfa (Þúfu-bjarg), which is the eastern crater wall. The volcano was composed of tephra (móberg) which, since being erod-ed by wave action has been replaced by Holocene lava flows. Looking westwards. (Photo Þ.E.)

Syrtlingur had been erupting in the sea 600 m east of Surtsey for a period of 5 months building up an island of ash and pumice almost 70 m high and 600 m long. The eruption ceased in October 1965 and a few days later the island was destroyed by wave ersion in bad weather. The volcanic island of Jólnir 800 m southwest of Surtsey suffered a similar fate. It emerged from the sea in December 1965 and continued to build up until August 1966 by which time it was 70 m high and 0.4 km² in area. By december 1966 it had disappeared. At present the depth is 30–40 m in the shallows where the islands once stood (Figures 18-2, 18-3 and 18-4).

Wave action works mainly in two ways on solid rock. As the waves break and run on shore the water is forced into cracks in fractured or columnar rocks and compressing the air in them. In the back flow the air is drawn out of the fractures causing a vacuum. This results in the rocks gradually loosening and breaking down. The broken down rock then rolls around in the surf becoming rounded as it erodes the underlying rocks. Where there is heavy wave action and a steep beach the backwash constantly transports sand and gravel back to sea while leaving rounded boulders behind. The sand and gravel settle where wave action ceases forming *foreset bedded banks* (Figure 18-5). The finest grain sizes are carried further away by the current. Wave action has eroded *wave-cut terraces* in solid rock on

Figure 18-7. The southern lowlands invaded by the sea at the end of the Pleistocene and beginning of the Holocene after the retreat of the ice sheet. Looking from Berghylsfjall in the Hrunamannahreppur district towards the SW. In the distance from left: Vörðufell, Ingólfsfjall and Búrfell in the Grímsnes district. (Guðmundur Kjartansson 1943.)

many headlands. Due to rapid undercutting a steep or sheer *wave-cut cliff* is formed, below which is a platform or ledge, the *wave-cut platform*, on which the surf abraids using its sediment (Figures 18-5 and 18-6). In Iceland very high wave cut cliffs are widespread and are usually recognizable by the suffix "bjarg" in Icelandic, as for instance Látrabjarg and Hornbjarg in NW-Iceland which are about 400 m in height. Wave action here is so powerful that even the largest boulders are carried away. At the junction between the cliff and the platform the waves often cut a notch or cave especially if the rocks vary in hardness or are well bedded.

In Iceland marine traces from late glacial time are very common: They were formed as the land adjusted isostatically after the weight of the last Pleistocene ice sheet was removed and the sea flooded the lowland because of the slow uplift of the land and world wide rise of sea level due to melting of big ice sheets, i.e. a eu-

static rise in sea level. At Reykjavík these old shorelines are at a height of 43 m, in the south of Iceland at 100 m but otherwise occur between 30 and 60 m elsewhere in the country (Figure 18-7 and 24-28). Such marine traces provide especially good evidence for the shaping of the landscape by wave action and also for the type of strata which form in shallow areas. Good sand and gravel quarries are widespread in former terraces at the highest shoreline.

A similar situation applies in the case of the large ice sheets which covered parts of the land in both the northern and southern hemispheres. Amongst the greatest uplift since the Pleistocene has been about 300 m in the gulf of Bothnia between Finland and northern Sweden. Sea level changes are of great importance to the landscape formation on the continental shelf throughout the world. During the glacial periods of the Pleistocene so much water was bound up in glaciers

Figure 18-8. Lónsfjörður has been closed off by a 15 km long gravel barrier. Inside this, on the right, is the salt water of the lagoon. The mountain furthest on the left is Vestrahorn, while the pass of Almannaskarð and main road separates it from the main mountain ridge. Looking to the southwest from Eystrahorn. (Photo Þ.E.)

that sea level fell by about 100–150 m in the world's oceans. This water was returned to the sea during interglacial periods and in the Holocene. Shoreline changes of this type are known as eustatic changes. If all the present day glaciers were to melt, a 60 m increase in sea level in the world's harbours would result. For this reason there is now concern in low-lying countries about the greenhouse effect due to increasing amounts of carbon dioxide in the atmosphere. This will lead to an increase in temperature with a corresponding melting of the glaciers and a rise in sea level. Fold mountain building processes, swelling and subsiding of the deep sea floor in connection with sea floor spreading, as well as slow epeirogenic uplift or subsidence also have an effect on the relative position of sea level.

Wave tops usually break at an angle to the coast except when the wind blows directly on to the land. The backwash on the other hand is always at right angles to the coast. Thus sand and gravel are transported along the coast steplike in the same direction as the wind and sea. In vigorous wave action the gravel is often carried inland to build up *beach ridges* while the sand is washed away, the current velocity being much stronger in the breaking waves than in the backwash. Along the south coast of Iceland south-easterly winds are predominant so that the waves reach the coast at an angle and transport sand and gravel gradually westwards. Through time bays and fjords have become filled by fluvial and marine

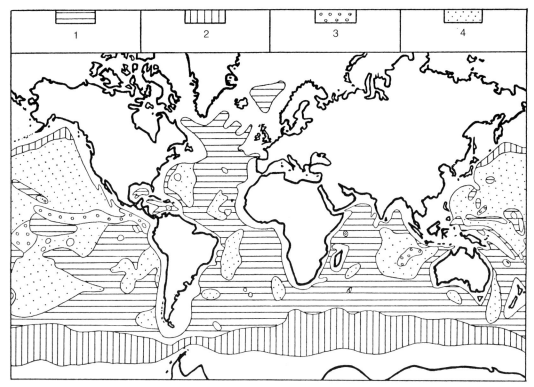

Figure 18-9. Sediment on the sea floor: 1) Globigerina oozes, 2) siliceous diatomea oozes, 3) Radiolaria oozes 4) red marine clay, white sediment on shelves and in arctic and antarctic seas.

sediments or else the transport has taken a shortcut across them, closing them off with a spit or bay barrier. Behind this a lagoon has formed (Figure 18-8). Good example are in (for instance) Lónsfjörður and Hornafjörður, SE-Iceland. Lagoons are really quite common in the country. The lake (Tjörnin) in Reykjavík is an example, the town centre standing on a 15–20 m thick gravel spit. The gravel banks on which most settlements and towns in NW-Iceland (Ísafjörður, Figure 17-9), the north (Siglufjörður, Oddeyri at Akureyri) and E-Iceland (Búðareyri in Reyðarfjörður) stand, have formed in a similar way to the gravel spits.

It was mentioned earlier that waves breaking often form a surf fringe around islands. If the waves are mainly from one direction as is often the case in fjords, then they transport sand and gravel along the island. On the lee side the waves break from both sides and deposit the gravel as a *spit*. One such spit formed in this way runs for instance southeastwards from the island of Engey in Faxaflói bay at Reykjavík. If the island lies a short distance offshore the gravel ridge forms a spit joining the island with the mainland as for instance the spit of Eiðið on Heimaey and the *spit* running out to Hólmurinn at Reykjavík. Fluvial sediment can also join islands to the mainland. This is the case at Dyrhólaey, Hjörleifshöfði and Ingólfshöfði on the south coast where the sediment from glacial rivers and jökulhlaup floods has joined islands to the land.

179

Sediment on the sea floor

Sediment on the sea floor varies to some extent in type depending on distance from land, depth and the temperature of the sea.

Shallow sea sediment. In shallow seas sand and gravel beds are found nearest the land, while further out they give way to silt and mud. Sediment in shallow seas also contains a considerable amount of organic remains such as bivalves and gastropods which sometimes form continuous beds cf. shelly sand deposits in Faxaflói. In hot seas corals live in expanses or on reefs in shallows and often form thick beds of limestone.

Sediment on the sea floor is water saturated while it is unconsolidated. As a result it sometimes slides downslope under its own weight, especially on the continental slope. Large turbidity currents sometimes slide down the slope and spread out on the deep sea floor. They have on some occasions broken submarine telephone cables. Turbidities and greywacke are very common in fold mountains where it has been hardened for a long time.

Deep sea sediment. The deep sea floor is mainly covered by three types of sediment all of which are very fine grained. In a broad belt surrounding Antarctica and in the north Pacific the deep sea floor is covered in silica diatom ooze. Otherwise the deep sea floor at a depth of 2000–4000 m is covered in sediment composed mainly of foraminifera shells which are protozoa with a calcium carbonate shell which live as plankton in the surface waters of the sea or at the bottom of the oceans, *foraminifera ooze*. Foraminifera ooze, covers about 35% of the deep sea floor and is rich in calcium carbonate (40–90%) as would be expected (Figure 18-9).

The sea floor deeper than 4000 m is covered by red clay, the red colour being due to iron compounds. At this great depth the sea is cold and the pressure enormous so that only organic remains which do not dissolve at high pressures or low temperature can accumulate there. Under these conditions for instance calcium carbonate is in solution. It is mainly radiolarian shells which withstand these conditions. They are protozoa having a silica skeleton. In certain areas in the Pacific and Indian oceans *radiolarian ooze* is dominant. Deep sea sediment, rich in shells of diatoms are also common, especially around Antarctica. Diatoms are single celled algae. *Red deep sea clay* is mainly composed of fine grained volcanic ash, or fine sediment transported by wind or ocean currents.

Shallow water sediment covers about 20% of the world's ocean floors while deep water sediment covers about 80%. On the other hand shallow water sediment accounts for about 99% of all marine sediments in amount.

Research in the oceans has made great progress in recent years. As well as biological and oceanographical research, investigations have also been made into the characteristics of sediments, thickness of sediments, igneous rocks, and magnetic, seismic, gravimetrical and palaeontological properties of bottom sediments and rocks. For nearly two decades, international drilling programmes from specially equiped ships (ODP) have been collecting information about sea floor sediments and the upper portion of the basaltic ocean crust. The oil and gas resources of the sea floor are already being exploited as for instance in the North Sea. Manganese ores also occurs in quantity in many deep sea sediments and will doubtless be exploited through time. Last but not least, certain light metals such as magnesium which are in solution are already being extracted from the sea.

Lakes

19

Depressions filled with fresh water are known as lakes. They originate in various ways and can be due to glacial erosion, volcanism, tectonic movements, landslides, to name but a few. Iceland has many lakes although most of them are rather small. The largest is Þingvallavatn, 83 km² and the deepest Öskjuvatn, 220 m. Altogether there are 34 lakes larger than 5 km², around 154 between 1 and 5 km² and at least 10 proglacial lakes larger than 1 km². The world's largest lakes are the Caspian sea in Russia, 484,000 km², Lake Superior, N-America 83,000 km² and Lake Victoria, E-Africa 69,000 km². Altogether lakes represent 2% of the area of dry land in the world. The deepest lake is Lake Baikal, 1741 m. The main types of Icelandic lakes will now be treated according to their mode of formation.

Lakes of glacial origin. The majority of Icelandic lakes lie in *glacially eroded depressions,* such as Lagarfljót, E-Iceland which is the third largest lake in the country, 53 km² and 112 m deep) and reaching 90 m below sea level. Other lakes of this type include Skorradalsvatn (14.7 km² and 48 m deep), lakes on the heaths of the Mýrar- Borgarfjarðar- and Húnavatnssýsla as well as various lakes around Reykjavík such as Rauðavatn.

In some places where moraine or flu-vioglacial deposits are very thick ice slabs have remained in the sediments. When they melt *kettle holes* form which become filled with water. Such lakes occur for instance at Blönduós, N-Iceland, at Ljósavatnsskarð and in the Reykjadalur valley in Suður-Þingeyjarsýsla, N-Iceland. Kettle holes are also common on the sandur e.g. Skeiðarársandur, of the south coast following jökulhlaup floods, though they are seldom long lived.

Outlet glacier tongues often push up unconsolidated till and glaciofluvial deposits, or else they are washed away by meltwater which bursts out from beneath the glacier snout. In either case a lake often remains in such hollows when the glacier retreats, which are known as *glacier tongue lakes or proglacial lakes.* The lake of Jökulsárlón on the Breiðamerkursandur is a good example of this type of lake. It is 8 km² in area and 100 m deep, though 160 m at the glacier edge where icebergs reach down to this depth when calving (Figure 17-1). Ljósavatn in Ljósavatnsskarð, N-Iceland (3.3 km², 31 m deep) is also of this type and formed at the close of the Pleistocene at the edge of a glacier.

Skriðjöklar which flow in the main valley often block ice free tributary valleys and lead to the formation of *ice dammed lakes.* When the water depth in the lake

Figure 19-1. General view of the south of Askja in Dyngjufjöll, northern highlands. Looking to the west. In the foreground is the explosion crater (maar) Víti and the lake Öskjuvatn which was formed after the Askja eruption of 1875. (Photo Páll Jónsson.)

reaches 9/10 of the glacier thickness, the glacier lifts, releasing the lake water as a jökulhlaup flood. The best known lake of this type in Iceland is Grænalón on the western edge of Skeiðarárjökull. It is about 15 km² in area and 200 m deep when the water level is at its maximum. It floods every year with a maximum discharge of 2000 m³/sec. At the close of the Pleistocene, ice dammed lakes were common in many parts of Iceland. In Fnjóskadalur for instance ice dammed lakes were produced when the Eyjafjarðarjökull dammed up water in Dalsmynni to the west and Bárðardalsjökull dammed up water in Ljósavatnsskarð, NE-Iceland.

The lake drained through Flateyjardalsheiði to the north and not Dalsmynni as gravel terraces and a step at 200 m furthest north and 260 m furthest south in Fnjóskadalur suggest. The inclination of the shoreline is the result of more uplift inland because of the greater ice thickness there than towards the sea.

Lakes due to volcanic eruptions. Lakes resulting from volcanic eruptions are quite common in Iceland.

Lakes form in craters, especially explosions craters, when they reach below the water table. Such lakes are called crater lakes or *maar* and are often small but

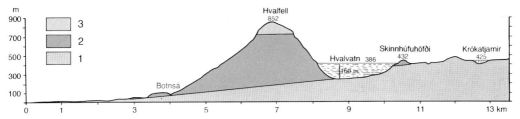

Figure 19-2. Cross section of Botnsdalur in Hvalfjörður, SW-Iceland. The lake Hvalvatn was formed when the subglacial móberg mountain (stapi) Hvalfell was built up during a glacial period, damming the valley. Symbols: 1) grey basalt Formation, 2) subglacial móberg, 3) lava shield. (Drawing Þ.E.)

deep. Examples are Kerið in Grímsnes, S-Iceland which has a depth of 7–14 m depending on changes in groundwater level, Veiðivötn in the southern highlands, Víti in Askja (Figure 19-1) and Grænavatn in Krýsuvík being the deepest, 44 m.

Lakes are also formed when lava flows across valleys or block their entrance thus damming up rivers. *Lava dammed lakes* are quite common, good examples being Hlíðarvatn and Oddastaðavatn in Hnappadalur on Snæfellsnes. Also belonging to this group are lakes formed when volcanoes erupt in valleys and block them. One of the best examples of this is Hvalvatn, W-Iceland, the second deepest lake in Iceland at 160 m, which was formed when the table mountain Hvalfell was built up in the valley of Botnsdalur in Hvalfjörður during an early late Pleistocene glaciation (Figure 19-2). Lakes can also form in the valley formed between two volcanic ridges. Belonging to this group are Kleifarvatn, Krýsuvík (9.7 km², 107 m deep) and Langisjór in the southern central highlands (26 km², 73 m deep).

Caldera formation often accompanies volcanic eruptions and when filled by water these are known as *caldera lakes*. The best known of these in Iceland is Öskjuvatn in Dyngjufjöll which was formed following the Askja eruption of 1875. It is about 11 km² in area and 220 m deep and is therefore the deepest lake in the country (Figure 19-1).

Lakes due to tectonic movements. Crustal movements have led to the formation of only a few lakes in Iceland. Lake Þingvallavatn is one example. It occupied the rift valley formed between Hrafnagjá and Almannagjá. Following the seismic events in Kelduhverfi, NE-Iceland in 1976 and 1987 a fairly large lake, Skjálftavatn, was formed on the sand plains near the coast. The lake was 5 km² in area and 1–2 m deep. Such lakes are fairly uncommon in the world although the Dead Sea and most of the lakes in eastern Africa have formed in rift valleys. The Caspian sea on the other hand occupies a depression which is the result of gradual crustal movement.

Landslides can cause lakes to form in two ways. Rockslides often block valleys so that rivers become blocked and lakes form. Examples of such lakes are Flóðið in Vatnsdalur, N-Iceland, formed behind the Vatnsdalshólar rockslide and Skriðuvatn, in Skriðdalur, E-Iceland, formed behind the Haugahólar rockslide. A depression also often forms between the rockfall scar in the cliff and the debris heap, which water can collect in.

Lakes at the sea. Due to the drift of sand and gravel along the coastal bays and inlets are frequently closed off by spits or bay barriers. Inside the spit is either a tidal saltwater lagoon such as Lónsfjörður,

SE-Iceland (Figure 18-9) or a fresh water lagoon such as Hópið in Húnavatnssýsla, N-Iceland. Tjörnin in Reykjavík is also of this type, the town centre standing on a gravel spit.

In addition to the types of lake mentioned there are some which have formed in various other ways. These include *oxbow lakes* which form when meandering rivers bypass a meander and thus close it off (Figure 16-3). Lakes also form when sediment deposition cones from tributary rivers block the main valley or divide an already existing lake. The series of lakes in the Svínadalur valley in the Borgarfjarðarsýsla district, W-Iceland, has formed in this way.

Many lakes have a complex origin and do not belong to any one group. Thus lake Þingvallavatn which has an area of 83 km² and is 114 m deep is the result of glacial erosion, tectonic movements in a rift valley as well as the build up of volcanic products in Hengill, Dráttarhlíð, Lyngdalsheiði and Hæðadyngja and also by lava flows when the Þingvallahraun lava blocked it north of Dráttarhlíð on the eastern shore 9000 years ago (Figure 10-1). An outflow channel from the lake was then formed between the lava flow and the subglacial móberg ridge. There is now a dam in the channel at the Steingrímsstöð hydroelectric plant. Mývatn has formed in a similar way. It lies in a glacially eroded depression while it is to some extent dammed up by lava flows, the last about 2000 years old, the Yngra-Laxárhraun lava. Mývatn is 37 km² in area with a maximum depth of only 4 m.

Finally, lakes formed as a result of the construction of hydroelectric plants should be mentioned. The largest is Blöndulón, 56 km², Sultartangalón on the Þjórsá river, 19 km², Sigöldulón, 14 km² and Hrauneyjarlón on the Tungná river, 9 km² and Kvíslarveituvatn in Þjórsárver, 20 km².

Erosion and sedimentation in lakes

The surface level of lakes is usually subject to certain changes. In lakes which have no surface run off such as Kerið and Kleifarvatn, the surface coincides with the water table and is therefore subject to the same changes. The level of lakes from which there is surface runoff is also changeable. In wet conditions and thaws the level is higher than in drought. Lakes have a stabilizing effect on river discharge and reduce the risk of floods.

Shoreline erosion on lakes closely resembles marine erosion (see chapter 18) while being at a much smaller scale. Wave cut platforms and gravel bars are formed along lakes shores for example.

Sedimentation in lakes is also similar in many respects to that in the sea. This is especially true of lakes into which rivers flow. Deltas form at the mouths of rivers and gravel bars and terraces along the shoreline. Where the depth is too much for wave action to be effective, fine grained sediment accumulates on the bottom. The situation is different for lakes which only have ground water inflow. In Iceland only organic sediment has been observed on the bottom of such lakes as for example diatomite which is, however, often mixed with volcanic ash and aeolian sediment. On the bottom of lake Mývatn for instance is a 5–10 m thick layer of diatomite which is at present exploited commercially. In shallow lakes, mainly tarns, peat also forms from various water and bog plants, so that they gradually become filled by peat and form bogs (Figure 22-1).

Aeolian processes and landforms

20

Iceland lies in the path of North-Atlantic depressions and the wind direction is therefore constantly subject to change and stable weather is rare. Winds which blow off the sea loose their moisture on mountain ranges in their path and are dry when they reach the lee side. Southerly winds are wet in the south but dry in the north while northerly winds are wet in the north but dry in the south. Aeolian processes are therefore most effective in northerly winds in the south of the country and in southerly winds in the north of the country.

The wind has little effect on vegetated land or bedrock, but in areas of scant vegetation where unconsolidated soil is at the surface it causes great damage. The wind swirls dust high into the air and often transports it for long distances, while sand and gravel roll along the ground tearing up the vegetation and eroding the soil while polishing the bedrock and boulders. In fresh winds (Beaufort 6) the wind can lift grains of 1–2 mm diameter but in storm force winds quite large boulders roll along the ground. The wind is therefore one of the forces of erosion and

Figure 20-1. Wind eroded stone at Sámsstaðaklif, Þjórsárdalur. The wind eroded facet (right) faces towards the northeast, i.e. inland. (Photo Þ.E.)

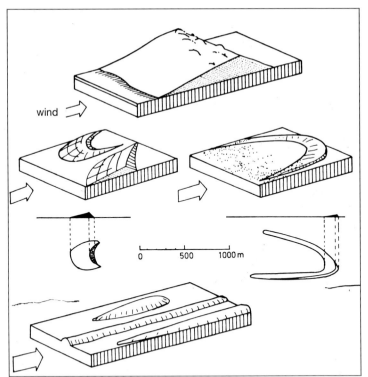

Figure 20-2. Sand dunes and drifts. At top is a sand dune (often at the coast), then crescent shaped dunes (common in deserts) and longitudinal dunes, which often form in the shelter of an obsticle. (Wagner 1950.)

its effects are very variable. The type area for aeolian processes are sub tropical deserts such as the Sahara and Gobi as well as the scantily vegetated wastes of the polar regions. Aeolian processes are also active along sandy coasts throughout the world and along rivers, glacier margins and in poorly vegetated mountainous areas. Wind transported debris usually has its origins in the weathering of rocks by differential temperature changes, frost processes or by marine, fluvial or glacial erosion. In volcanic areas the wind also transports a lot of ash and pumice.

Aeolian denudation refers to the lifting and transport of rock debris, while *wind erosion or abrasion* implies the erosion of rock, soil or vegetation by the windborne debris. During transport the grains are also ground down.

Windborne sand smoothes and polishes rock outcrops making them completely smooth and giving them a greasy lustre resembling polish. It also erodes loose boulders producing a smooth facet on the weather side. Such boulders often turn, due to frost heaving or solifluction, so that new wind eroded facets are formed, often with a sharp angle between the facets. Such boulders or ventifracts are called *dreikanters* although the facets may be more numerous. Wind polished outcrops and wind eroded boulders are common in Iceland. The wind eroded surfaces usually point landwards, or in the direction from which the dry winds blow (Figure 20-1).

The effects of wind erosion depends greatly on the type of rock. In well bedded rocks of varying hardness the softer beds are eroded first so that the harder beds stand out as ledges. This is particularly common in the late Pleistocene móberg formations where caves or overhangs also sometimes form (Figure 20-6).

Figure 20-3. Wind eroded soil bank (Icel. rofbarð) at Kópasker, NE-Iceland. The light band by the shovel is tephra layer H₃, 2800 years old. The distance to Hekla is 300 km and tephra layer 5 cm thick. From its position it can be seen that the soil which formed from between the end of the Pleistocene and up to 2800 years ago, is much thinner than that formed since. The investigator is Sigurður Þórarinsson, founder of tephrochronology. (Photo Þ.E.)

The transport of debris by wind closely resembles that by running water. The largest grains hop along the surface downwind like bed load in running water and can even be carried up mountain sides to a considerable height. In strong winds sand grains can reach up to 10 m height, the effects of which can be widely observed in the highlands. For instance wind borne sand has eroded the vegetation off the Tjörvafell area in the Landmannaafréttur, southern highlands, up to this height. The finest grains on the other hand are swirled upwards and carried like fluvial sediment. It is quite common for dust clouds to obscure the sun in Iceland, while sand dust from the Sahara has been carried by wind to Scandinavia.

Aeolian sedimentary formations occur mainly where the wind meets an obstacle or where the wind velocity is reduced.

The largest grains are first to settle and accumulate in drifts or sand dunes. Their crests usually lie across the wind direction and the sand drifts off the windward side to collect on the lee side. Thus the dunes gradually shift and are cross-bedded internally. High dunes of this type are common in hot deserts and along beaches in many parts of the world, but are rare in Iceland. Early Holocene sand dunes of considerable height occur, however, at Dyrhólaey and Mýrdalur, S-Iceland. Low dunes are on the other hand common on the shelly sand expanses of NW-Iceland and on the volcanic tephra of the highlands. Otherwise most dunes in Iceland have formed in the lee of rocks and cliffs. Quite high dunes often form in the vicinity of lime grass (Elymus mollis) tufts, producing a characteristic landscape (Figure 20-2).

187

The smallest grains or dust is usually carried much further than the sand, being carried high into the air and causing clouds thick enough to obscure the sun. In Iceland this occurs mainly in summer droughts or during long frosty spells in snow light winters. In areas bordering deserts thick layers of fine aeolian sediment or *loess* have formed. In China for example several hundred metres of loess have been carried there by westerly winds from the Gobi desert. Thick loess beds are widespread in mid and eastern Europe, Canada and the U.S.A. and have formed as the result of wind removing rock dust from fluvioglacial plains or poorly vegetated moraine expanses at the margins of Pleistocene ice sheets. Loessal soil is composed mainly of small quartz grains (silt) bonded by calcium carbonate. The porosity is around 50% so that loess retains water and fertilizer well. It is very fertile and in loess areas are found some of the richest grain cultivation areas of the northern and southern hemispheres.

Icelandic loess

During the climatic optimum of the Holocene practically all the land area of the country was covered in loess which was widely vegetated by birch or brushwood. The aeolian sediment which forms the soil originates in two ways. On the one hand ice expansion, marine-, glacial-, fluvial- and aeolian erosion break down rocks, while on the other hand volcanic eruptions have supplied the soil with tephra (ash and pumice) which has been distributed over the land according to the wind direction at the time of eruption. The ash layers are often clearly defined in soil profiles and provide excellent evidence on the formation and history of the soil (Figure 20-3). Wind has then removed fine grained debris from alluvial plains and from coastal sand expanses and spar-

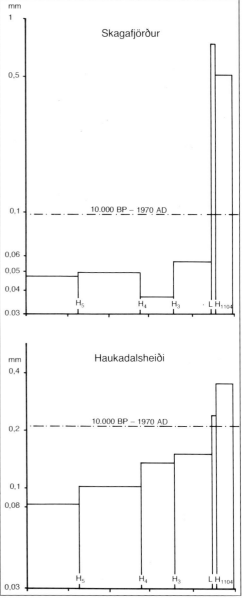

Figure 20-4. Comparative diagram of the mean accumulation of loessial soil in millimetres per year in 20 soil sections at Haukadalsheiði, S-Iceland (Guttormur Sigbjarnarson 1969) and in 27 sections in Skagafjörður, N-Iceland (Grétar Guðbergsson 1975). Tephra layers: H = tephra from Hekla, H_5 = 6600 years, H_4 = 4000 years, H_3 = 2800 years, H_1 = from 1104 and L = tephra from the settlement period i.e. 1100 years old.

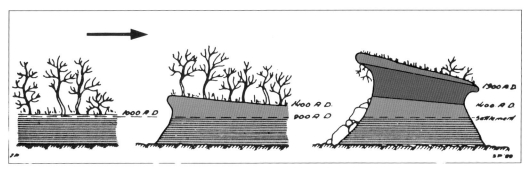

Figure 20-5. Accumulation of loessial soil and formation of wind eroded soil bank on the 8000 years old Þjórsárhraun lava in the Landsveit district, S-Iceland. The space between the lines represents accumulation in 500 years and shows that this has been rapid during historical time. The arrows show the direction of the eroding wind and accumulation is clearly most upwind of the bank. AD = Anno domini or after Christ. (Sigurður Þórarinsson 1961.)

sely vegetated mountain areas, depositing it on vegetated land.

Observations on the accumulation rate of loess soil in Iceland are fairly straightforward being greatly facilitated by the use of tephra layers. The rate of accumulation is usually measured between ash layers, for example between H_4 and H_3, the latter covering about 80% of the country (Figures 24-25 and 24-26). The accumulation rate was much lower between the close of the Pleistocene and up to the Settlement period 1100 years ago, than it has been during historical time. In the period between the Hekla eruption H_4 (4000 years ago) and H_3 (2800 years ago) the rate was on average 0.08 mm per year while inland in the south it was 0.28 mm per year due to the proximity of active volcanoes. In the same areas the accumulation following the Hekla eruption of 1104 (H_1) reached up to 0.4 mm per year in the north and 0.8 mm per year in the south. Thus the accumulation rate since settlement in Iceland has been 3–5 times greater than in the period from 4000–2800 years ago. In the earlier period the land was mostly covered by vegetation but after 1104 denudation was dominant. In soil profiles (Icel. rofabörð) it can often be observed that the soil which formed from between the close of the Pleistocene and up until settlement is only 20–50 cm thick, while the aeolian deposits formed since then are several times thicker. (Figure 20-3, 20–4 and 20–5).

Soil erosion

During the climatic optimum of the Holocene in Iceland 3000–4000 years ago, at least 3/4 of the country was covered by vegetation and it is unlikely that less than half was covered in woodland or brushland. At present just less than one quarter is vegetated and only 1/100 wooded. The woods began to decline due to a worsening climate 2500 years ago, but following settlement there was a sudden change in the growth and the country was well populated in a short time. The woods had already disappeared in most districts during the first few centuries of settlement due to the encroachment of both man and livestock, though also to some extent due to the worsening climate (Figures 24-24 and 24-35). Land previously covered with woods became grass-covered and this had far reaching effects on the run off characteristics. In rain or during rapid snow melt, the water in woodlands mainly percolates down through the soil, but on grassland part of it is surface run off

189

Figure 20-6. Layered and consolidated fine sand deposit, formed in the early Holocene. This "coarse" grained soil has accumulated on vegetated land and contains scattered plant stalk traces. Photographed west of the Eystri-Rangá river, S-Iceland, where wind erosion has been severe in the past few centuries. Hekla in background. (Photo Þ.E.)

which cuts channels in the soil cover (Figure 24-35). Wind erosion then spreads from the channel banks outwards and becomes rapid. Erosion is most active on móberg and lava areas where the bedrock is highly porous and the precipitation sinks rapidly through the soil. In a few areas historical explosive eruptions, with much ash and tephra production, have initiated soil erosion. For instance the Hekla eruptions of 1104, 1693 and 1766–68 are to some extent to blame for soil erosion inland in southern Iceland as well as in the Rangárvellir district. During the 19th century around 40 farms were deserted in these areas due to sand drifting and soil erosion.

Much of the dust carried upwards by the wind settles in rivers, lakes and finally in the sea and thus plays no further part in soil formation. Some settles in bogs and peat formed since settlement is coloured yellow brown by it in many areas (Figure 24-34). It is the aeolian dust in fact which makes Icelandic bogs as easily cultivated and fertile as they are, following drainage. Destruction of the vegetation and soil erosion by wind form one of the biggest environmental problems facing Icelanders today. While there are programmes for preventing sand drifting and for planting in various areas, they are unfortunately still on too small a scale. Destruction of vegetation and soil erosion represent one of the worst problems facing mankind today.

Rockslides and landslides

21

Figure 21-1. Debris flow at Víðivellir in Fljótsdalur, E-Iceland, which followed heavy rainfall at the end of October 1979. (Photo Oddur Sigurðsson.)

The transport of rock debris is always dependent on the earth's gravity, either indirectly though transport by rivers, glaciers or wind, or directly due to solifluction, soil creep, rockfall or landslides. For gravity to be effective, however, other processes such as glacial, fluvial or marine erosion, must have produced slopes

191

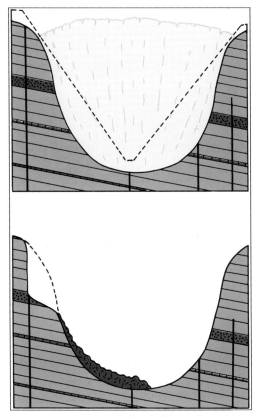

Figure 21-2. Formation of rockslide in the Tertiary Basalt Formation. Upper picture: The dotted line shows the original V-shaped valley which is being widened by the glacier. Lower picture: The glacier has melted so that its support is lacking. Rockslide follows the bedding dip and flows on to the valley floor. The interbasaltic beds are red, the lavas blue-grey. The vertical lines are dikes. (Sigurður Þórarinsson 1954.)

or sheer cliffs. Movement can be slow as for instance in the case of solifluction, or very rapid as in the case of rockfall or landslides.

Debris flows occur mainly where water accumulates in steep screes or soil slopes during heavy rainfall. They also occur in the spring when the waterlogged thawed top layer on sloping ground gives way over the frozen ground. The water increases the weight of the scree or soil and reduces their cohesive strength. Debris flows of this type often spread out over a large area on the lowland (Figures 21-1 and 21-3).

Rockfalls occur mainly when ice expansion and differential heating loosen rock in cliff faces so that they fall. Through time the slopes become covered in screes whose steepness depends mainly on the coarseness of the material, the coarser screes being steepest. Huge screes of this type occur for example on the slopes of Hafnarfjall at Borgarfjörður, W-Iceland and also on the slopes of Vestrahorn and Eystrahorn in Lón, SE-Iceland (Figure 7-12). Rockfall is often dangerous especially where roads traverse steep screes, such as at Óshlíð between Bolungarvík and Hnífsdalur in NW-Iceland.

Landslides are piles of broken and pulverized rocks, formed when entire mountain sides collapse in a single event. In Iceland landslides have occurred mainly in the Tertiary basalt areas where Pleistocene glaciers and rivers have steepened slopes and broadened ancient valleys (Figure 21-2) or where marine erosion has led to the formation of high cliffs and upset the equilibrium of the slopes. Landslides occur either while the erosion processes are still at work in which case they are destroyed immediately, or sometime later, in which case they leave a scar in the mountain side and debris at the bottom of the slope or in the valley. An example of the former is the landslide which occurred on 15th January 1967 at Steinholtsjökull, a valley glacier on the northern side of Eyjafjallajökull, S-Iceland. To the west of the glacier is a 400 m high sheer cliff. Sometime earlier it had been noticed that a fracture had begun to form some distance from the edge of the

Figure 21-3. Rockslide at Móberg in Langidalur in the Austur-Húnavatnssýsla district, western N-Iceland. The dip of the beds is about 15° towards the valley. Crescent-shaped lobes are evident in the debris pile to the right. Looking northwards across Langidalur valley. Blanda river in centre of valley. The slide is about 2.5 km wide. (Photo Ólafur Jónsson.)

cliff and this gradually widened until the huge rock slab separated from it. On the date mentioned the slab became unstable and collapsed. According to seismographs at Kirkjubæjarklaustur, 100 km to the east, the fall occurred at 13:47 based on a small earthquake whose epicentre was recorded in the landslide area. The rock slab disintegrated on falling, depositing a huge debris pile on the glacier. The landslide caused break-up of the glacier and a the same time forced a huge flood wave out of the lake which lies in front of the glacier snout. The flood water carried with it an enormous amount of ice debris and huge boulders. The debris pile has moved with the glacier and the evidence

of the slide will eventually disappear, but the scar and the boulders which the flood wave carried will remain as evidence for the landslide for a long time.

The landslide at Steinholtsjökull must be regarded as rather small compared with the landslides which occurred in the Tertiary basalt areas after the glaciers of the last glacial period melted. While the glaciers occupied the valleys they eroded and steepened the sides while at the same time supporting them and preventing landslides. The landslides occurred when the glaciers melted and they appear to have been most frequent at the end of the Pleistocene and early in the Holocene. Some are from Historical time however, such as the landslide Loðmundarskriður in Loðmundarfjörður in E-Iceland which is mentioned in the Landnáma or Settlement book. A landslide on the south of Lómagnúpur west of Skeiðarársandur is probably from 1784.

Clay rich red interbasaltic sediments undoubtedly play an important part in the formation of the numerous landslides in the Tertiary basalt areas, producing an ideal failure surface. The dip of the beds also plays an important part in landslides. They are extremely rare where the bedding dip is low or the beds horizontal, but common where there is a considerable dip. Landslides have occurred mainly on down-dip slopes (Figure 21-2).

Landslides crush the rock slab although quite large slabs or even entire section of the strata can occur amongst the debris. The material is therefore very porous and retains water poorly, spring water often originating in such debris or rock fill. They usually have a very rough relief, occurring in steep piles and hillocks though in between there are often irregular curved lobes or ogives.

Occasionally landslides extend right across a valley floor and even high up the opposite valley side. A good example of this is a 2 kilometre wide landslide Köldukinnarhólar, which occurred on Langadalsfjall in Húnavatnssýsla, N-Iceland, between the farms Fremstagil and Geitaskarð and ran across the valley and just over 200 m up the opposite side. Landslides thus often close off rivers causing lakes to form behind the debris dam. Such lakes are usually short-lived since the river easily cuts its way through the loose debris piles. In Iceland however there are still lakes behind old landslide debris, an example being the lake Flóðið in Vatnsdalur in Húnavatnssýsla which is blocked by large landslide debris and the landslide Hólar in Öxnadalur west of Akureyri where there is still a lake, Hraunsvatn, between the sheer cliff and the rock debris.

Avalanches or snowslides resemble debris flows in many respects. They occur in winter when snow accumulates on steep slopes or forming sharp edges so that an overhang forms. Because of the weight the snow suddenly starts sliding often travelling long distances and even right across valleys. Avalanches are either dry or wet when they start to slide but are always slushy further down and quickly change to firn. Avalanches are not of great significance from a geological viewpoint but have often led to great loss of life in Iceland, especially in the mountainous NW-, N- and E-Iceland. The last severe snow avalanche accident occurred on 12th December 1974, in Neskaupstaður, E-Iceland, when several homes and factories were destroyed and 12 people were killed.

Peat, coal and oil

22

Bogs and peat

Peat. Each autumn plants wither and shed their leaves. On dry land the plant remains rot and become mixed with the soil, but in bogs where the water table is at the surface, or in lakes, they hardly rot at all provided external conditions do not change with the result that they accumulate and form dark brown peat layers. Anaerobic bacteria and fungi then transform the plant remains into peat. By removing oxygen from the remains they gradually increase the carbon content of the peat. The best peat is therefore usually in the lowest layers of the bog since it is the oldest and most developed.

Icelandic peat is mainly composed of sedges and mosses remains. In most bogs there are, however, two layers with birch stems which were formed in the warmest and driest periods of the Holocene, i.e. the early and late birch periods.

Icelandic peat formed before the Settlement contains 10–30% ash while that formed later contains 50–70%. The ash content of peat in neighbouring countries is 1–2% (cf. chapter 24).

Peat has been dug from early times in Iceland (Figure 22-2) and used as domestic fuel. However, it contains rather a lot of ash as a result of aeolian sediment and volcanic tephra layers which have settled in the bogs. Peat digging in Iceland had now ceased but used to be the main fuel in the country. Peat is also used in horticulture, in gardens and in potting composts. In Ireland, Finland and Russia peat is used widely for electricity production and for domestic heating.

Peat bogs cover about 1/10 of Iceland or almost half of all the vegetation cover in the country. Icelandic peat bogs are of two main types, blanket bogs (Icel. hallamýrar) and topogenic bogs or fens (Icel. flóamýrar).

Blanket bogs occur only in the northernmost part of the cold temperate climatic zone where precipitation is relatively high and evaporation low and in particular where the bedrock is impermeable. In these conditions the soil retains moisture so that the water table coincides with the ground surface. Even where the bogs occur on sloping ground plant remains can accumulate to become peat. Blanket bogs also form where springs emerge on mountain sides or where water trickles out of scree deposits. The greater part of wetland in Iceland belong to this type.

Topogenic bogs and fens on the other hand depend on the landscape and occur mainly in depressions, especially in lake localities and along rivers. The lakes

Figure 22-1. Flóamýri in Þjórsárdalur, southwest of Búrfell, S-Iceland. (Photo Þ.E.)

gradually become shallow as organic remains and inorganic sediment settle out. At the same time peat forms from the lake banks until the lake is completely filled in. At this stage the surface of the bog starts to rise and becomes dome-like, being highest in the centre. Following this they dry out and can become wood covered in time. This type of bog is seldom found in Iceland but is common in neighbouring countries as raised bogs. They occur in S-, W-, and central E-Iceland and often still have a small lake remaining at their centres (Figure 22-1).

Marshy meadows and fens are widespread on lowland along river courses and palsa bogs, which contain ice all year, on the highlands (Figure 14-7).

In the past few decades the drainage and reclamation of bogs in Iceland has been intensive and has gone too far, upsetting irrevocably the natural habitat of various wetland wading birds. The blanket bogs in particular have proved suitable for cultivation, being easily drained. The raised bogs on the other hand are difficult to reclaim, lying usually in depressions and behind rock thresholds.

Coal

Peat is found world-wide in cooler climates and the tropics in Holocene deposits, although peat formation has almost certainly occurred in humid climates of all the geological periods since land plants started to appear in the middle Palaeozoic era, about 400 million years ago. As seen above, plant remains gradually become peat as the result of the activity of anaerobic bacteria. Ancient peat has become covered by other strata, especially sediments, which have led to the cessation of the bacterial activity. The organic

Figure 22-2. Peat cutting at Laugarnes, Reykjavík in the early part of the century. (Photo Peter Sorå. Photograph collection of Reykjavík City Council.)

transformation of plant remains to peat is replaced by chemical transformation of the peat to lignite and coal in which carbon increases proportionately while oxygen and hydrogen decrease. Production of various gases, or coal gas, accompanies *carbonization*. This is mainly marsh gas (methane) as well as carbon dioxide and carbon monoxide. Coal gas is used for lighting and heating purposes and is produced by heating the coal. The coal is thereby transformed to coke which is for example used in iron smelting. Coal gas sometimes collects in mines causing explosions and has resulted in mining disasters.

The rate of carbonization is also dependent on the overburden, i.e. the thickness of the beds deposited on top of the coal beds, as well as on the temperature. It has therefore usually progressed further in old geological formations than in young formations, the likelihood of thicker strata being much greater over a longer period of time. Thus in strata from the latter part of the Palaeozoic era i.e. the Carboniferous period 300 million years ago, are found only coal beds, while lignite occurs in younger formations, for instance in Tertiary sequences. An increase in overburden involves an increase in temperature, which speeds up the carbonization. In fold mountain regions, particularly in metamorphic rock and in volcanic areas, carbonization can go so far that organic remains are transformed to pure carbon in the form of graphite. Graphite has been found at Siglufjörður, N-Iceland, where lignite has probably been affected by heat from magma in a dike.

According to the stage of carbonization, coal is classified as follows:

Carbon content of coals
Wood 50%	Peat 60%
Lignite 70%	Coal 80%
Anthracite 90%	Graphite 100%

The table does not include ash and moisture content. The value of coal as fuel depends mainly on its carbon content but a high ash content can even make the coal unusable. Coal is usually black and shiny while lignite is brown in colour.

The Tertiary Basalt Formations in Iceland contain widespread thin beds of *surtarbrandur*, which is a variety of lignite. It is usually black and sometimes shiny resembling coal although its combustibility is that of lignite. Surtarbrandur has a high ash content since eruptions were frequent during the of formation. The Icelandic lignite beds are always thin, the peat formation being constantly interrupted by lava flows. During the first World War lignite was mined in a few places such as Jökulbotn in Reyðarfjörður, E-Iceland, Tungubakki on the Tjörnes peninsula, N-Iceland and at Bolungarvík and Botn in Súgandafjörður in NW-Iceland.

It is now thought that the swamps in which the coal beds formed in earlier geological timesresembled tropical swamps rather than cool temperate swamps. The coal swamps were mainly situated in rift valleys or in coastal lagoons at the margins of fold mountain ranges. The coal beds of the Ruhr district and in Britain were for instance formed at the margin of the fold mountains of the Hercynian or Vascarian in Europe and Alleghenian orogeny in the U.S.A. during the Carboniferous period.

The lignite beds at Cologne on the Rhine were on the other hand formed in a rift valley during the late Tertiary period. There the thickest individual coal bed is about 100 m, although this is rather an exceptional thickness. It was much more common that crustal movements were uneven and peat formation irregular so that rivers or the sea deposited sand and mud in the intervening time. Thus Carboniferous sediments in the Ruhr are about 3000 m in thickness while the coal beds are only about 80 m or 2.7% of the total thickness.

The chief coal mining areas today are in the U.S.A., Russia, China, Australia, South Africa, Great Britain, France, Germany and Poland. It is thought that the world's known coal reserves will last at least 1000 years at the present rate of consumption. Coal is used for domestic heating, electricity production and in various industries such as in iron smelting as well as for carbon electrodes in aluminium production. Coal import in Iceland 1990 was about 74,000 tons.

Oil

Crude oil is a mixture of various gaseous, liquid and solid hydrocarbons. It is divided into natural gas, oil and tar (asphalt). The simplest hydrocarbons are gases and are known collectively as *natural gas* which in addition to marsh gas (methane) usually contains some ethane, propane and butane and other gases in small amounts. Natural gas has no smell or colour. The actual *crude oil* is brown or dark in colour and is a viscous liquid when it emerges. It is composed of fairly heavy hydrocarbons. *Asphalt* is composed of heavy solid carbohydrate compounds.

Plant remains found in coal testify to

their origin. The origin of oil is on the other hand not nearly so clear since it contains no fossils and also because it never occurs in the bedsin which it formed.

As pointed out earlier the hard body parts of plants and animals such as shells accumulate in many areas in sediments on the sea floor (cf. chapter 18) whereas other plant and animal remains usually rot immediately. Where currents are absent the sea is poor in oxygen. Here soft plant and animal remains can accumulate without rotting. In the bottom sediments of the Black Sea the amount of organic remains is for example about 35% and the water at depth being therefore poor in oxygen and saturated with hydrogen sulphide. In ordinary deep ocean sediments, however, the amount of organic material is seldom more than 2.5%. Furthermore oil occurs almost entirely in marine sediments, suggesting that it originates in the remains of marine organisms. For these reasons oil is thought to originate in marine plant and animal remains, especially plankton which has accumulated in clay-rich bottom sediment. During formation anaerobic organisms were active in transforming the organic material. Later the organic sediment became covered by other sediments and the biological activity stopped, although the organic material has continued to change chemically due to the addition of overburden and increase in temperature. In this way the organic remains have in time been transformed to hydrocarbons or in other words natural gas and oil. The overburden weight then gradually forced the oil and salt water out of the sediment or rock source. The oil rose along fractures and through permeable beds, mainly sandstone and limestone until it reached impermeable strata, in particular clay beds. In pervious beds the oil floated on salt water due to their density difference. Then it moves along pervious beds, finally collecting in

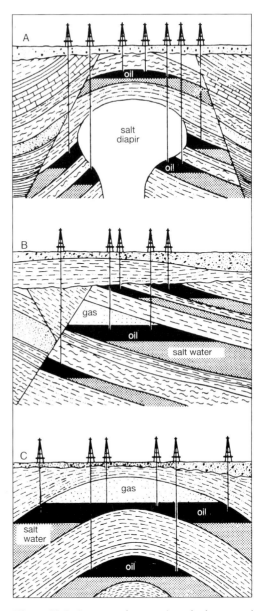

Figure 22-3. Source and reservoir rocks for natural oil and gas. Pictures show from top to bottom, oil associated with: salt dome, fault and anticline. Gas and oil float on salt water in porous beds between impervious clay beds.

reservoir rock underneath impermeable beds as for example in anticlines, at faults or at the edges of salt domes (Figure 22-3).

In oil traps the oil separates according to weight, the gas being uppermost, then the oil and underneath it marine salt brine. In some oil areas the gas has escaped from the trap leaving practically only oil. Due to erosion of oil regions both gas and oil sometimes escape leaving only asphalt.

In drilling for oil it is usual to drill directly to the oil while the gas uppermost in the trap pushes it upwards. As can be seen, crude oil is a viscous liquid composed of various liquid hydrocarbons. In oil refineries the various compounds are separated by distillation, giving liquids which have different properties and uses, such as petroleum, paraffin, and diesel, etc. Icelandic oil imports amounted to 742,000 tons in 1992.

It is estimated that the known oil and gas reserves in the world will last for 50 to 100 years at the present consumption rate. A lot of oil and natural gas has undoubtedly yet to be discovered.

The earth's oil and gas reserves should actually last even longer when sensible use of energy resources becomes a reality and governments, guided by an informed public, appreciate that such resources are not renewable except for wind, water and geothermal energy which are renewable within limits. At present the waste of energy is excessive. Automobile engines are unnecessarily powerful and the traffic speed in some countries too high while building insulation in cold countries is poor and in various hot countries air conditioning is ridiculously energy-demanding in relation to needs. Among the worst examples is the waste of raw materials and energy for military purposes. Hopefully the problem of excessive energy consumption will be dealt with in this decade, for limited energy resources and other resources make it a question of survival for mankind while in addition reduced energy consumption would decrease pollution of the ground water, rivers, lakes and the sea as well as the soil and at the same time help conserve living organisms, both animals and plants such as the forests. The atmospheric pollution is mainly due to carbon dioxide and sulphur compounds, which result in the greenhouse effect and PCB hydrochloric compounds which result in thinning of the ozone layer. Oil, natural gas, coal and peat are not renewable. They are known as fossil fuels. Water power is already used to capacity in most countries, but solar energy, geothermal heat, wind and tidal power could doubtless be exploited more than at present for energy production. Nuclear power will not be utilized more than at present unless there are considerable technical advances and the risk of pollution from the power plants themselves and from the radioactive waste can be prevented. In the future it should be borne in mind that no matter how carefully the world's natural resources of energy, raw materials, food and clothing are managed, only their conservation and moderate use can help mankind.

We have mainly dealt with coal, natural gas and oil as energy sources. The total energy consumption of mankind is a somewhat uncertain figure even though coal and oil are mainly used as fuel for cooking and heating in industrialized countries. Water power is barely 2–3%, nuclear power 10% of the energy consumption and geothermal heat barely more than 1%. In the developing countries wood is a substantial energy source and the greatest cause indirectly of deforestation and soil erosion. Furthermore, manure and rubbish are used as fuel. The use of solar energy, tidal energy and wind power are still at early stage.

Historical geology

23

During the long course of geological time, strata have constantly been formed or worn down, magma has emerged from the earth's interior to form intrusions or lava flows, sedimentary beds have piled on top of each other, the stratigraphic pile has become compressed to become fold mountains and the ocean floor has formed at divergent plate margins from spreading oceanic ridges and been destroyed at subduction zones on converging plate margins. This course of events is recorded in the earth's strata although nowhere in a complete section since crustal movements and denudation have constantly interrupted the build-up of geological formations and produced gaps. The geological record is most complete in marine sediments, which usually form horizontally. This fact has led to one of the two fundamental principles of geology, on the relative position of strata, put forward by Nikolaus Steno of Denmark in Florence in 1669. *The uppermost bed in a sequence is always younger than those beneath it* (Principle of superposition and original horizontality). In fold mountains, however, beds can have turned over so that the older beds can lie on top of younger. Intrusive igneous rocks are always younger than the surrounding country rocks. The main principle of stratigraphy was proposed by James Hutton of Scotland (1795) and Charles Lyell of England (1830). It states that *the present is the key to the past*, based on the assumption that the same processes have always been at work on the earth and have left the same traces as they do at present (uniformitarianism and actualism). Although old, these principles still hold good today, in spite of progress within earth sciences and new technology.

Origin of the earth

Many theories have been proposed for the origin of the solar system. In some theories it is assumed that the sun and planets were formed by condensation of a glowing gas cloud, and in others that the planets have separated as "dust balls" from the sun due the gravity effect of other suns as they passed by at some distance. Others believe that the sun and planets have formed when a rotating cloud of gas, cosmic dust and asteroids coalesced under gravitational pull to form the sun and planets and this theory is generally favoured today. It should be pointed out that the sun contains 750 times more matter than all the planets together. Geological history thus first starts when the crust solidified. The remains of this original crust are nowhere to be found, the oldest surface rocks on the earth being granites and gneiss which are about 500–700 million years younger than the formation of the earth, as will be explained.

Theories on the origin of the atmosphere and oceans are also somewhat divided. If the earth was initially glowing then the present atmosphere is the remains of the original, while water which condensed from it collected in depressions to form the oceans. If, on the other hand, the earth formed from "cold" cosmic dust it is probable that the atmosphere gradually formed from oxygen-poor volcanic gases from the earth's interior. On the one hand water has then formed by condensation, while on the other hand the atmosphere has through time attained its present composition later on by photosynthesis in which water and carbon dioxide combine due to solar energy. Photosynthesis produces free oxygen which is one of the main requirements for life on earth.

Geological time – Geochronology

As pointed out earlier, marine sediments form practically horizontally. Due to uplift they emerge from the sea and formation of *concordant* beds ceases. Weathering and erosion then cause denudation and are often accompanied by disruption of the strata, causing dipping and faulting. When the area sinks beneath sea level again, sedimentation commences and the new sediment lie horizontally on top of the older disturbed beds, producing a difference of dip between them. A change of dip of this kind is known as an *unconformity* and represents a gap in the geological history of the area. Information on the history of events taking place during the hiatus, or gap, is obtained by research in other areas where strata were

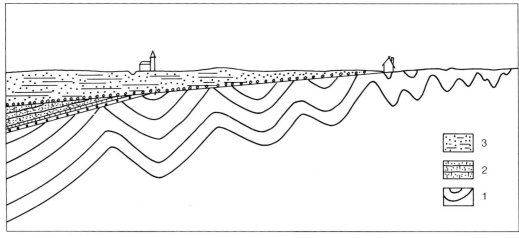

Figure 23-1. Section of geological formations in the Ruhr district, Germany, showing three unconformities. The strata were formed in the Carboniferous (1), Triassic (2) and Cretaceous (3) periods, the area being frequently under the sea. The beds from the Carboniferous period were deformed in the Hercynian folding period. The unconformities were formed when the land was uplifted from the sea and was at the same time tilted with the result that there is a difference in dip between the formations. Erosion took place while the area was above sea level. The section thus provides much information on crustal movements, sea level changes etc. (Wagner 1950.)

The geological time scale

Era	Period	Epoch	Age in million years	Folding (orogeny)
Cainozoic	Quaternary	Holocene	10,000	Alpine-folding
		Pleistocene	1.64	
	Tertiary	Pliocene Miocene Oligocene Eocene Palaeocene	65	
Mesozoic	Cretaceous Jurassic Triassic		250	
Palaeozoic	Permian Carboniferous Devonian Silurian Ordovician Cambrian		570	Hercynian folding Caledonian folding
Proterozoic Archaean	Precambrian		4,600	

The names used in stratigraphy are taken from the evolution of life (eras, epochs of the Tertiary period), geographical locations where the strata from particular periods outcrop (Cambrian, Devon, Permian, Jurassic), ethnic groups which lived in areas where the rocks of periods were first described (Ordovician, Silurian), or characteristic rocks, chalk (Cretaceous), coal (Carboniferous). In North America the Carboniferous period is divided into two, the older Mississippian and the younger Pennsylvanian. Cambria is the ancient name for Wales. Ordovicians and Silurians were Celtic groups in Wales. Devon is a county in southwest England. Perm is a district in E-Russia. Trias is coined from the threefold division of this period in Germany and Jurassic from the Jura mountains. The Tertiary (third) and Quaternary (fourth) periods are leftovers from an older stratigraphic system, secundus (secondary) and primus (first) being the periods before these. The names of the epochs of the Quaternary and Tertiary periods are Greek and related to the increase of present day shells in marine sediments; palaeo = ancient, eos = red of dawn, oligos = few or small, meion = less, pleion = more, pleistos = most and holo = all, caino = new.

forming when the unconformity took over (Figure 23-1). By tracing and comparing formations in many areas the overall stratigraphical picture can be obtained. Unconformities relate the history of crustal movement and along with the type of strata it is possible to work out the changes the land has undergone and the distribution of the oceans during past periods of geological history.

Animal and plant remains are widespread in geological strata and the history of life on earth is interwoven with its history. Remains of animals and plants found in rocks are known as *fossils*. They are either formed of hard body parts such as shell or bone (Figure 23-7), or are impressions of them. Sometimes the original material is gone and has been replaced by another, as for instance silica in place of wood in petrified wood. Occasionally, traces of soft animal and plant parts have been preserved, such as replicas of leaves (Figure 24-9), or even footprints or traces of crawling organisms. Most of the animals and plants found as fossils are long since extinct while others are represented by closely related living descendants. Fossils of marine animals are of most value in research in historical geology since many of them live or lived in extensive ocean areas and some even in all the oceans of the world. Connections between the continents have not been constant due to continental drift and fold mountain movements and as a result animal or plant species have sometimes evolved separately according to continent. For instance Australia became isolated early in the Cainozoic with the result that only two mammalian orders, the marsupials and monotremata, succeeded in evolving.

Usually individual families or species of plants or animals live for a rather short time viewed geologically. This makes it possible to use fossils in determining the *relative age of geological formations* and to correlate formations over large areas. In this way the geological time scale or column has been put together, the names of the geological eras being based on the evolution of life forms. Fossilized plants or animals which characterise a particular period of geological time are known as index fossils.

Research in volcanic areas is subject to the same main rules as research on sedimentary formations. The youngest lava lies on top of the older lavas, the youngest tephra layer on top of the older and so on. However, intrusions are younger than the surrounding country rock in which they have solidified. Fold mountains are always younger than the youngest sediment from which they have been formed.

Around the middle of the last century the *relative geological column* was more or less established in its present form, but attempts were made even then to find ways of establishing the absolute age of formations as well as of the earth itself. This was done by comparing the present day sedimentation rate with the total thickness of sediment in older formations. From this it was estimated that 35–75 million years had elapsed since the beginning of the Palaeozoic era. In a similar way attempts were made to estimate the age of the world's oceans from their salinity, most of the salt having been brought there in solution by rivers. Such calculations suggested that the age of the sea was just under 100 million years old.

With the discovery of radioactive elements in rocks, new possibilities arose for dating. Radioactive elements or their isotopes decay to form new elements at constant rates and can be compared to a clock which is started when an igneous or metamorphic rock forms. Thus half of the original uranium in rocks decays to lead and helium in 4500 million years (the half life of uranium). By measuring the ratio of uranium to lead in the rock its age can be determined. This method is mainly used in dating ancient rocks. In the same way half of the radioactive potassium in rocks decays to argon gas in 1300 million years. This method is mainly used for age determinations on fairly young rocks.

Due to cosmic radiation in the upper atmosphere a radioactive isotope of carbon, carbon-14 or ^{14}C is constantly formed from nitrogen. Its half life is about 5570 years. Radioactive carbon behaves chemically like ordinary carbon, ^{12}C and combines with atmospheric oxygen to form carbon dioxide. By photosynthesis of the carbon dioxide in plants the radioactive carbon is bound to the tissue in the same proportion as in the atmosphere. When the organisms die absorption of carbon dioxide ceases and the radioactive carbon begins to decay. After 5570 years only half of the original radioactive carbon in the organic remains is left, after 11,140 years a quarter remains and so on. The proportion of radioactive carbon to ordinary carbon in organic materials thus indicates the age. The maximum age which can be determined using the *radiocarbon method* is 70,000 years. The method can also be used in dating various animal remains since animals live on organic material photosynthesised by plants. It is also possible to date for example shells and snails which use carbon dioxide from the sea in forming their shells. Radiocarbon age determinations are of most value in samples taken from continuous sections and which can be correlated with bog profiles for which pollen analysis is available, or with soil profiles which include tephra layers or lavas. This provides a useful comparison when establishing the retreat of glaciers, shoreline changes, volcanic events, or vegetation or climatic change. The radiocarbon dating method is also very useful in determining the age of archaeological remains, either directly or indirectly and often in conjunction with tephrochronological research and pollen analysis.

With the exception of the radiocarbon method the dating methods discussed can only be used on igneous rocks. This has the disadvantage that it is difficult to correlate age determinations of intrusive rocks with relative events in geological history. Usually, it is only possible to state that sediments are younger or older than the dated igneous rock.

The availability of age determinations has opened new means of research for instance on Precambrian strata where sediments are scarce and fossils rare.

The oldest rock yet to be found on the continents is gneiss[7] at Isua in Godthaabsfjord in western Greenland which is 3800 million years old and granites and gneisses in Labrador (3800 m.y.), North-Norway (3500 m.y.) and in Australia (3900 m.y.) and in South Africa (3500 m.y.) (Figure 23-2). Since gneiss is metamorphic and granite intrusive, there must have been still older rocks in the area though there is no longer any trace of them. From these age determinations as well as the age of meteorites and moon rocks the earth is now estimated to be 4600 million years old.

---

7 The rock type gneiss is used as a general term for metamorphic rock which has formed from igneous rock (metavulcanite), sedimentary rock (metasediment) or even older metamorphic rock deep within the crust or at the base of fold mountains at high temperatures and pressures. Through metamorphism both the chemical composition and crystal structure of the original rock change. Mudstone for instance becomes first schist, then mica schist and finally gneiss. Sandstone becomes quartzite and limestone becomes marble. Igneous rock changes to gneiss, which resembles the original rock, but is generally coarser grained and banded, either composed of the minerals of acid rocks (quartz, feldspar (orthoclase) and mica), or basic rock (pyroxene, olivine and feldspar (plagioclase)). See chapter 12.

Figure 23-2. The geological structure of the continents. Symbols: 1) Precambrian shields older than 570 million years, 2) Caledonian folds around 400 million years old, 3) Hercynian folding around 300 million years old, 4) Alpine folds younger than 140 million years, 5) little disturbed sedimentary sequence on older formations, 6) major lava areas and 7) major rift valleys. (Geological Museum, Copenhagen.)

Figure 23-3. The basement rocks of Scandinavia. Pre-cambrian series and their age. The Caledonian series is from the early Palaeozoic era.

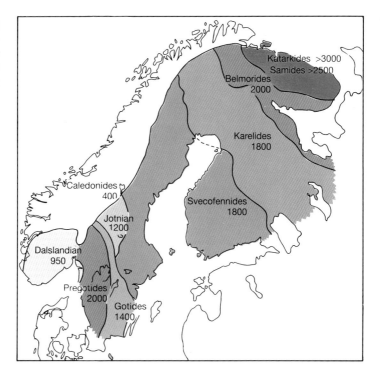

Geological history is divided into *eras* in the same way as the history of mankind. Eras are divided into *periods*, which are further divided into epochs.

The Archaean and Proterozoic eras – Precambrian

By tradition the Archaean and Proterozoic eras are discussed here as one, under the name of *Precambrian*, which accounts for over 9/10 of earth history. During this long period the continental cores were formed, being mainly composed of metamorphic rocks, especially gneiss, basic igneous rocks and plutonic rocks, in particular granite, which has formed at the base of long since denuded fold mountains. Fold mountain building episodes have occurred at long intervals and sometimes practically contemporaneously on almost all the continents during the Precambrian. On the other hand the division of the Precambrian into periods and suberas is difficult due to the nature of the rocks.

Precambrian rocks occur mainly in continental cores, the shield areas of which have mostly become very flat due to extended periods of denudation although soaring mountains at one time existed there. The main areas are Canada-Greenland, Brazil, Africa-Arabia, India, Siberia, China, Australia and Scandinavia-Russia (Baltic shield). In Scandinavia, Finland and north-west Russia the bedrock can be divided into several sections on the basis of the relationships of formations and age determinations (Figure 23-3). The oldest rock formation here is on the Kola peninsula, in northern Norway and in northern Finland (3500–2000 million years), while somewhat younger rocks occur in central Sweden and Finland (1800 million years) and the youngest formation occurs in southern Norway and south-west Swe-

207

Figure 23-4. Gneiss (meta-gneiss) in SW-Finland. The light bands are feldspar and quartz while the dark bands are dark mica and other dark minerals. The boulders are granite. The rocks are about 1800 million years old. (Photo Carl Ehlers.)

den. The latter is known as Sveconorvegium and the last folding event occurred there about 1000 million years ago. This folding event is often referred to as the Dalslandium. The other Precambrian shields are similar in type, the oldest rocks being in the centre while the younger fold formations have been added at the edges.

Formations from the latter part of the Precambrian contain a fair amount of only slightly metamorphosed sediments,

and occur for instance in central Sweden (Dalarna), northern Scotland (Torridonian sandstone) and western Greenland (Igaliko sandstone at Garðar and Brattahlíð near Narssarsuak).

Precambrian sediments contain calcareous concretions which are believed to be fossilized blue-green algae or bacteria and known as stromatolites. *The oldest fossils* of this type were found in South Africa being more than 3000 million years old and first becoming common around 2200

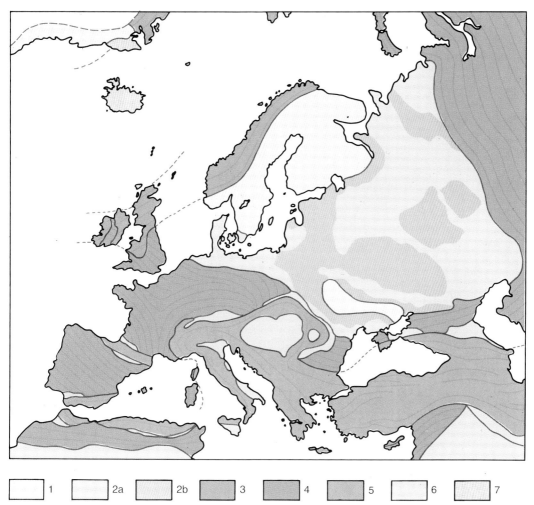

| | 1 | | 2a | | 2b | | 3 | | 4 | | 5 | | 6 | | 7 |

Figure 23-5. The basement rocks of Europe. 1) Precambrian rocks, 2a) Precambrian rocks covered by sediment, 2b) Precambrian rocks covered by very thick sediment, 3) Caledonian folds, 4) Hercynian folding, 5) Alpine folds, 6) postorogenic sedimentary areas in the Alps, 7) Tertiary and Quarternary volcanic rocks. (Wienberg-Rasmussen 1975, simplified by G.H.I.)

million years ago. The history of life on earth must, however, be much longer for a considerable period of time elapsed from the appearance of viruses and bacteria until the advent of more complicated organisms. In sediments 3300 million year old from South Africa for example microscopic organic remains have been found which are probably fossilized bacteria. Otherwise fossils are very rare in

strata from the early Precambrian although they start to be noticeable towards the end of the Precambrian, especially fossils of animals like coelenterates, annelids and brachiopods. Most organisms which lived at this time appear not to have had hard body parts which could become fossilized.

Little is known about the climate and sea temperature in the Precambrian, al-

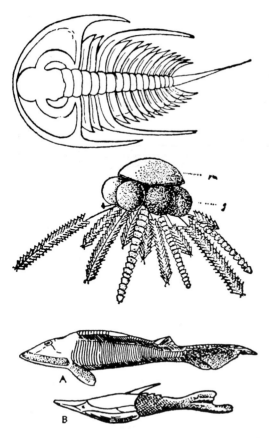

Figure 23-7. Top: trilobite, Olenellus, index fossil in the early Cambrian. Middle: Graptolites, colony. They were the characteristic colonial animals in the Ordovician and Silurian periods which became extinct in the middle Palaeozoic. Bottom: armoured fishes. A: Hemicyclaspis, B: Pteraspis. They lived during the Devon period.

Metal resources are widespread in Precambrian rocks as for example iron deposits in northern Sweden (Kiruna), Russia and North America. Various precious metals also occur, formed in association with igneous rocks, both volcanic and intrusive, while widespread iron silicate deposits also occur which formed as sediment 2000 million years ago. In some places there is also some graphite which is believed to have formed from algae.

The Palaeozoic era

The early Palaeozoic era is divided into the Cambrian, Ordovician and Silurian periods. In the beginning of the Palaeozoic the climate became warmer again following the long cold periodsof the late-Precambrian ice age. Denudation of the old continental shields continued and at the same time large land areas sank below sea level to become shallow seas. In addition huge oceans started to form at spreading ocean ridges on divergent plate boundaries as well as trenches on converging plate margins where widespread accumulation of sediments took place. For example a large ocean existed where the North Atlantic is at present (Iapetus Ocean) and in the Silurian period the sediments in this trench and on the shelves were compressed due to plate movement when the north American and European plates collided compressing the trapped sediments and igneous rocks and the rest of the ocean bottom between them pushing up the Caledonian fold mountains (Caledonia was the Roman name for Scotland). One arm of this great fold mountain chain extended from the British Isles along western Norway and from Spitsbergen to eastern Greenland thereby joining the land areas of the Scandinavian shield and the British Isles to the North American shield and Greenland. There was considerable volcanism

though at times it was warm (chalk beds) or warm and dry (rock salt). Glacial remains have been found and suggest that the climate was at times cold. Very extensive glacial remains are for instance known from around 2000 million years ago in Canada and especially from the close of the Precambrian in Norway, Greenland, South Africa, China and Australia. Widespread glacial remains are known from all the continents from late Precambrian time around 600 million years ago.

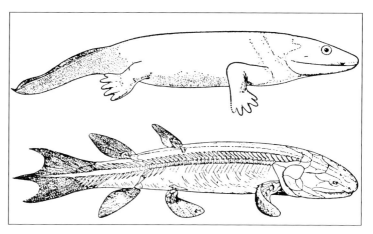

Figure 23-8. Top: The oldest land vertebrate, a primitive amphibian (Ichthyostega) which resembled a fish in many respects but walked on four feet. "Amphibious fish", this example was found in Upper Devonian rocks in E Greenland. Bottom: Crossopterygia, a fish also from the Upper Devonian. The fins are strongish and were used for walking.

connected with this orogeny. Among the best preserved stratigraphical sections is in Wales although it was subject to folding during the Caledonian orogeny. The names of the periods have their origin in Wales (Figure 23-5).

Fauna. Marine sediments from the Cambrian period contain fossils including representatives from all the phylums of the invertebrates such as protozoa, sponges, echinoderms, brachiopods, annilids, molluscs, arthropods and especially crustaceans. All of these were marine animals, most of them having hard shells. Animals belonging to some of these phyla were just beginning to appear at the end of the Precambrianbut suddenly increase greatly in numbers in the Cambrian period.

Index fossils of the Cambrian period are the *trilobites* (Figure 23-7a) which were crustaceans which became extinct by the Palaeozoic era. In the Ordovician period *graptolites* (Figure 23-7b) become dominant. They lived in colonies and drifted with the current as plankton. Nothing is known about their relationship with other phyla but they became extinct in the middle of the Palaeozoic era. Brachiopods (Figure 23-12) were also very common. One of them, *Lingula* still exists and is the most conservative of all

the animals, having barely changed or evolved since the beginning of the Palaeozoic. Corals also became common forming reef deposits during the Silurian period for instance as in Gotland, Sweden.

Amongst the new species which appeared in the Ordovician period are the first vertebrates. They were known as *placodermi*, primitive jawless proto fish covered in bony scales (armoured fishes) (Figure 23-7c). They became extinct in the middle of the Palaeozoic period.

The *flora* evolved little up until the end of the Silurian period when the forerunners of land plants became established thereby initiating colonization on land although algae had already been common in the sea for a long time or at least since the Precambrian. These plants were primitive and fern-like and known as Psilophytes. Around the same time the first land animals appeared, which were scorpions and millipedes.

The climate became much warmer during the Cambrian and still warmer during the Ordovician and Silurian periods. In the Silurian period thick chalk beds were formed such as in Gotland and at Niagara Falls (the threshold rock). In places the climate was actually so dry and hot that it led to the formation of rock salts by evaporation as for example

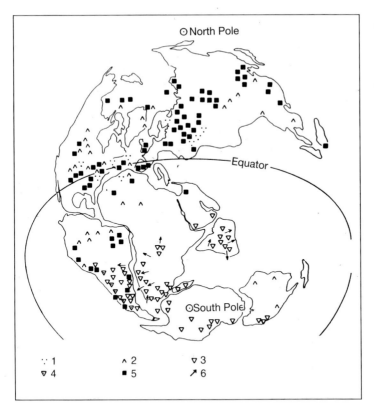

Figure 23-9. Probable position of the continents during the younger Carboniferous period 320–286 million years ago. Symbols: 1) Dotted triangles: Red sediments (desert). 2) Inverted V: salt deposits. 3) Triangles: tillite. 4) Triangles with dot: mountain glaciers. 5) Filled triangles: Coal. 6) Arrows: glacial striæ. (Schmidt and Walter 1990.)

in Siberia and North America. However, during the Ordovician an ice sheet covered the Sahara, which was then situated at the south pole.

The middle Palaeozoic-Devonian period. The Caledonian orogeny ended with the Silurian period and during the Devonian period weathering and erosion led to the denudation of the fold mountain ranges. In the folding area and surrounding areas thick beds of red-coloured conglomerate and sandstones were formed (old red sandstone). In the British Isles (on Caithness and the Orkney Islands), in W-Norway, in eastern Greenland and on the east coast of U.S.A. the beds are at their thickest, in places being several kilometres thick. These areas became a supercontinent (Old red continent). The red colour is thought to be due to a rather dry cli-

mate with seasonal rainfall. It should be pointed out, however, that land vegetation was at a very early stage and therefore sparse. There were, however, lakes bordered by clubmosses (lycods) and horsetail (Equisetum) forests. During the late Devonian period on Bear Island (Björnöya) the oldest known coal beds formed from their remains. In the lakes swam *lungfish* which could survive in dry conditions between rainy periods like their descendants do today in Australia. Related to them were the lobe finned fishes (Crossopterygii) which had very strong fins and whose descendants were the first amphibians (Ichthyostega). Their fossils have been found in the red late Devonian beds in eastern Greenland (Figure 23-8). During the Carboniferous period their descendants, became dominant, many of which were quite large. Most became ex-

Figure 23-10. Probable position of the continents during the Permian period 286–245 million years ago. Symbols are the same as in Figure 23-9. (Schmidt and Walter 1990.)

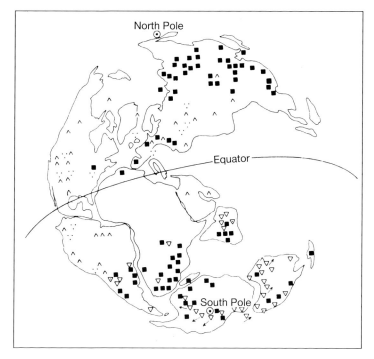

tinct at the end of the Palaeozoic era although certain of their descendants still exist and spend the first stage of their life in water as frog tadpoles breathing through gills which become lungs as they grow and crawl on to land.

The later part of the Palaeozoic era is divided into the Carboniferous and Permian periods. While the red sediments were being deposited on the "northern continent", a geosyncline or trough formed by plate movement extended from the east coast of the U.S.A. to the British Isles and eastwards across middle Europe to the Urals. During the Devonian period mainly clays and sandstones were deposited in the trough, accompanied by volcanism but this was replaced by deposition of limestone beds during the earlier part of the Carboniferous. In the mid and late Carboniferous folding of the beds took place due to northward drift of the African plate, forming the Hercynian (Va-

riscan) orogeny which can be traced from Spain and the south of the British Isles eastwards through Belgium, Germany, Poland and Crimea to the Ural mountains (Figure 23-5). On the east coast of North America the Appalachian mountains were formed in an orogeny at the same time.

On the margins of the fold mountain ranges the Carboniferous strata, sediments composed of debris from the mountains, accumulated lowlands. In the warm and wet climate huge swamps formed in depressions on land which were covered by forests of ferns, clubmosses, lycopods and Equisetum and horsetail. The peat was then later transformed into coal, from which the period draws its name. The main coal areas are at Don in Russia, in Poland, the Ruhr in Germany, Belgium, northern France and in Britain. Extensive coal beds were also formed on the margins of the Appalachian mountains in the U.S.A., especially in Pennsylvania.

213

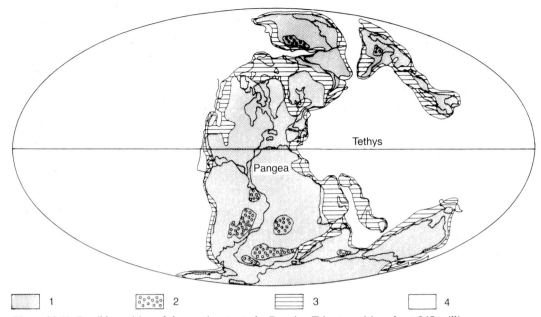

1   2   3   4

Figure 23-11. Possible position of the continents at the Permian-Trias transition about 245 million years ago according to the ideas of Alfred Wegener 1915. Practically all the continents were assumed to be joined as Pangea. Between certain continents however were shallow seas, especially in the northern hemisphere. Symbols: 1) continents, 2) depressions with sedimentation, 3) shallow seas and 4) ocean. (Ziegler 1976.)

The climate in the lower Permian period was dry and warm in Europe and the U.S.A. and coal formation largely ceased as a result. Along the edges of fold mountains thick beds of red sandstone formed from debris from the Hercynian chain which had already started to be denuded. During the mid Permian period the sea flooded the area between the Hercynian fold mountains and the continent to the north in the North Sea as well as the area between Greenland and Norway and, but also North America and Siberia. In shallow enclosed seas huge salt beds were formed in the upper Permian period in the hot, dry climate. During later crustal movements the salt was deformed and intruded as salt domes upwards through the overburden. Widespread oil deposits now occur associated with them (Figure 22-3). Permian salt was previously mined but nowadays they are exploited mainly for potassium.

Between the land areas of the northern and southern hemispheres an extensive Mediterranean sea "Tethys" (Figures 23-9 and 23-10) existed during the Mesozoic and up until the Cainozoic era. The Alpine fold mountain chain rose from this during the Cainozoic. To the south of the sea lay the super continent of Gondwanaland which comprised the present day continents of Australia, India, Antarctica, Arabia-Africa and South America. The fauna and flora evolved in a rather different way in this area than on the continents of the northern hemisphere. The land areas of the southern hemisphere were probably joined to Europe and North America by continental drift in connection with the formation of the Hercynian fold mountains during the Carboniferous period and to Siberia through the formation of the Ural mountains during the middle Permian. This super continent has been named Pangea. It may well be, however, that a shallow sea existed between the continents. In the beginning of the Trias period and especially in the Jurassic period the super continent broke up and the present day continents began to drift in various directions (Figure 23-11).

On Gondwanaland at the end of the Carboniferous and during the Permian period huge ice sheets formed. Evidence for them is found in all the present day continents of the southern hemisphere. The main explanation for these extensive glacial features is that at the end of the Palaeozoic era all the continents of the southern hemisphere were joined together around the south pole which was "situated" in the present day Indian ocean, but they then drifted apart. No glacial evidence exists in the northern hemisphere from this period, the north pole of the time having probably lain in the ocean. The flora and fauna were very similar at this time in all the land areas of the southern hemisphere. The typical vegetation was Glossopteris (a seed fern) while in polar regions conifers were dominant in the Permian period.

Igneous activity was widespread during the Carboniferous and Permian periods. In geosynclinal troughs and fold mountains there was a lot of igneous activity and large granite batholiths were formed such as in Cornwall, Schwarzwald and the Hercynian area while there

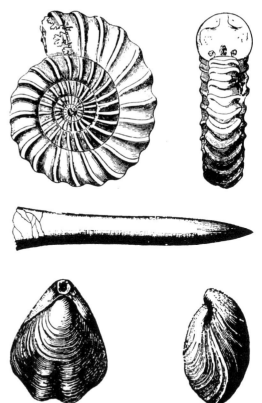

Figure 23-12. Index fossils from the Mesozoic era. Top: ammonite (Aegocerus capricornu, Jurassic). Middle: belmnite (Belemnite paxollosus, Jurassic). Bottom: Brachiopods (Telebratula gregaria, Triassic).

was also volcanic activity as in the Oslo area in Norway (rhomboporphyre) and in Scotland where the "volcano" of Arthur's

Figure 23-13. Fish-like dinosaur (Ichtyosaurus). This 3 m long fossil is unusually well preserved. It was found in black shales from the Jurassic period at Holzmaden in S Germany. (Hauff 1938.)

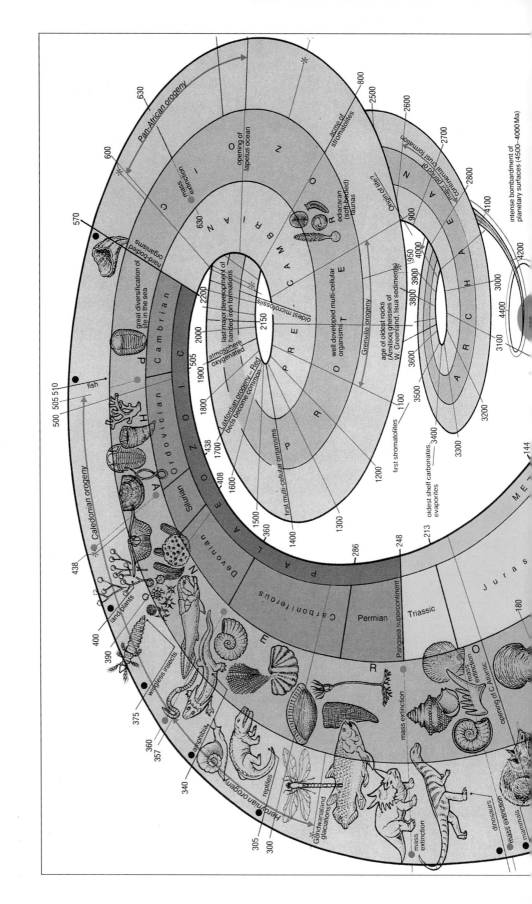

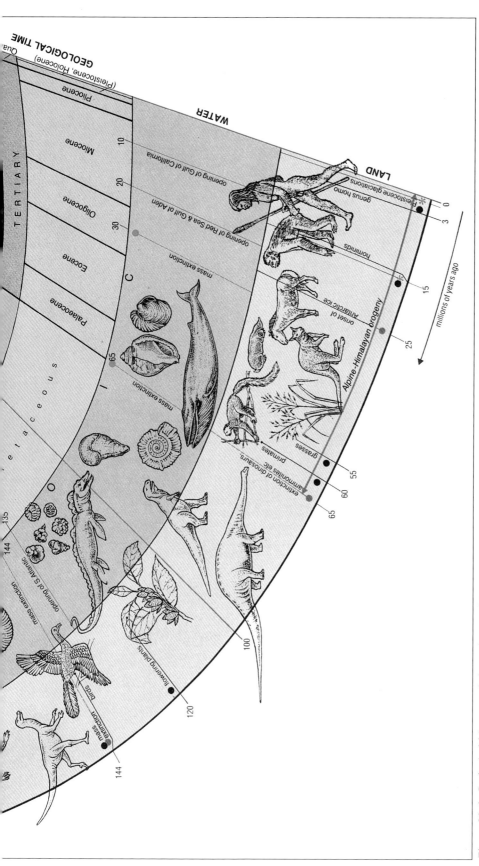

Figure 23-6. Geological history and the evolution of life. (Times Books Ltd.)

Figure 23-14. Dinosaurs from the Mesozoic era. 1) and 2) Pterosaurus from the Jurassic and Cretaceous periods. Wingspan of the largest reached up to 7–8 m. 3) Brontosaurus. 30 m in length and 7 m high. The largest land animal to exist. Herbivore from the Jurassic period. 4) Allosaurus up to 10 m in length. Jurassic period. 5) Triceratops. Well protected vegetarian 7 m in length. Cretaceous period. 6) Whale-like Plesiosaurus. Lived in the sea. Jurassic and Cretaceous periods.

seat in Edinburgh was active at the end of the Carboniferous period.

Fauna. As mentioned the first land vertebrates appeared during the Devonian period. They were amphibians, labyrynthodonts, which then became dominant during the Carboniferous. Their dominance diminished during the Permian and they were replaced by the reptiles, which first appeared in the Carboniferous. Primitive fishes decreased in numbers and some became extinct such as the placodermi which were replaced by the cartilaginous (sharks and skates) and bony fishes (e.g.lung fishes). Among the invertebrates the most noteworthy are brachiopods and shelled squids, goniatites, related to the ammonites (Figure 23-12). They were the index fossils in the late Precambrian.

Flora. Higher plants evolved rapidly and during the Devonian and Carboniferous ferns dominated on land. From them evolved the seed ferns and from them the cycads and gymnosperms which replaced the ferns and dominated from the mid-Permian.

Mesozoic

The Mesozoic is divided into the *Triassic, Jurassic* and *Cretaceous*. There were weak folding movements but sediments continued to accumulate in the Tetys geosynclinal trough, which was the result of the separation of N-America, Asia and Europe from Gondwanaland. There was also folding during the later part of the era around the Pacific.

Volcanic activity occurred during the

Figure 23-15. Bedded coral limestone from the Triassic period at Dachstein near Salzburg in the Alps. The cliff face is 1000 m high. Overthrown folds, the overfolding to the right. (Photo Þ.E.)

Mesozoic, especially during the Triassic when huge, thick lava plateaus were formed associated with the beginning of continental drift in Siberia, S-Africa and during the Jurassic in S-America where the largest lava area on the earth's surface occurs at the Parana river (1.2 million km²).

The global climate was mild, dry to start with, but becoming humid with the formation of coal beds, e.g. in Europe during the early Cretaceous.

At the end of the Jurassic the sea flooded the lowlands of Europe and extensive beds of limestone were formed. During the Cretaceous the sea inundated an even larger area and first sandstones and then limestone beds were formed Figure 23-19). Towards the end of the period major beds of white chalk (Figure 4-8) were formed, e.g. in Britain and France (Dover and Calais) and in Denmark (Mønsklint).

Fauna. The marine index fossils in the Mesozoic were two groups of squids, the *ammonites* (Figure 23-12 which had a spiral calcareous shell and the *belemnites* (Figure 23-12) which resembled the present day squids although the back extended to the tail as a point. Both groups became extinct at the end of the Mesozoic. Other fauna included corals, sponges, shells, gastropods and brachiopods.

At the end of the Palaeozoic most of the fishes which had dominated the marine life disappeared from the scene while the evolution of cartilaginous fishes (e.g. sharks) and bony-fishes continued. In the Jurassic period the true *bony fishes* appeared. They were rather small and of the herring family. The amphibians had al-

219

Figure 23-16. A very primitive bird (Archaeopteryx). Fossils of 3 species have been found in limestone from the late Jurassic period in southern Germany.

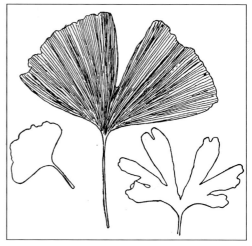

Figure 23-17. Fossilized leaf of maiden hair tree, Gingko, the oldest genus of trees at present on earth, has been living for 250 million years. Middle: Ginko biloba which has not changed in at least 50 million years.

ready started to decrease in numbers during the Permian period and as the Mesozoic progressed only those resembling present day families continued.

By the end of the Palaeozoic era the *reptiles* had already begun to increase in numbers and in the Mesozoic they reached the high point of their evolution and dominated on land, in the sea and in the air. With the arrival of the reptiles the colonization of the land by the vertebrates began in earnest. They were independent of water and in this respect unlike amphibians which have to hatch their eggs

in water and pass the first stage of their life there. Certain groups of reptiles evolved slowly and have remained almost unchanged since the Mesozoic, such as the tortoises and crocodiles. On the other hand the evolution of the dinosaurs was extremely diverse. Early in the Mesozoic certain groups turned to the sea and evolved there in a similar manner to the whales later on. They are known as *Ichtyosaurus* (Figure 23-13) and reached up to 15 m in length. Other reptiles chose the air, *Pterosaurus*, their wing span reaching 8 metres. Among the land dinosaurs there was great diversity and many lifestyles. Some were herbivorous and others carnivorous, some quick footed and resembling the kangaroos while others were heavy footed and armour plated. Some of the *dinosaurs* (Figure 23-14) became the largest of all land animals before or since, one of them (Brontosaurus) being around 30 metres in length, 13 metres high and about 50 tons in weight. Dinosaurs, along with the squids (Belemnites, Ammonites) were index fossils during the Mesozoic

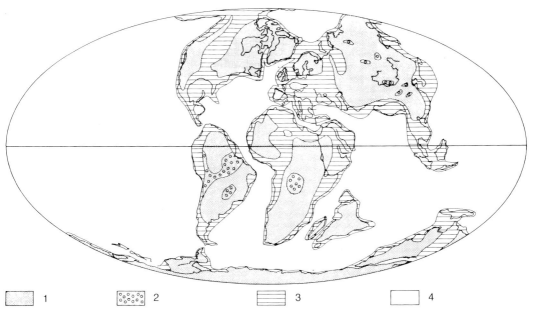

1   2   3   4

Figure 23-18. Probable position of the continents in late Cretaceous period about 100–60 million years ago. The continents and sea floor have begun to take on their present form. The North Atlantic is still a continent with shallow sea straits. Symbols: 1) continents, 2) depressions within continents with heavy sedimentation, 3) shallow seas and 4) oceans. (Schmidt and Walter 1990.)

both flourishing and becoming extinct during the era.

In Jurassic chalk beds the Solnhofen in southern Germany fossils of three *primitive birds* (Archaeopteryx, Figure 23-16) have been found. They were of similar size to ptarmigan and had feathers like birds. On the other hand they had claws on all their limbs, teeth and feathers in place of the present day tail. From the close of the Jurassic there is a gap in the series of feathered birds but by the end of the Cretaceous period the true birds had appeared.

During the Triassic period the *mammals* appeared. They were primitive and rather small, probably related to the present day monotremata (egg laying mammals) and probably hatched out eggs. Their evolution was slow but higher mammals first appeared in Cretaceous beds. They had a womb (uterus) which enabled the young to be born at an advanced stage.

Flora. Horsetail- and clubmoss trees of the Palaeozoic had disappeared by the Mesozoic but the ferns survived. The representative vegetation of the Mesozoic was *conifers (Gymosperms)*, and *ginkgotrees* (Figure 23-17). During the middle Cretaceous period there was a sudden revolution in the plant kingdom when *flowering plants (Angiosperms)* appeared, especially *broad leaved trees* which quickly became dominant.

In the sea were many microscopic single celled animals such as Foraminifera with calcareous shells and Radiolaria with silica shells, as well as algae, e.g. siliceous diatoms and microalgae having calcareous plates (Coccoliths) which formed widespread thick sediments on the sea floor, such as chalk (Figures 4-8 and 23-19).

The Cainozoic era

The Cainozoic is the youngest era of ge-

Figure 23-19. Stevns Klint in the southeast of the island Sjælland in Denmark. The bedding plane in centre of picture also marks the transition between the Mesozoic and Cainozoic eras, i.e. Cretaceous-and Tertiary periods. Below the transition is chalk with flint beds, while above is bryozoan limestone. A very thin bed of clay occurs between the beds, which is of great significance in discussion about the major faunal changes, such as the extinction of the dinosaurs and many species of squid etc. around this time. This thin bed is very rich in iridium, thought to have originated in a huge meteorite which collided with the earth around that time. (Photo Þ.E.)

ological history. During this period the Alpine fold mountain chain (Figure 23-2, 23–5) was formed and volcanism was very active throughout the world. The landscape and distribution of land gradually achieved its present state not least due to relative sea level changes but in particular due to plate tectonic movements. It is now thought that all the oceans have formed since the Jurassic period, or in the last 150–200 million years and mainly in the Cainozoic. For instance the North Atlantic was formed by continental drift during the Cainozoic (Figure 24-4).

Strata from the Cainozoic era are naturally better known and preserved than from older periods of geological history. Over wide areas sediments are unconsolidated and in some cases undisturbed. They have either formed on dry land or in shallow seas, the strata which formed in deeper water being still on the deep sea floor.

The Cainozoic is divided into two periods of different lengths, the *Tertiary* period which spans most of it and which began about 65 million years ago and the *Quaternary* period which began about 1.64 million years ago and extends to the present day.

The Tertiary period

The Tertiary period is divided into *early Tertiary (the Palaeocene, Eocene and Oligocene)* often referred to as the Palaeogene and the *late Tertiary (Miocene and Pliocene)* often referred to as the Neogene, which began about 23 million years ago. The geological history of Iceland falls into the Neogene and will be treated in more detail in chapter 24.

Folding of strata in the great Mediterranean or Tethys geosyncline had already started in the latter part of the Mesozoic era (Andes and Rocky mountains), but folding reached a maximum during the early Tertiary period. This folding is not yet finished as frequent large earthquakes in fold mountain regions show (Figure 10-8). Most of the major mountain ranges of the world are the result of folding and uplift in this orogeny. Examples are the Atlas mountains, the Pyrénées, Alps, Balkan, Caucasus, Himalayas, mountain ranges in Japan and New Zealand as well as the Andes and Rocky mountains mentioned earlier (Figure 23-2). With the folding and uplift of the Alpine chain ended the history of the great Mediterranean Tethys sea. The final traces of this great sea are the Mediterranean and Black Sea. Through the folding movements new land was added to the continental cores of Europe and Asia in the northern hemisphere, which was joined to part of the broken up Gondwanaland i.e. India, Arabia-Africa, by their northward drift and forming the fold chains of the Atlas mountains and Alps as well mountain ranges in Asia Minor, Iran and the Himalayas. In the late Cretaceous the oceans had reached their greatest extent in geological history, but with the uplift of the Alpine chain and other continental shelf areas during the Tertiary period the area of dry land greatly increased. With uplift the erosive capability of rivers was re-newed and they gradually established their present day channels. Rivers transported large amounts of sediment and deposited it on lowland and in shallow seas. In this way inland seas and bays became filled in to form dry land. Sediment infilling and uplift formed the lowlands of Denmark, Poland, Northern Germany, the Netherlands and in the London and Paris basins, while in the Alpine countries it formed the Po basin, the Donau basin and Hungarian plains and in North America at the northern Gulf of Mexico to Florida and along the east coast of the U.S.A. In many areas rivers have also added to lowland during the Quaternary epoch since erosion and sedimentation were rapid at this time. The landscape on the newly formed Tertiary lowlands with many grabens was similar to that in the Carboniferous period and the climate humid at times. Great bogs were formed in many areas thick peat layers which subsequently became lignite. As regards the amount of coal the Tertiary period is second to the Carboniferous. Great lignite deposits occur for instance in Germany, North America, Spitsbergen and Asia. Tertiary marine sediments also contain widespread extensive natural gas and oil reserves.

With the opening of the present day oceans which began about 200 million years ago the modern continents began to drift to their present positions. Following the break up of the Pangea super-continent in the Permian and Triassic periods the formation of rift valleys and then spreading ocean ridges, the oceans gradually increased in size although at rather different rates. Thus the drift rate on the mid-Atlantic ridge is 1 cm per year in the North Atlantic, 2 cm per year in the south Atlantic while in the south-east Pacific it reaches 10–20 cm per year in each direction on the East Pacific ridge. The formation of the ocean floor through sea floor

223

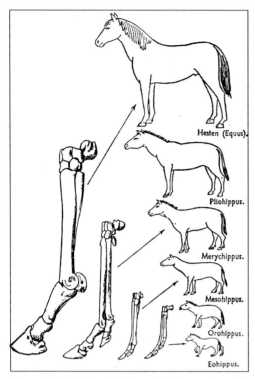

Figure 23-20. The evolution of the horse from the Eocene epoch (Eohippus) and up to the present (Equus = horse). At left are bones of the front feet. Scale proportions normal. (Heintz 1966.)

sent as for instance around the Pacific and in the Mediterranean. In addition plutonic rocks were intruded into the roots of the fold mountains although there is rather little evidence of the plutons since erosion of the mountains is still continuing and nowhere nearly complete. However, granite batholiths have been exposed by erosion in the Sierra Nevada in western North America and in the central Alps.

At the beginning of the Tertiary period great eruptions took place in the north of the Atlantic in a belt extending from Northern Ireland and Scotland westwards to the Faeroe islands, Iceland, E-Greenland, W-Greenland and Baffin Island (Figure 24-4). These were mainly basalt flood eruptions accompanied by a lot of lava production from fissures and central volcanoes, but in between the lava beds are beds of volcanic tephra, soils, lacustrine and fluvial sediment. This basalt formation everywhere closely resembles the Icelandic Tertiary Basalt Formation and its thickness is commonly 1000–10,000 metres. The eruptions began everywhere in connection with the opening of the Atlantic as a result of plate tectonic movements early in the Tertiary period.

Great lava eruptions also occurred in the Tertiary period in Siberia, on the Indian sub-continent, in Ethiopia, Patagonia, north-west North America (the Columbian and Snake River plateaus). Some volcanism also occurred in central Europe for instance in the Eifel, W-Germany and Massif Central in France.

Along with plate movements and folding were tectonic movements which for example led to the formation of rift valleys within the continents such as the Rhine-Rhone valley and the Dead Sea, Red Sea and east African Rift Valley combined with volcanism.

There are also large subsidence areas either within the continents or on the

spreading did not in fact start everywhere at the same time. In the Pacific and south Atlantic it began in the Jurassic period, 200 million years ago but farthest north in the Atlantic it commenced at the Cretaceous-Tertiary transition about 65 million years ago.

Associated with the opening of the oceans and upheaval of the Alps there was great *volcanic activity*. On the ocean ridges large amounts of magma rose to the surface and erupted as pillow lavas. In a few places the volcanism succeeded in building up islands of which Iceland is the largest. In fold areas on convergent plate margins eruptions had already started at the beginning of folding in Triassic times and continues to the pre-

224

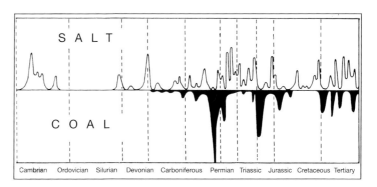

Figure 23-21. Salt and coal formation in a stratigraphical context clearly shows the climatic changes which have occurred on the earth in the last 570 million years. Coal formation suggests a warm humid climate while salt formation suggests hot dry conditions. (Schmidt and Walter 1991.)

edges at plate margins. Thus subsidence has been taking place since the early Permian period or during the last 300 million years, with the accumulation of thick sediment in the North Sea area which in fact extends from the Carpathian mountains and central German mountains through Denmark, the North Sea northwards along the west coast of Norway to the Barents Sea and Spitsbergen. The sediment reaches a maximum of 10,000 metres in the Central rift valley in the North Sea and in the Viking rift valley

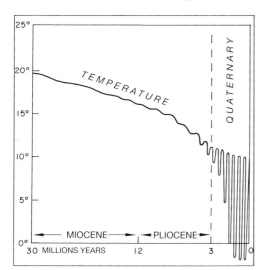

Figure 23-22. Changes in mean annual temperature in central Europe during the late Tertiary and Quaternary periods. Changes in mean annual temperature in Iceland were similar but about 5° C lower overall. (From Woldstedt 1954.)

northwards along the Norwegian coast. Here beds of clay, sand limestone, chalk and salt alternate. There are large quantities of natural gas and oil in the strata of these areas.

Climatic changes during the Tertiary period are much better known than in earlier geological times since the strata are better preserved and living organisms more closely related to those of the present day. During the early and middle Tertiary the climate was warm and humid (lignite and bauxite) but became gradually cooler. Changes of the positions of the continents as a result of plate tectonic movement and the formation of higher fold mountains because of isostatic movement also had an effect on the climate. For example with the uplift of the coastal ranges and the Rocky mountains the climate of western North America became dry and in fact still is. In the late Tertiary the climate became colder and in the Oligocene, Miocene and Pliocene glaciers formed on the mountains as for example in Antarctica, in Alaska and in Iceland (Figure 23-22).

Flora. During the mid Cretaceous flowering plants made their appearance and quickly became dominant, although conifers were also very common, as they still are. Among the main conifers were giant firs and other related trees and they played an important part in the formation of lignite. Amongst flowering plants the

225

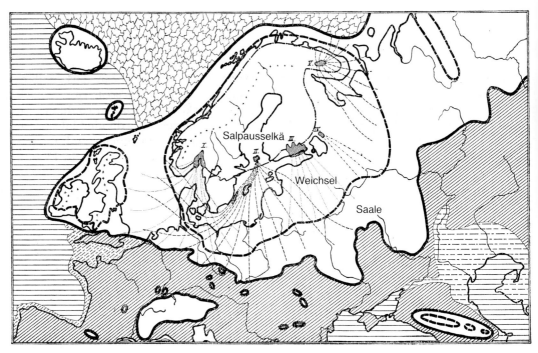

Figure 23-23. Extent of glaciers in Europe in the second last (Saale) and last (Weichsel) glaciations. The continental shelf was at this time dry down to the 100–150 metre depth line. Also shown is the glacier extent in Scandinavia 11,000–10,000 years ago (Salpausselkä = Younger Dryas cold period). The bedrock in shaded areas in Scandinavia is composed of easily identified rock types, fragments of which are found extensively and are widespread in glacial till and provide information on the extent and movement of Pleistocene glaciers. The North Atlantic was covered by drift ice. (Wagner 1950.)

broad leaved trees were most common. Pollen analyses suggest, however, that there was also very diverse plant growth in the lignite bogs. There is little evidence of latitudinal distribution of vegetation in the warm climate of the early Tertiary period as is exemplified by the existence of palms, vines and giant firs in Greenland. The latitudinal distribution starts to become noticeable in the mid and late Tertiary when various warm-loving plants disappear from northern areas. In central Europe various warm-loving trees still survived, however, such as palm trees, fig trees and giant firs.

Fauna. Great changes affected animal life at the close of the Mesozoic and start of the Cainozoic. The squids, ammonites and belemnites became extinct and in their place the *shells* and *gastropods* became dominant in the marine environment and the chief index fossils in the sea. Brachiopods decreased greatly in numbers and are insignificant today (200 species). Of the Arthropods the crabs and insects were most common having been evolving slowly since the Palaeozoic. Among Protozoa in the early Tertiary are very large foraminifera, the so called nummulites which reached as much as 10 cm in diameter. In places they form thick limestone beds as for example in Egypt where the rock has been used in the construction of the pyramids.

At the end of the Mesozoic era the dinosaurs had disappeared and the amphibians seldom evident. Most species of present day cartilaginous fishes had made their appearance in the Mesozoic and their evolution was largely finished. True bony fishes (Teleostei), e.g. herring and salmon, continued to evolve and in the late Tertiary most present day species had appeared. Fossils of birds are rare but their evolution appears to have been rather rapid and at the close of the Tertiary period most present day species were established.

The *mammals* first made their appearance in the Triassic period and their evolution was for a long time slow but with the beginning of the Cainozoic they evolved extremely rapidly with new species continually appearing while others became extinct. *Mammals are the characteristic life type for the Cainozoic.* Late in the Mesozoic insectivores appeared on the scene and all the higher mammals have evolved from them. There were three main branches: carnivores (e.g. predators), herbivores (e.g. hoofed animals) and monkeys. The predators evolved quite rapidly and in late Tertiary all the present day groups had emerged. Of them, the whales had already turned to the sea and evolved in the Eocene and the seals in the Miocene. The herbiverous animals quickly separated into many groups and claws changed early into hooves while the teeth became flat. Elephants appeared for instance early in the Tertiary and were trunkless and the incisor teeth grew bigger. Horses also appeared in the early Tertiary. They were small forest animals at first with 4 hooves on the front feet and 3 on the rear (Eohippus, 40 cm). They then gradually increased in size and became steppe animals while at the same time the number of hooves decreased (Figure 23-20). The apes also appeared in the Eocene and by the Miocene period primates-hominoids had entered geological history.

Quaternary

The Quaternary period is divided into two periods of different length, the *Pleistocene epoch* which began 1.64 million years ago and the *Holocene epoch* which began 10,000 years ago and continues today. The Pleistocene is divided into *glacial stages* having a cold climate, and *interglacial stages* having a warm climate. During the interglacials the climate was similar to what it is at present and at the beginning of the Pleistocene, even warmer. The Holocene in many ways resembles the interglacials of the Pleistocene and it will be treated here outside of Iceland as such.

During glacial stages the snowline lay 500–1000 m lower than at present and the mean annual temperature was 5–10°C lower when the climate was at its harshest (Figure 23-22). During glacials the glaciers covered all of N-Europe, the British Isles and the Alps. During the last glacial period but one the ice sheet extended from the ice divide in Scandinavia as far south as London, the central mountains of Germany and Moscow. The great distribution can be determined from glacial striae, glacial deposits, erratics and the position of end moraines. In the east of the British Isles there are for example a large amount of erratics which originate in Norway suggesting that the ice flowed across the North Sea (Figure 23-24). The whole of northern North America was covered by a huge ice sheet which extended south of the Great Lakes which are in fact ancient proglacial lakes. There were also large glaciers in most mountain areas as for example the Caucasus and Himalayas as well as on mountains in the tropics. A similar situation applied to the southern hemisphere, where there were for instance large glaciers in New Zealand and in the southern part of South America and in Tasmania. In the second last glacial period (Saale)glaciers covered about 45 million km^2.

During glacials the precipitation in the present day deserts was considerably more than now. It should be borne in mind, however, that evaporation was less because of the lower air temperature. Many of the great deserts were covered by vegetation and there were widespread large lakes in the depressions. The best known of these now dried up lakes is "Lake Bonneville" in Utah which was about 50,000 km^2 in size and which was a fresh water lake. The remains of this great lake exist today as the Great Salt Lake which is brine and "only" about 4500 km^2 in size.

Up until the end of the last century it was believed that the Pleistocene was one long continuous winter. Later, glacials were considered to have been 4, based mainly on research in the Alps. It is now believed that in Iceland there have been 14–23 such glacial stages during the last 3 million years and even more according to research on sediment on the ocean floor which spans the past two million years. Glacials have different names in various parts of the world and their correlation is often difficult. The names are either coined from rivers or areas where moraine or fluvioglacial sediment from the past few glacial stages is preserved.

Names of the past few glacial stages in N. Europe, the Alps and N. America

N-Europe	Alps	N-America
Weichsel	Würm	Wisconsin
Saale	Riss	Illinoian
Elster	Mindel	
Cromer	Günz	

Little is known about the length of individual interglacials and glacials. The last glacial period ended 10,000 years ago and is believed to have started 70,000 or even 120,000 years ago, while the interglacials are thought to have been shorter than the glacials. The glacial stages have therefore probably lasted for about 100,000 years.

Little is known about the extension of the glaciers in the earlier glacials since traces of them were largely destroyed by the glaciers of the second last glacial when glaciers had the greatest extent in the Pleistocene. Traces of them are best seen in volcanic areas such as in Iceland where lavas have covered till deposits and protected them from glacial erosion younger glaciations. Traces of the glaciers of the last glacial, their retreat and melting stages are well known. In northern Europe there were two large ice sheets during the last glacial stages, one over the British Isles and the other in Scandinavia (Figure 23-24). In the Alps there was a large glacier and Iceland was almost entirely ice covered. The Scandinavian glacier of the last glacial, Weichsel, reached its greatest extent 18–20,000 years ago. At that time it covered all of Scandinavia and its limits can be traced southwards in Jutland, eastwards in Germany south of Berlin to Valdai hills in Russia and as far north as the White Sea. The glacier then melted quite rapidly and about 13–14,000 years ago the ice limit lay through the Danish archipelago. The retreat was accompanied by readvances, however, for the climatic improvement was not constant but interrupted by cold spells. In one such cold spell 11,000 years ago the glacier advanced in Scandinavia pushing up huge end moraines which can be traced from Oslo Fjord (Ra) across central Sweden to Finland (Salpausselkä). The end of the Pleistocene is considered to be when the glacier started to retreat from these end moraine complexes about 10,000 years ago and the Holocene epoch began. The Scandinavian glacier was completely melted 8000 years ago.

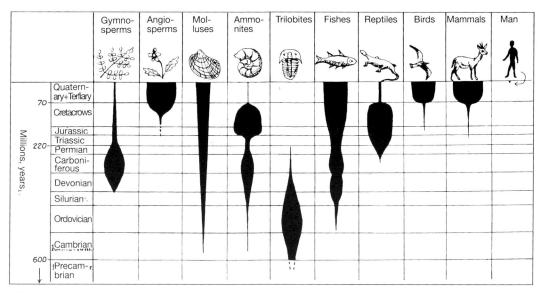

	Gymno-sperms	Angio-sperms	Mol-luses	Ammo-nites	Trilobites	Fishes	Reptiles	Birds	Mammals	Man

Figure 23-24. Stratigraphical evolution of fauna and flora. The diagram shows for instance when various groups and classes appear or become extinct and when they were dominant. (Schwarzbach 1954.)

Pleistocene glaciers have strongly shaped the landscape in their respective areas. Close to the ice divide they eroded the bedrock and carried the debris away. At their margins they deposited the till and formed a wave-like drumlin and end moraine landscape such as in Ireland, northern Germany, the Baltic lands and Denmark. The glaciers also eroded and built up flat extensive sandur plains such as for example the Danish heath lands on Jutland. The wind removed the fine grained debris from the expanses of till deposits and the sandur and gravel plains, depositing it elsewhere in thick beds (loess). On this loessial sediment are now some of the most fertile grain agricultural areas of the world as for example in the United States, Ukraine and Russia.

Volcanism was similar to that in the Tertiary and most volcanic areas are still active. In some areas sub-glacial eruptions occurred such as in Iceland, Canada and Alaska.

Folding movements occurred mainly in areas around the Pacific Ocean and Mediterranean Sea and in the Himalayan mountains.

During glacial stages much of the world's water reserves were bound in glaciers and sea level was about 100–150 m lower than at present. Thus ocean areas at present shallower than 100–150 m were dry land and the distribution of land different than at present i.e. eustatic sea level changes. North America was joined to Asia through Bering land. The British Isles were one area joined to the continent since the North Sea and English Channel were dry land. Britain was thus a peninsula which extended outwards from Europe. When the glaciers melted the water returned to the sea which flooded the land areas anew. The British Isles became separated from the mainland 7000 years ago when the sea flooded the English Channel and the North Sea.

The ice sheets on the continent were 2000–3000 m thick at the centre. The burden of the ice depressed the land surface underneath with the result that the sea flooded a large area when the glacier melted since the land rose more slowly than sea level. Sea level increase due to meltwater from retreating and melting glaciers and uplift due to the decrease in load therefore competed for dry land in areas which had been under ice. To start with the increase in sea level had the upper hand but later on the isostatic uplift exceeded this. Sea level nearly stopped increasing 5000 years ago, the glaciers being similar in size to what they are now. Uplift has since dominated in some places such as in Scandinavia while in others the land is sinking such as in the south of the North Sea where a large area has sunk below sea level in the past few thousand years.

Regarding the causes of climatic variations, which affected the world during the Pleistocene not much is known accurately but they occurred at the same time in both the northern and southern hemispheres. The climatic belts shifted towards the equator during glacials and towards the poles during interglacials. A number of theories have been proposed for the cause of climatic change, including changes in ocean currents, the inclination of the earth's axis and varying radiation from the sun.

With the first glacial stages conditions for life in northern regions greatly worsened. Plants and animals had three alternatives: to adapt to changed conditions, to move, or to die. Changes to the flora and fauna were slower than might be expected, however, for the early glacial stages were less severe than those that came later, the second last glacial period being harshest.

Flora. Most of the warm loving trees which flourished north of the Alps and in Asia north of the Himalayas during the Tertiary period became extinct at the start of the Pleistocene or moved, never to return even when conditions improved. The east-west mountain ranges proved insurmountable barriers for many species. In America the situation was different. Here the mountain ranges run from north to south and did not act as a barrier to plant and animal movement associated with climatic change. During glacial stages the ice free area in Europe between the glacier expanses in the north and the mountains in the south formed treeless steppes and frozen bogs and tundra. The representative vegetation was dwarf-birch, willow, heather and mountain avens (Dryas octopetala). At the beginning of interglacial stages birch was the first vegetation to be established followed by pine. When the climate had become warmer, resembling today's, other trees followed such as oak, hazel, maple, elm, and spruce.

Fauna. The icy conditions of the glacial stages had a similar effect on animal life as on the vegetation. Many species died out during the Pleistocene, some moved, while others became adapted to changed conditions. Thus among species to emerge during the Pleistocene were wool haired rhinoceros, mammoths and cave bears, all of which were well protected against the cold. They all became extinct at the end of the Pleistocene. Herds of reindeer and musk ox also roamed the steppes and tundraduring glacial stages. During interglacial stages warm-loving plants re-colonized their original areas and elephants, rhinoceros and hippopotamus survived in central Europe up until the middle Pleistocene as well as horses, deer and sheep families. Among invertebrates, shells and gastropods (snails) were important index fossils.

Geological history of Iceland

24

Geologically Iceland is a young country, which has been built up during the latter part of the Cainozoic era, i.e. Miocene, Pliocene and Quaternary. It is almost entirely composed of lava flows and eruptive móberg (hyaloclastites) while in between are widespread, thin sedimentary beds. Igneous intrusions are also quite common in the older geological formations.

Iceland differs geologically in many ways from neighbouring countries, which are composed of much older rocks. There denudation by weathering and erosion has dominated during the Cainozoic although there has been volcanism at times in certain areas. In Iceland on the other hand volcanism has rapidly caused piling up of volcanic beds which is still going on. Weathering and erosion are nowhere more active than here although they have not succeeded in wearing down the volcanic structures because the build up has been so rapid.

The geological formations of Iceland are divided into four main groups according to stratigraphical age and differ considerable from one another. Oldest is the *Tertiary Basalt Formation* which was formed in the late Tertiary period. Next in order of age is the *Grey Basalt Formation* which was formed in the late Pliocene and early Pleistocene and the *Móberg Formation* which was formed in the late Pleistocene. These three formations form the bedrock of the country on which the fourth and youngest formation rests and which consists of unconsolidated or poorly hardened beds such as till and glaciofluvial deposits, marine and fluvial sediments and soil, as well as volcanic tephra and lava flows (Icel. hraun). This youngest formation was formed at the end of the Pleistocene and in Holocene.

The Tertiary Basalt Formation

The Tertiary Basalt Formation is the oldest geological formation in Iceland being formed in the late Tertiary period i.e. Miocene and pliocene epochs. It occurs mainly in two areas, on the one hand the east of the country extending from Þistilfjörður in the northeast, across the eastern fjords to Skeiðarársandur in the southeast and on the other hand the west of the country from the mouth of Hvalfjörður in the southwest across W-, NE-and N-Iceland to Bárðardalur. Formations from the Pleistocene and volcanic formations from the Holocene fill the gap between the two main Tertiary basalt areas on the surface. There are also areas of Tertiary rocks at Tjörnes, NE-Iceland and in the Hreppar area in mid S-Iceland (Figures 24-2 and 24-3).

Figure 24-1. Búlandstindur in Berufjörður, seen looking southwards across the fjord. This is a typical mountain of the Tertiary Basalt Formation, built up from many tens of lavas. The cirque on the right, Hvítárdalur, is the result of erosion by a corrie glacier. (Photo Þ.E.)

The Tertiary Basalt Formation in neighbouring countries

The Icelandic Tertiary Basalt Formation is part of an extensive basalt area which was formed by intensive volcanic activity at the start of sea floor spreading in the North Atlantic region when the European and North American plates began to separate. Tertiary basalt areas occur in Northern Ireland the Hebridean Islands and Scotland, the Faeroe Islands, Iceland, eastern Greenland, western Greenland, Baffin Island and also on Spitsbergen.

In western Greenland on Disco Island and in the surrounding area volcanism started on the sea floor during the Palaeocene and continued into the Eocene. Tephra and pillow lavas accumulated first in the sea and

were then overlain by a lava pile of several kilometres thickness.

In eastern Greenland between Kangerdlugssuag and Scoresbysund there is also a large Tertiary basalt area. The highest mountain in Greenland, Gunnbjarnarfjall 3733 m, is composed of Tertiary basalt lavas and is in this area. The formation is about 10 km thick here and rests in most areas on Precambrian rock but in places on marine sediments, clay and sandstone from the late Cretaceous period. In the north of the area marine sediments from the late Eocene and Oligocene epochs overlie Tertiary basalt. Intrusions are common in the Tertiary basalt formation in eastern Greenland and some are very large indeed as for instance the petrologically famous Skaergaard intrusion complex.

The Faeroe Islands are almost entirely

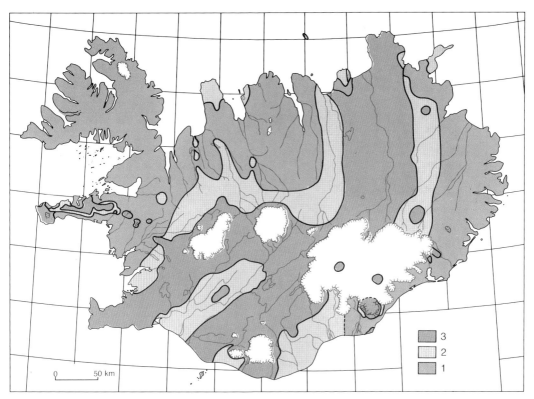

Figure 24-2. The extent of the Icelandic geological formations. Bedrock: 1) Tertiary Basalt Formation; 2) Grey Basalt Formation, late Pliocene and early Pleistocene; 3) Móberg Formation, late Pleistocene. (Drawing Þ.E.)

composed of Tertiary eruptive rocks. The Tertiary basalt formation is about 3 km thick above sea level and is divided into three. Lowermost there is a series of thick basalt lavas with red intercalated sediments (900 m). On top of it there is a series of flow units of pahoehoe type lavas (1200 m) and uppermost a series of thin basalt lavas with red beds in between (700 m). A series of 10–15 m thick sediments containing lignite separates the lowermost series from the shhield volcano section. Drilling on Suðurey has revealed that the lowest basalt series reaches at least 2000 m below sea level so that the basalt pile is altogether at least 5000 m thick and is probably underlain by continental crust.

In Northern Ireland (Ulster) and in the inner Hebrides and W-Scotland the Tertiary basalt formation lies on top of formations of varying age. The youngest of these are sediments from the Cretaceous period. The basalt lavas reach a maximum of around 2000 m.

In Greenland, the Hebrides and Northern Ireland gabbro and granophyre intrusions are also found in the Tertiary Basalt Formation or are associated with it, Most of these have formed in the roots of central volcanoes.

Fossilized plants in interbasaltic beds from all the areas mentioned indicate that the lava piles are of early Tertiary age, 50–60 million years. This is supported by potassium-argon age determinations.

Volcanism has also been active on Jan Mayen, probably mainly during the Pleistocene, the island being mainly volcanic in origin. The highest mountain is Bjarnarfjall (Beerenberg) a 2267 m high strato volcano

233

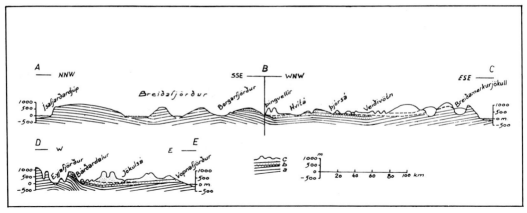

Figure 24-3. Stratigraphical section from NW-to E-and SE-Iceland. Symbols: a) Tertiary Basalt Formation, b) Grey Basalt Formation and c) Móberg Formation. Dips approximate, but vertical scale exaggerated. (Drawing Þ.E.)

similar to Snæfellsjökull, which is still active, the last eruption in 1970–71. Jan Mayen lies on a transform fault zone which joins the northern part of the Kolbeinsey ridge with the Mohn's ridge.

For a long time it was thought that the Tertiary basalt areas of the North Atlantic region was all one, the submarine ridge between Scotland through the Faeroes and Iceland to Greenland joining the areas together. According to this the ridge had then sunk in the sea breaking the land connection.

In more recent years the Tertiary basalt region and its connection with the North Atlantic and the formation of Iceland have been explained by the plate tectonics theory. It is assumed that at the beginning of the Cainozoic Greenland, Scandinavia and the British Isles formed one continental plate where the North Atlantic is at present situated. About 65 million years ago this continent broke up and the countries drifted apart where the Mid-Atlantic ridge runs through the North Atlantic. The northernmost part of the ridge south of Iceland is known as the Reykjanes ridge. The present day continents east and west in the Atlantic have then steadily moved apart, the rate of drift being about one centimetre per year in each direction. The Atlantic ocean has thus formed

gradually through sea floor spreading. At the very initial stages of the break up volcanism began at the edges of the continents and on the Mid-Atlantic ridge. Volcanism has since been restricted to the Reykjanes ridge south of Iceland and Ægir ridge. The history of the Mid-Atlantic ridge in the northernmost part of the Atlantic appears, however, to be somewhat more complicated than for other ocean ridges. Thus it is thought that in the early Cainozoic the northern part of the active Reykjanes ridge lay between Iceland and Norway, the so called Ægir ridge (Ægir was the god of the seas in Nordic mythology). In the middle of the Cainozoic around 25 million years ago, the activity moved to the west, north of 64–65° N and to the Kolbeinsey ridge leading to the formation of Iceland. The Kolbeinsey ridge runs northwards from the mouth of Skagafjörður through the skerry Kolbeinsey and to the transform fault zone associated with Jan Mayen at 71° N. The oldest rocks in the crust underlying Iceland could thus be about 25 million years old. The oldest rock yet dated using the potassium argon method are just over 14 million years and occur on Breiðadalsheiði, near the town of Ísafjörður, NW-Iceland. Still older rocks should therefore occur on the edge of the continen-

234

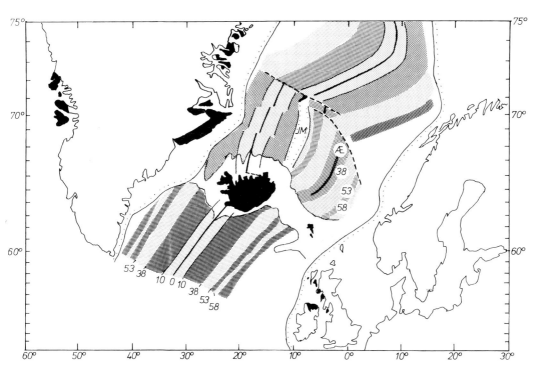

Figure 24-4. The Tertiary basalt formation in the North Atlantic, i.e. in the British Isles, Faroes, Jan Mayen, east and west Greenland. The North Atlantic originated through sea floor spreading and continental drift at the start of the Cainozoic era 60–70 million years ago when volcanism also started. Through volcanism on the ocean ridges new crust was constantly formed which drifted to both sides. On the map, the junctions between stripes on the sea floor connect points of the same age in million years, according to geomagnetic measurements. Symbols: Æ = Ægir ridge (between Iceland and Norway), JM = Jan Mayen ridge. The value 0 shows the axes of the Reykjanes and Kolbeinsey ridges. (Sigurður Steinþórsson 1981.)

tal shelf off the west and east coasts of Iceland (Figure 24-4).

In keeping with the regional dips in the Tertiary Basalt Formation in Iceland there have been two volcanic zones from the beginning when the Ægir ridge became inactive and volcanism and spreading moved to the Kolbeinsey ridge about 25 million years ago. These two ridge sections, the inactive Ægir ridge (which died out) and the Kolbeinsey ridge, lie at latitudes of between 64–65° N and 70° N. The Reykjanes ridge south of 65° N has, since the early opening of the Atlantic, been in much the same position as today. The eastern volcanic zone was probably in a similar area as at present. On the other hand the western volcanic zone lay from Faxaflói bay to the northeast through central Snæfellsnes near Stykkishólmur, W-Iceland, Hvammsfjörður to Víðidalur and Húnaflói, joining the Kolbeinsey ridge north of Skagafjörður. The strata formed in this rift zone have drifted to the northwest and southeast. The south east dipping strata of NW-Iceland and the northwesterly dip of the eastern Snæfellsnes peninsula and the Mýrar district from Borgarnes at Borgarfjörður support the idea that the dips of the Tertiary Basalt Formation are due to the weight and accompanying sagging of newly formed and accumulated volcanic rocks in the active zones. Thus the oldest rocks of the

235

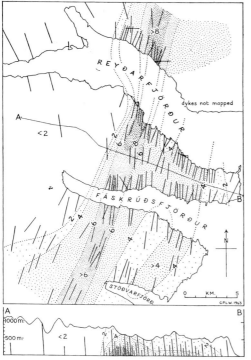

Figure 24-5. Dike swarm in eastern Iceland. Each line represents 5 dikes. They are orientated from north to south and the mean thickness about 3 m. The figures give the percentage of dikes in the rock at sea level. The shading is darker where the dikes are more numerous. The section at the bottom is from A to B on the map and shows that dikes decrease in number upwards in the succession. Among the better known dikes are those at Helgustaðir, the site of an extinct central volcano. (Walker 1966.)

north-westerly dips in the west of Árnessýsla district in middle S-Iceland.

The eastern volcanic zone has probably always been in a similar position to that at present, as the westerly tilted pile in the east and south-east of the country shows, as do the south-easterly dips on the penninsula between Skjálfandi and Eyjafjörður in middle N-Iceland. The oldest rocks produced in the eastern volcanic zone can thus be found farthest east in the country at Gerpir where they are about 13 million years old and in the anticline in the mountains west of the Skjálfandi bay where they are at least 12 million years old.

The great volcanic activity in the North Atlantic area is believed to be associated with strong up welling of magma in a mantle plume where magma ascent is more than at a normal divergent plate margin on sea floor ridges, i.e. a hot spot.

The plume which fed the Ægir ridge probably moved 25 million years ago to the west and resulted in the formation of the Kolbeinsey ridge. The plume is now situated underneath Iceland and nowhere else does more magma reach the surface in a limited area of the world. It is to this that Iceland owes its very existence.

The first eruptions in the area of Iceland would have resembled the Surtsey eruption. First of all, islands were formed of pillow lavas, tephra (pyroclastite) and lavas which, by continued volcanic activity, gradually grew together to become Iceland, the largest island on a spreading ocean ridge. Little is known about the size and shape of Iceland during the Tertiary period. Probably it was similar to its present size in the late Miocene about 5 to 10 million years ago although the coastline would have been quite different. Drift from the volcanic zones and production of volcanic products would have been similar to at present but marine, fluvial and then glacial erosion have removed strata on the edges of the country to form the coastal shelf such as off the east and west coasts where it is formed of similar rocks to those on land.

formations from this volcanic zone are found farthest out to the northwest off the Ísafjarðardjúp and are, according to Potassium-Argon dates more than 14 million years old on Breiðadalsheiði and about 13 million years old in an anticline at Borgarnes (Figure 24-3). About 7 million years ago volcanism shifted from this volcanic zone to the Reykjanes-Langjökull zone which is still active. This is supported by for instance the south-easterly dip from Borgarfjörður in under younger volcanic formations in to the presently active western volcanic belt and

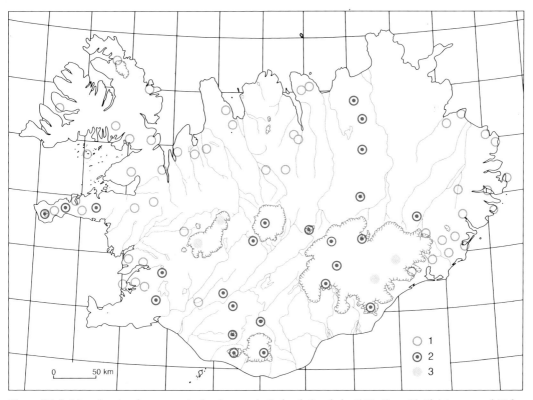

Figure 24-6. Map showing known central volcanoes in Iceland. Symbols: 1) Tertiary, 2) Pleistocene and Holocene, 3) probable central volcanoes. (Drawing Þ.E. and G.H.I.)

With the westward shift of the Mid-Atlantic ridge in the Iceland area in the mid Tertiary period, the Kolbeinsey ridge became positioned under the eastern continental shelf of Greenland with the result that part of it drifted to the east of the ridge. This continental strip became the Jan Mayen ridge which lies from the Icelandic coastal shelf in the northeast, northwards to Jan Mayen. In other words the Jan Mayen ridge is formed of continental crust such as quartz-rich sediments which are not Icelandic in origin and thus differ from other ocean ridges which are formed mainly of basalt. For this reason the Jan Mayen ridge could be a source of oil.

Although the N-American and European plates were joined to form one continent 400 million years ago, through the formation of the Caledonian fold mountain chain, shallow inland sea occupied a rift valley at their margins along the coasts of Norway and Greenland through the North Sea and southwards to the central German mountains. The formation of this inland sea on the plate margins began in the Permian 300 million years ago. Subsidence continues today and up to 10,000 m of sediment have accumulated. Some of the richest gas and oil resources in the world occur there. Part of these sediments is now in the western Atlantic on the eastern Greenland shelf north of Scoresbysund.

Structure of The Tertiary Basalt Formation

The Tertiary basalt formation in Iceland is mainly composed of basaltic lava flows,

237

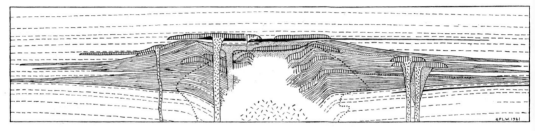

Figure 24-7. Section through the Breiðdalur volcano, an extinct central volcano in eastern Iceland. Horizontal shading indicates basic and intermediate lavas which originated in the strato volcano. Rhyolite lavas are cross hatched. Rhyolite tephra is shown in heavy dots, ignimbrite in black. Intrusions and feeder dikes to rhyolite lavas are shown with irregular dashes. Lava flows from other volcanoes, especially eruption fissures, which underlie the volcano or have become intercalated with lavas from it or have buried it, are shown with dotted lines. The section is about 35 km in length and 4 km high. (Walker 1963.)

(Figure 24-1). Igneous activity during the Tertiary period was probably similar to that at present. Most eruptions occurred in eruptive fissures while others occurred in central volcanoes or shield volcanoes. Individual volcanoes are now admittedly seldom found since the crater walls have often been worn down before the next lava buried them. On the other hand the feeder conduits are well known as dikes which cut through the lava pile. Each dike is thought to relate to a lava flow farther up in the succession so that they become much fewer in numbers on moving upwards through the lava pile, as is to be expected (Figure 24-5). Some dikes could, however, be the result of lateral dike intrusion from central volcanoes. Through repeated eruptions an enormous thickness of lavas was accumulated through time. In the east of the country the Tertiary basalt formation is believed to be about 10,000 m thick if the thickness of individual lavas from Gerpir inland towards Fljótsdalur is added together, i.e. the stratigraphic thickness. This is of course not the case due to the drift of the lava pile out of the volcanic zone. In Reyðarfjörður the mountains are about 1000 m high and a 2000 m deep research drill hole was sunk there in 1980. Since it did not reach through the Tertiary Basalt Formation, as expected the thickness of the succession there is at least 3000 m.

Volcanoes and lava flows. The Tertiary lava pile has accumulated mainly in *lava or flood eruptions* which appear to be restricted to particular zones which are typified by dike swarms i.e. ancient volcanic systems. The dyke frequency can often be very high and the horizontal thickness in places reaches 10–15% of the rock (Figure 24-5). In a road tunnel through the mountain Strákar in Siglufjörður, N-Iceland there are for instance 28 dikes over a 780 m section having a total thickness of about 120 m or 15.5% of the rock. Due to landscape lavas in active volcanic zones are usually rather regular and extensive (Figure 24-1 and 17-9). They are usually of aa lava type and often referred to as tholeiite or porphyritic basalt if they contain feldspar phenocrysts.

The lava pile contains ancient *strato volcanoes called central volcanoes* which are buried in the lava pile. Amongst the largest volcanoes of this type are those named after Breiðdalur (Figure 24-6 and 24-7) and Reyðarfjörður or Helgustaðir (Figure 24-5) in eastern Iceland, while in northern Iceland Kerling-Vindheimajökull and Víðidalsfjall are examples and in western Iceland Hafnarfjall at Borgarfjörður and Setberg at Grundarfjörður on Snæfellsnes. Altogether around 50 central volcanoes have been found in Iceland (Figure 24-6). They probably have closely resembled Hekla and Snæfellsjökull in appearance and type. Eruptions have usually been on a limited area through a summit crater with the result that high strato volcanoes or ridges were built up from lavas and tephra. The magma was either basaltic, andesitic or rhyolitic similar to the products of present day strato volcanoes, variability in rock composition being one of the main characteristics of strato volcanoes. In fissure eruptions, on the other hand, the composition is almost without exception basaltic. This suggests that there have been magma chambers underneath central volcanoes (Figures 8-7 and 8-10). When activity ceased in the volcano the magma in the chamber usually solidified as plutonic rock (gabbro or granophyre) and many plutonic intrusions in the Tertiary basalt formation have most likely originated in this way. Sometimes the magma chamber was suddenly emptied with the result that the volcano collapsed producing a caldera (see Figure 8-6 and 19-1). A good example of such a caldera is in Setberg on Snæfellsnes where the caldera has later become filled by rhyolitic tephra.

The succession in Breiðdalur central volcano is about 2000 m, although it probably never stood more than 500–1000 m above its surroundings. This is mainly due to the fact that fissure eruptions were frequent in the neighbourhood and lavas from them flooded the base of the strato volcanoes and became interfingered with lavas from them in the same way that the Þjórsá and Tungná lavas are now interfingered with Hekla lavas north of Hekla. Some central volcanoes have, however, doubtless been higher than the Breiðdalur volcano.

It is fairly easy to distinguish between lavas from eruptive fissures and central volcanoes since in addition to petrological compositional variations in the rocks from the latter they are also more limited in distribution and more irregular than lavas from fissures. The comparison between the Hekla and Tungná lavas also applies here. The longest Hekla lavas have only flowed 25 km

but the biggest Tungnárhraun lava (Þjórsárhraun 8000 years old) has flowed a distance of 130 km from the eruption site at Hófsvað on Tungná to the south coast in the Flói district.

In addition to lava flows from fissures and central volcanoes, there are in places in the Tertiary basalt formation thick series of thin belted lavas made of "flow units" of pahoehoe type (helluhraun) produced in *shield volcano* eruptions and often termed olivine tholeiite with no interbasaltic or even intercalated beds.

Tephra layers. Explosive eruptions occurred in some volcanoes, particularly central volcanoes and the tephra was distributed over a large area. Thin basalt tephra layers are not very conspicuous since they have weathered rapidly and become incorporated in the soil. On the other hand widespread light-coloured *rhyolitic tephra layers* are easily observable in interbasaltic beds and such sections resemble soil profiles in present day soil sections containing for instance Hekla tephra layers (Figures 20-3, 24–8 and 24–26).

Among the thickest tephra layers are, however, *welded tuff (ignimbrite)* beds which were formed from glowing ash avalanches in rhyolitic eruptions. The most significant of these is the Skessa bed which was formed in an eruption of the Tertiary "Breiðdalur" volcano. It occurs as a light band in mountains from Berufjörður northwards to Reyðarfjörður and Fagridalur in E-Iceland. It covers about 430 km^2 of which around 260 km^2 are welded tuff deposits (Figure 24-7). The average thickness is about 15 m and the total amount about 4 km^3 or considerable more than was produced in the greatest explosive eruption of Hekla, H_3, 2800 years ago (3 km^3).

Thick beds of volcanic breccia (tephra) are to be found in mainly in the central volcanoes. Pillow lavas are rare in the Tertiary Basalt Formation and are found mainly where lava has flowed into lakes such as in calderas, or in rivers.

Figure 24-8. Red interbasaltic beds at Óshlíð between Bolungarvík and Hnífsdalur, NW-Iceland. The upper surface of the lower bed is very weathered, the lower part is clear cut. The white streaks are weathered tephra layers composed of rhyolite. (Photo Þ.E.)

Intrusions. The most common intrusions in the Tertiary Basalt Formation are *basalt dikes* which cut directly upwards through the lava pile (Figures 24-5 and 7-16). As mentioned, their frequency at sea level is in places very high and in certain areas their cumulative thickness reaches up to 15% of the rock. Most dikes are ancient feeder conduits to eruptive fissures although some have doubtless been the result of lateral dike intrusions. The majority of dikes in the Tertiary basalt formation are oriented NE-SW, but in some areas other orientations are common such as the south of NW-Iceland where it is A-W. Dikes are often many kilometres in length. Most of them are basaltic. Few *sills* have yet been found.

Batholiths and laccoliths of plutonic rocks are not common in the Tertiary Basalt Formation but most are found mainly in southeast Iceland (Figures 6-7 and 7-14). The best example of a *laccolith* is Sandfell in Fáskrúðsfjörður (Figure 7-14). The largest *batholith* yet known in Iceland is in Slaufrudalur and Endalausidalur in the Lón district in SE-Iceland. It is formed of granite and granophyre and is about 10 km^2 in size at the surface. Smaller granophyre batholiths and laccoliths occur for instance in Reyðarártindur in Lón and Flyðrur in Hafnarfjall at Borgarfjörður, W-Iceland. Most batholiths are of both gabbro and granophyre as for instance in western and eastern Horn in Lón (Figure 7-12). These intrusions are all of Tertiary age.

The Tertiary Basalt Formation also contains batholiths intruded during the Pleistocene such as granophyre in Lýsuhyrna on Snæfellsnes.

It should be pointed out that intrusions are always younger than the country rock. The plutonic rock in Lón is therefore far from being the oldest rock in Iceland, the surrounding rocks being much older.

Amygdules in the Tertiary Basalt Formation

Amygdules are quite common in the Tertiary basalt formation, particularly zeolites, calcite (Iceland Spar) and quartz minerals. Geological research in eastern Iceland has revealed that the amygdules are arranged in belts. Close to central volcanoes the rock is usually highly altered and contains many amygdules, quartz, calcite and high temperature zeolites being dominant. The calcite of Helgustaðir is for instance found at the roots of the Reyðarfjörður central volcano. Iron sulphide is also commonly found surrounding central volcanoes.

It has also been demonstrated that the horizontally belted distribution of amygdules can be used to assess the original surface height of the lava pile during the Tertiary. When volcanism died out in the east the surface of the lava pile appears to have been 1000–1500 m above present sea level in the eastern fjords and 1800 m in the south-east of the country. Relative to the average height of the mountains of the eastern fjords, around 500–1000 m have been eroded off the top of the Tertiary Basalt Formation forming a "peneplain" (Figure 24-38) while valleys and fjords have since cut through this to much greater depths.

Interbasaltic beds. Widespread sediments of various thickness occur between the lavas of the Tertiary Basalt Formation as well as tephra layers as previously mentioned.

In places interbasaltic beds of clay, silt and sandstone or conglomerate occur which are *fluvial and lake sediments* in origin. There is, however, much less of such sediment than might be expected compared to the denudation capability and sediment transporting capability of present day rivers in Iceland. The porosity of the lavas has probably largely resulted in the thinness and scarcity of the fluvial sediments. Precipitation has percolated down through the permeable bedrock in the same way as it does in lava areas today. The ground water has then emerged as springs in depressions and valleys and producing spring-fed rivers. As is the case today, they have not transported much sediment or cut downwards during the Tertiary. The fraction of the precipitation which was surface runoff has also reached the rivers slowly since the country was covered with vegetation. Heavy snow cover has also been rare in the mild and warm Tertiary climate and meltwater infrequent as a result. The Tertiary bedrock is now very impervious so that direct runoff rivers have their sources there. The impervious nature of the bedrock was acquired long after the strata were formed, sediments at their time of formation being unconsolidated and amygdules not yet having formed in the surface rocks. The sediments have since become compressed and consolidated under the overburden weight while amygdules precipitated from thermal ground water in vesicles and fractures in the lavas. Both these factors have resulted in the present day impervious nature of the Tertiary basalt areas.

Much more common than fluvial or lacustrine sediments in the Tertiary basalt formation are red coloured clayey, silt or sandstone beds. They are probably *soil* in origin formed from volcanic tephra and surface scoria on lava flows. Through chemical weathering iron has been released, colouring them red. Some clay has also formed in these beds. Such weathering only occurs in a humid climate and at considerably higher temperatures than at present in Iceland. In soil produced in Iceland since the Pleistocene no new formation of clay has taken place. Red interbasaltic beds often contain carbonized plant remains which also suggests that they are soil in origin. As regards the red colour it should be pointed out that lavas often oxidize the top 10–20 cm of the underlying sediment. In the Tertiary Basalt Formation beds many metres thick are completely red throughout so that the effect of heat alone can not be the only explanation. Red interbasaltic beds today often impart a peculiar appearance to barren mountain sides in the Tertiary Basalt districts (Figures 17-9 and 24-8).

The interbasaltic beds contain widespread *lignite* beds, which is peat in origin which has become carbonized through the effects of overburden weight and geothermal heat. Peat bogs have occupied depressions where the ground water table was high. The lignite beds are always rather thin, usually only a few centimetres in thickness and seldom more than 0.5–1 m since the peat never thickened appreciably because of the frequent interruption by lava flows. For this reason some sections contain many separate beds of lignite.

The interbasaltic beds weather much more rapidly on mountain slopes than do the lavas. As a result sloping ledges often form, the underlying lava forming a step while the sedimentary bed above forms a ledge farther in. The traps are often grass covered and form long vegetated bands in the mountain side.

Volcanism was not continuous while build up of the Tertiary basalt formation took place, and no more so than it has been in the past few thousand years. The interbasaltic beds thus bear clear witness to the fact that longer periods of quiescence have passed between eruptions. Thick sediments can indicate a long quiescent period while thin sediments indicate frequent eruptions.

Some of the main rock types and the succession comprising the Tertiary Basalt Formation have now been described. The formation is well known from eastern Iceland. In a 4500 m thick succession from Gerpir and inland to the head of Reyðarfjörður, which is actually only the lower half of the Tertiary formation in E-Iceland above sea level, *the proportion of the various rocks is as follows:*

basalt lavas	83%
rhyolite lavas	8%
andesite lavas	3%
interbasaltic beds (tephra and sediment)	6%

The proportion of rock types in the Tertiary Basalt Formation in general is probably similar although it naturally varies according to area, sediments being especially thick in certain areas. They are usually 2–10% of the total thickness.

Long sections have been measured through the Tertiary Basalt Formation in certain areas. This research has been carried out to establish the geomagnetic time scale supported by potassium argon age determinations. The research avoided "central volcanoes" because of irregular stratification in their vicinity so that really only basalt lavas are included in the measured succession.

In eastern Iceland a section was measured from Gerpir through Norðfjörður to Fagridalur and onwards to Hamarsfjörður and Fljótsdalur. The stratigraphic thickness of the succession proved to be around 9000 m and comprised around 700 lava flows. The oldest beds in the succession are about 13 million years old at Gerpir and the youngest about 2 million years old in Fljótsdalur. These 9000 metres have thus formed in about 11 million years which means that one lava flow has been erupted every 16,000 years on average. While accumulation of the lava pile was taking place there were at least 50 reversals of the earth's magnetic field.

Figure 24-9 a. The picture shows a fossil leaf imprint of maple (Acer sp.) at approximately half size.

Figure 24-9 b. The picture shows an imprint of maple fruit. Scale in cm. Locality of both fossils is at Surtarbrandsgil, Brjánslækur. (Photo Walter Friedrich.)

In Borgarfjörður, W-Iceland a section was measured from Húsafell through Hvítársíða, Þverárhlíð to Norðurárdalur, a distance of about 35 km. The thickness of the succession is about 3500 m and it was formed from 7 million years ago in Norðurárdalur up to about 2 million years ago at Húsafell. During this 5 million years about 430 lava flows were formed or one lava flow about every 11,000 years. There are about 25 magnetic field reversals in the succession. Sediments represent almost 15% of the rocks in Borgarfjörður.

It is much more difficult to estimate the amount of dike and plutonic rocks than eruptive rocks. Over an 8000 km^2 area in eastern Iceland the volume of intrusive rocks seems to be about 80 km^3.

Tectonics; dips and faults

While the accumulation of the Tertiary Basalt Formation was taking place and after it was complete, internal crustal movements and overburden weight led to dipping and faulting of the strata.

Faults are quite common in the Tertiary Basalt Formation, particularly normal faults. Normally the movement on the fault face is rather little, being seldom more than 10–20 m, although in some cases it is more than 100 m. Generally the strike of the main faults is from north-east or north to south-west or south. In some areas the direction is different such as in NW-Iceland where it is E-W and Snæfellsnes where it is WNW-ESE.

Dip. Dipping strata characterize the Tertiary Basalt Formation in many areas (Figure 24-1 and 24-3). The dip is mainly due to crustal movement (plate tectonics) and to the overburden weight of newly formed volcanic rocks in the volcanic zones. The lavas commonly dip from 5–15° but the but the direction of dip is variable according to locality or region. Crustal movement leading to dipping and faulting probably occurred more or less simultaneously. In central vol-

243

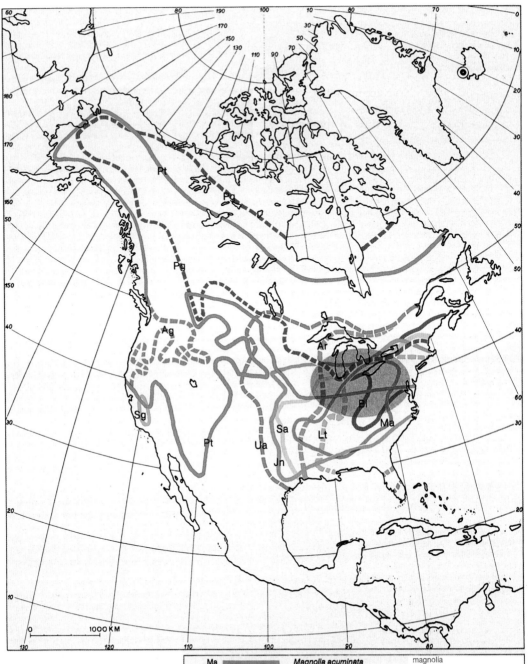

Figure 24-10. The map shows the distribution of several tree species in N-America today, which grew in Iceland during the Tertiary. (W. Friedrich and Leifur A. Símonarson 1981.)

Ma		*Magnolia acuminata*	magnolía
Lt		*Liriodendron tulipifera*	túlípantré
Jn		*Juglans nigra*	valhnot
Bl		*Betula lenta*	birki
Ar		*Acer rubrum*	rauðhlynur
Ag		*Abies grandis*	stórþinur
Ua		*Ulmus americana*	álmur
Sg		*Sequoiadendron giganteum*	risafura
Sa		*Sassafras albidum*	lárviður
Pt		*Populus tremuloides*	ösp
Pg		*Picea glauca*	hvítgreni

canoes the dip is often very variable since the lavas have flowed down steep slopes in various directions from the craters (cf. Figure 8-9) and the same applies to the thick tephra beds which have accumulated around the craters on the volcanoes.

Measurement of the dips in the Tertiary Basalt Formation show that it comprises rather flat *synclines* and *anticlines* (Figure 24-3). In the Borgarnes area and in the west of Borgarfjörður there is an anticlinal axis with a SW-NE orientation while a syncline runs from NNE to SSW from Snæfellsnes through Hvammsfjörður to the Skjálfandi area, W-Húnaflói. In the north the Tertiary formation dips to the east and south-east, east of Flateyjardalur-Leirdalsheiði-Hörgárdalur in Eyjafjörður, but west of this line the dip is westerly or south-westerly as far as Víðidalur west of Blönduós. The line referred to is thus an anticlinal axis which runs as far south as the Hreppar district (the Hreppar anticline) in middle S-Iceland. In the east and south-east of Iceland the dip is generally westerly or north-westerly so that this area forms the eastern flank of a syncline, the western flank being in the Eyjafjörður-Skjálfandi area. The syncline between them is thus underneath the eastern volcanic zone.

The landscape during the Tertiary

The build-up of the Tertiary basalt formation has been described. From a consideration of its formation and the position of the strata it is possible to reconstruct what the landscape was like during the Tertiary period in Iceland. The land was probably rather flat with long crater rows, though here and there were shield volcanoes and quite high strato volcanoes. In the depressions between the lava flows and in rift valleys, bogs and lakes were widespread while in the valleys meandered slowly flowing spring-fed rivers. In the red-coloured soil which covered almost the entire country warm-loving veg-

Figure 24-11. Fossil of an insect, march fly, from sediments in Mókollsdalur, Kollafjörður in the Strandasýsla district, NW-Iceland. Scale in millimetres. (Leifur A. Símonarson 1981.)

etation thrīved. Lava flooded the vegetation and soil cover every so often. The lava surfaces broke down and decomposed rather rapidly due to chemical weathering so that they were soon covered anew by vegetation which flourished until new lava covered it once more and the cycle was repeated.

Flora and fauna during the Tertiary period

In the interbasaltic beds of the Tertiary formation especially in clayey silt and sandstone and lignite beds there are frequently fossilized plant remains which covered the land during the Tertiary period (Figure 24-9a and b). These are mainly tree trunks, leaf imprints, fruits, seeds and pollen grains which in places are so well preserved that they can be identified by family, genus or even species.

Plant fossils are best preserved in the Tertiary formation of the western fjords. The main fossil localities are Húsavíkurkleif in Steingrímsfjörður, Þórishlíðarfjall in Selárdalur, Surtarbrandsgil in Brjánslækur and Mókollsdalur in Kollafjörður in Strandasýsla.

Altogether around 50 genera or species of plant fossils, particularly trees have been

Figure 24-12. Fossilized bone fragments from a mammal, probably a small deer, found in red interbasaltic beds in Þuríðargil in Vopnafjörður, NE-Iceland. Scale in centimetres. (Leifur A. Símonarson 1990.)

found. Among *broad leaved trees* alder (Alnus), birch (Betula), willow (Salix), aspen (Populus), hazel (Corylus), beech (Fagus), maple (Acer), oak (Quercus), elm (Ulmus), tulip-tree (Liriodendron), plane-tree (Platanus), hickory (Carya), horse chestnut (Castanea), holly (Ilex), walnut (Juglans), magnolia, vine (Vitis) and laurel have been found. Among *conifers* pine (Pinus), spruce (Picea), fir (Abies), larch (Larix), swamp cypress (Taxodium), dawn-redwood (Metasequoia) and grand sequoia (sequoiadendron giganteum) have been found. The Icelandic lignite flora appears to be most closely related to the present day flora of the broad leaf forest in the east of the United States from the south of New York state and southwards to the Gulf of Mexico. Many species also flourish still in central and southern Europe and others in south east Asia, (Figure 24-10).

In the oldest strata (from the Miocene) trees which grow in warm temperate climates characterize the flora (swamp cypress, dawn-redwood and giant Sequoia) but in the younger strata (from the Pliocene) temperate conifers and broad leaved trees which flourish today in the temperate belt of Europe and N. America become more noticeable.

These vegetation and climatic changes are well indicated by the youngest Tertiary plant remains, which are found in lignite beds in the lower part of the Tjörnes succession between Kaldakvísl and Hallbjarnarstaðaá, which belong to this period. Many warm-loving tree species have disappeared here but temperate conifers with pine, spruce, fir and larch have become dominant. Birch, willow and alder flourished in between but in addition oak, beech, platanus, hazel and holly still flourished.

Little is as yet known about the Tertiary fauna in Iceland. Fossilized remains of insects have been found in lake sediments in

Mókollsdalur in Kollafjörður in Strandasýsla but the sediment probably accumulated in a caldera lake. These are fossils of march-flies, and aphids (green-fly), related species living today in south-east Asia and the south-eastern United States of America respectively(Figure 24-11).

Recently fossilized bone remains of a mammal have been described from red interbasaltic beds in Burstafell in Vopnafjörður, E-Iceland. Although the remains are small and broken they are believed to be from a small member of the deer family (figure 24-12). The beds in which the remains were found are estimated to be 3–3.5 million years or from the late Tertiary period. The find raises hopes that a closer examination of the interbasaltic beds in the Tertiary formation may produce fossils of land animals although conditions for their preservation have been poor because of active chemical weathering during the Tertiary in Iceland and a lime shortage in the rocks, also because Icelandic soil has been and still is very poor in lime.

It could well be and is indeed likely that during the build-up of the Tertiary basalt formation there was a land connection between Iceland and either Greenland or even via the Iceland-Faeroes ridge to the British Isles which were at that time part of continental Europe. The number of genera and species of the Icelandic lignite flora as well as the bone-find in Vopnafjörður suggest this. The water depth on the Greenland-Iceland-Faeroes-Britain ridge is generally 400–600 m except in the strait between Iceland and Greenland where it is just over 600 m and in a channel in the ridge between the Shetland and Faeroes where the greatest depth is just over 800 m. In addition, deep sea drilling has revealed that the rock in the ridge between Iceland and the Faeroes is basalt, probably lavas with red interbasaltic beds similar to those in the Tertiary formation in Iceland and surrounding countries and they formed above sea level (Figure 24-4).

Subsidence of around 600–800 m on the ridge joining Greenland, Iceland, the Faeroes and Britain over several million years is not out of the question. Subsidence and sediment accumulation in the North Sea area has for instance reached up to 1000 m in 2–3 million years, in Holland for instance around 600 m. Subsidence on the sea floor is also due to crustal cooling as the rock sequences drift out from the plate margin where they are formed. This is accompanied by an increase in density because of cooling so that the depth increases with distance from a spreading ridge. From the above it can be concluded that Iceland was probably joined to Greenland and even continental Europe i.e. the British Isles, during the late Tertiary and that there was even a land bridge between the continents through Iceland at that time.

Nothing is known about marine life around Iceland before the end of the Tertiary period, marine sediments not occurring in the true Tertiary Basalt Formation. Towards the end of the Tertiary period the sea flooded the Tjörnes area and several hundred metres of sediment were formed, the Tjörnes sediments. The lowest sediments are Pliocene in age and contain a considerable amount of fossilized shells which need a much higher sea temperature than at present around Iceland.

The climate during the Tertiary

From fossil plants and the nature of the interbasaltic sedimentary beds it is clear that the climate during the formation of the Tertiary Basalt Formation was warm and fairly humid. Evidence of particular aspects of the weather is, however, scant. Fossils such as of walnut and holly suggest that the mean temperature of the coldest month was above freezing point. Precipitation appears to have been considerable as suggested by the lignite beds which occur widely in the interbasaltic beds. The formation of red, clay-rich soils suggests a humid and warm climate since considerable chemical weathering occurs only under such conditions.

As mentioned, the older part of the Icelandic lignite flora which is common in interbasaltic beds in the Tertiary formation appears to be most closely related to the present flora of the eastern United States. From this it can be concluded that the climate in Iceland was similar to that of the present while the older part of the Tertiary formation was being built up,i.e. during the Miocene. The mean temperature of the warmest month was probably 15–20°C and the coldest month above freezing. Precipitation was probably fairly evenly distributed throughout the year.

Later in the Tertiary period, or during the Pliocene the climate deteriorated and glaciers formed on high mountains in Iceland. The oldest tillites found are in the Tertiary Basalt Formation in Hornafjörður SE-Iceland and are rather localised. The glaciers probably occurred on high strato volcanoes. This climatic cooling affected the vegetation, warm-loving trees having disappeared by the end of the Tertiary and conifers had become dominant as fossilized plants in the lower Tjörnes sediments show. The climate was, however, still mild and the mean temperature of the coldest month above 0°C, or similar to that of the present time in western central Europe. The sea temperature was at least 5°C higher than at present as fossils of various warm-loving shells which are found in the same beds indicate. Some of these do not live in waters colder than found on the south coast of England today.

Age of the Tertiary Basalt Formation

For a long time it was thought that the Tertiary Basalt Formation in Iceland was similar in age to Tertiary basalt in surrounding countries. The lignite flora was also thought to be of similar age in all the areas. New research on the fossil flora shows, however, that the Icelandic flora is considerably younger or from the late Tertiary (Miocene

and Pliocene) as mentioned earlier. Potassium-argon dates also confirm this. The oldest rocks dated are just over 14 million years old. They are basalts from Breiðadalsheiði near the town of Ísafjörður. Next come rocks from Gerpir and Borgarnes which are about 13 million years and from Skjálfandi and Eyjafjörður, N-Iceland which are around 12 million years. The Tertiary formations in surrounding countries are on the other hand 50 to 60 million years old.

The Grey Basalt Formation and Móberg Formation

The later part of the Cainozoic is known as the Quaternary period. It is divided into two periods of various lengths, the Pleistocene and Holocene. The Pleistocene period began around 1.64 million years ago and ended 10,000 years ago. During the Pleistocene icy cold *glacial stages* i.e. glacials alternated with *interglacial stages* i.e. interglacials, when the climate was similar to at present. During glacials ice sheets covered the country although nunataks and small areas, particularly in the north, were probably ice-free (Figure 24-24). It was believed for a long time that there were 4–5 glacial periods but recent research both here and abroad suggest that they have been more numerous or at least 14 on the Tjörnes peninsula in the past 2 million years when the ice sheet reached a similar size to that of the last glacial period. In the period between 2–3 million years ago glaciers were mainly in the active volcanic belts and probably did not cover the entire country. The number of cold spells at this time according to the number of glacial tillites and tillite-like beds (diamictite) in individual areas are 3–9 in number.

Rock formations from the Pleistocene occur mainly in a zone across the middle of the country from the southwest to the northwest i.e. on the margins of the volcanic zones with outliers in Skagafjörður and on Snæfellsnes (Figure 24-2). They overly the Tertiary Basalt Formation on either side and in

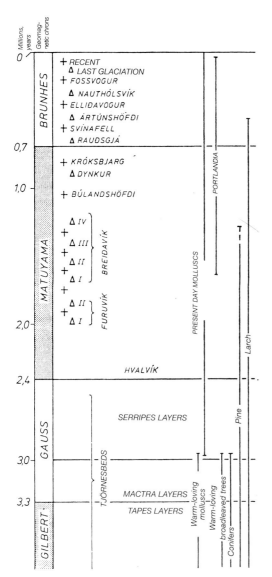

Figure 24-13. Table showing the division of the late Pliocene and Pleistocene by geomagnetic epochs. Furthest left: age in million years and main geomagnetic epochs-shaded : reversed magnetism, unshaded : normal magnetism. Δ represents glacial periods, + interglacial periods. Changes in flora and fauna on right. Based on Tjörnes stratigraphic sequence. Two more tillite horizons have been found on Tjörnes, both 0.7 million years The divisions are not exact. Other localities are in text except Rauðsgjá, which is on E-Tjörnes. (Drawing Þ.E.)

these regions Tertiary rocks are widespread low in the succession and Quaternary rocks farther up in mountain sides, in particular rocks from the early Pleistocene.

Pleistocene formations differ in many ways from Tertiary strata, the climate during their formation being quite different and has affected the strata as well as the vegetation and animal life. During interglacial periods lava flows were formed which are similar to lava flows form the Tertiary and the Holocene, but during glacial periods i.e. móberg hyaloclastite volcanic structures were built up by subglacial eruptions. Nothing comparable exists either from before or after the Pleistocene. The red sediments which are typical of the Tertiary Basalt Formation disappear and are replaced by glacial tillites and yellow or brown hardened silt-and sandstones. In addition fossils give useful information about relative age. The were radical vegetation changes immediately at the start of the Pleistocene. The warm-loving plants of the Tertiary period became extinct and did not return, Iceland being an island. There were also great changes to the mollusc fauna at the end of the Pliocene and beginning of the Pleistocene. Warm sea molluscs disappeared and the present day fauna took over. There are normally fewer amygdales in volcanic rocks from the Pleistocene than form the Tertiary.

Stratigraphy and geochronology

It was for a long time considered difficult to fit Icelandic Pleistocene formations into the geological succession since there were few significant changes in the flora and fauna here since the outset of the ice age. With the advent of modern research methods, mainly *palaeomagnetic measurements* and *radiogenic age determinations* of igneous rocks this view has completely changed and there are few areas where a better relative as well as an absolute time scale for the Pleistocene can not be worked out more successfully.

249

Figure 24-14. Móberg ridges, which are subglacial volcanoes are characteristic for the late Pleistocene Móberg Formation. The móberg ridge of Jarlhettur. Lake Hagavatn and Langjökull on left. Hofsjökull in background. (Photo Þ.E.)

When molten lava solidifies it becomes magnetized in accordance with the magnetic field of the earth at that particular time. At fairly lengthy intervals there have been reversals of the earth's magnetic field in which the magnetic poles have been reversed. The north end of the compass needle has either pointed as at present or in the completely opposite direction. If the direction is the same as at present the rock is said to be *normally magnetized* and if opposite it is said to be *reversely magnetized*. The main geomagnetic periods appear to have lasted for about a million years but in between were short events which were hardly more than a hundred thousand years.

The present *Brunhes geomagnetic epoch* began 0.7 million years ago. Since then the compass needle has pointed in the same direction as at present (Figure 24-13). During the period 0.7–2.5 million years or *Matuyama epoch* the compass needle pointed in the opposite direction while during the geomagnetic epoch before this or *Gauss epoch* which lasted from 2.5–3.35 million years it was normal. According to an international agreement the Pleistocene period is considered to have commenced 1.64 million years ago, or in the mid Matuyama geomagnetic epoch.

Geomagnetic reversals were also frequent while the Tertiary Basalt Formation was being piled up. There have been at least 50 magnetic reversals in eastern Iceland from 13.5 to 2 million years ago.

Because of differences and certain changes in character in lithology (beds) and biostratigraphy (fauna and flora) the author finds it appropriate to divide the rock sequences from late Pliocene and Pleistocene stratigraphy into two chronostratigraphical units (sub-epochs), the *Grey Basalt Formation* and the *Móberg Formation*. The Grey Basalt Formation is the oldest, covering the time from about 3 million years to 0.7 million years, i.e. the second half of the Gauss geomagnetic epoch (3–2.5 million years) and the Matuyama geomagnetic epoch (2.5–0.7 million years). The Móberg Formation is the youngest, its strata having formed during the present Brunhes geomagnetic epoch or from 700,000 years to the end of the Pleistocene, 10–15,000 years ago. A similar stratigraphical division is used on the geological maps of Iceland at scales of 1:500,000 and 1:250,000 published by The Icelandic Geodetic Survey and Icelandic Museum of Natural History.

Structure of Pleistocene strata

Igneous rock. At the start of the Pleistocene volcanic activity was mainly restricted to a broad zone lying across the country from SW to NE which, as time passed shifted to narrower belts which form the present day volcanic areas (Figure 8-1 and 24-2). However, there were also considerably active areas far out in Skagi, Skagafjörður and on Snæfellsnes, volcanism continuing into the Holocene in the latter area.

Volcanic rocks differed in appearance depending on whether they erupted on ice-free land during interglacial periods or subglacially during glacial periods, even though the magma was the same.

During interglacial periods *lava flows* flowed over long distances and often far beyond the volcanic belt. Most are grey in colour. They erupted either from *fissures* and *shield volcanoes*. Few volcanoes are known from older interglacial periods since they have either been buried under younger strata or been eroded away. However, in places dikes are found in the Quaternary bedrock and some of them are undoubtedly feeder

dikes to volcanic fissures. Þórðarhöfði and Ketubjörg in Skagafjörður are, however, clearly early Pleistocene volcanoes with plugs in the crater vents. Some lavas have originated in *strato volcanoes* some of which still tower over the landscape even though extinct, as for instance Snæfell in E-Iceland, while others are still active such as Snæfellsjökull, Eyjafjallajökull and Öræfajökull (Figure 24-6). Extensive lavas have also originated in Pleistocene shield volcanoes. The oldest of them have either been severely eroded or are covered by younger lavas while the youngest Pleistocene shield volcanoes still have the appearance of shield volcanoes. Examples are Vaðalda and Urðarháls in the north and Ok, Lyngdalsheiði and Mosfellsheiði in the southwest. The Pleistocene basalt on which Reykjavík stands (Reykjavíkurgrágrýti) was erupted from Mosfellsheiði 25 km northeast of Reykjavík. Large areas of young Pleistocene basalt lavas also occur on Melrakkaslétta, Snæfellsnes and Garðskagi on which Keflavík stands. Shield volcano lavas are always belted and good cross sections in such lavas are commonly found in the Reykjavík area.

During glacials magma erupted underneath thick ice sheets and melted cavities or openings in them (Figure 8-13, 8–14 and 24–14). The volcanic products accumulated in the meltwater supported by the ice walls. In the beginning of the eruptions pillow lavas were formed and later on explosive activity set in and on being quickly cooled by water the magma disintegrated into tephra (ash and pumice). The basaltic glass has since generally become altered to brown palagonite which has become cemented together as *móberg*. The móberg mountains were mostly built up on fissures and formed *móberg ridges* which did not reach above the glacier surface, or *table mountains (Icel. stapi)* which reached above the glacier surface so that the meltwater could not cool the flowing lava, with the result that they were capped by a lava shield. Móberg mountains thus provide

Figure 24-15. Striated rock surface of Tertiary basalt underlying tillite at the bottom of the Búlandshöfði succession at Stöð, Grundarfjörður, W-Iceland. (Photo Þ.E.)

evidence about glacier thickness while they were being piled up. The ridges show the minimum thickness while the table mountains indicate the maximum thickness of the ice sheets. Móberg mountains which were built up during the last glaciation are a dominant feature of the landscape and have been slightly eroded, such as the móberg ridges of Sveifluháls at Krýsuvík south of Hafnarfjörður and Jarlhettur south of Langjökull (Figure 24-14) and the table mountains Hlöðufell south of Langjökull and Herðubreið, northern highlands, while older examples probably from the second last glacial period are significantly more eroded (Sellandafjall, south of Mývatn) though they are still important features in the landscape. Móberg features formed during the early Pleistocene are on the other hand buried under younger strata or have been eroded. No table mountains are known from early Pleistocene for as might be expected their lava caps have doubtless long ago eroded. From their remains it is impossible to say whether the "móberg beds" were originally ridges or table mountains.

There is some *rhyolite* in the Pleistocene succession. Some has been extruded as lava flows but more often it has accumulated as lava domes such as Hlíðarfjall at Mývatn and various mountains in Kerlingarfjöll and in the Torfajökull area.

Up to now little *andesite* has yet been found in Pleistocene sequences but it should occur mainly in strato volcanoes. Andesite lavas from the early Pleistocene occur, however, in Grundarmön on Snæfellsnes, for instance.

Intrusions are rather rare in the late Pliocene and early Pleistocene Grey Basalt Formation but very rare in the Móberg Formation. Basalt dikes occur in places though they are of course fewer than in the Tertiary bedrock. There are also rhyolite dikes here and there. Some plutonic intrusions are of Pleistocene age although they occur in the Tertiary formation. Thus the granophyre of Lýsuhyrna on Snæfellsnes is around a million years old according to potassium-argon age determinations. That such young plutonic rocks should outcrop at the surface is unique and shows clearly the extent and depth of denudation which has occurred in some areas in Iceland during the Pleistocene.

Sediments. Sediments in Grey Basalt and Móberg Formations are much thicker than

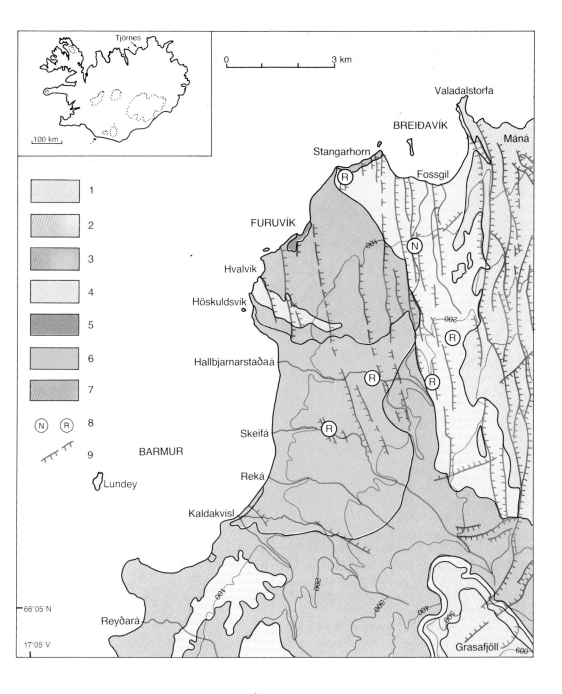

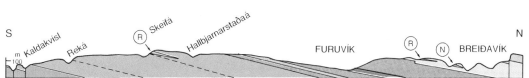

Figure 24-16. Geological map of the Tjörnes area (above) and geological section from Kaldakvísl to Breiðavík. Symbols: 1) Reyðará grey basalt (late Pleistocene), 2) reverse magnetized lavas, 3) normally magnetized lavas, 4) Breiðavík beds, 5) Furuvík beds, 6) Tjörnes beds, 7) Tertiary basalt, 8) individual lavas in sediments; N normally and R reverse magnetized, 9) faults. The vertical scale is 5X thus greatly exaggerating the dip. (Drawing Þ.E. and G.H.I.)

in the Tertiary Basalt Formation since fluvial and glacial erosion were very active during the late Pliocene and Pleistocene-and sedimentation rapid as a result. The sediments are either *fluvial, lake or marine* in origin and formed mainly during interglacial periods, or *glacial till*, subsequently lithified to tillites, which was deposited by glacier during glacial periods. The tillites commonly rest on glacially striated bedrock (Figure 24-15) and usually contain glacially smoothed boulders. Nearly all the sediment formed in glacial and interglacial periods is lithified and forms solid rock, siltstone, sandstone, conglomerate or tillite. The sediments have been covered by lavas in many areas and thereby been protected from erosion. This is not the case in many places abroad where glaciers from the more recent glaciations have reworked and removed sediment and till from earlier periods. For this reason late Pliocene and Pleistocene rock sequences are better preserved in Iceland than in most other places.

Between interglacial lava flows *soil beds* also occur. They are seldom red in colour except where lava has baked (oxidized) the top few centimetres and in this respect they differ from the Tertiary soil beds. They often show signs of frost heaving and solifluction similar to soils formed in the last few thousand years.

For many reasons it is rather difficult to judge the *total thickness of late Pliocene and Pleistocene formations*. During interglacial periods lavas covered large areas but during glacial periods móberg volcanic structures were piled up and as a result the thickness of the strata is very variable. It should also be borne in mind that due to erosion only the remains of the original succession are preserved in some areas. Among the most complete is the Tjörnes succession where beds from almost every period of the Pliocene and Pleistocene period appear to have been preserved. The sediments are usually thick here while the lavas are rather few in number and thin. Among the most complete is the Tjörnes sequence where a practically continuous succession of strata from the late Pliocene and Pleistocene is preserved. Altogether the late Pliocene and Pleistocene succession at Tjörnes is about 1000 m thick (Figure 24-16).

The Grey Basalt Formation

Strata belonging to the late Pliocene and early Pleistocene Grey Basalt Formation outcrop mainly at the margins of the Quaternary bedrock (Figure 24-2). In most places the formation is composed of grey basalt lavas but in between are beds of móberg, andesite, rhyolite and sediments. Typical of the formation are tillite beds. As mentioned above the Grey Basalt Formation falls into the period between 3 and 0.7 million years ago.

In the following discussion successions from the late Pliocene and early Pleistocene are described from some areas, in particular series with fossiliferous sediments.

Tjörnes

A very complete geological section occurs at Tjörnes (Figure 25-16) which spans the from the Pliocene and up to the late Pleistocene with few gaps. The succession at Tjörnes is remarkable for many reasons. lava flows, fluvial, lacustrine and fossiliferous marine sediments alternate with glacial tillites. The Tjörnes beds thus provide important evidence for changes in the fauna, flora and climate over several million years.

There are three main sediment groups which are separated by lava flows, but in addition thin sedimentary beds are common between the lavas. The youngest sediments are the Breiðavík beds, underlain by the Furuvík beds while the oldest are the Tjörnes beds which rest unconformably on altered and a faulted 8 million years old lava

Figure 24-17. The Hallbjarnarstaðakambur cliff at Tjörnes. Looking north. The buildings on the beach are at the mouth of the Hallbjarnarstaðaá river, where the Serripes layers overlie and replace the Mactra layers. (Photo Þ.E.)

formation. Altogether the sediments at Tjörnes amount to some 1200 m in thickness.

The Tjörnes beds. At the Kaldakvísl stream in the west of Tjörnes the Tjörnes sediments rest on the Tertiary basalt formation, and they can be traced for about 6 km in a coastal section northwards to Höskuldsvík as well as in river sections where they disappear under lavas landwards. The beds dip 5–10° to the north-west and are in places faulted. Their total thickness is about 500 m. The Tjörnes sediments are mainly formed of marine sediments and are rich in fossilized shells and snails (gastropods), while in between are fluvial and lacustrine beds, as well as lignite. During formation the area has therefore been either below sea level as indicated by the shell deposits, or above sea level as indicated by the lignite. The Tjörnes sediments are divided into three groups each associated with its particular index shell deposit. The lowest and oldest are the Tapes layers, followed by the Mactra layers while above them are the Serripes layers (Figure 24-16).

The Tapes layers, between the Kaldakvísl stream (Tunguá) and Reká river are characterized by the *Tapes layers* which today are not found farther north than the North Sea. In these layers, thin lignite beds and shell deposits alternate. The Tapes layers are, along with Tapes sp. rich in Arctica islandica Cardium sp. and Mytilus sp. The deposits have either formed in shallow seas or above sea level.

The Mactra layers, which outcrop between the Reká river and the Hallbjarnarstaðaá river are named after the shell Mactra sp. *(Mactra,* Figure 24-18) which are now extinct. In this group lignite beds also alternate with shell deposits. Many mollusc species in the Tapes and Mactra layers only live today in warmer seas than those surrounding Iceland or are extinct. An example is *Glycimeris* which now lives farthest north in the North Sea and as far south as the Canary Islands. Pollen analysis from lignite seams show that when the lignite beds were forming there were coniferous forests: fir, spruce, pine and

255

Figure 24-18. Fossilized shells from the Tjörnes sediments. 1) Glycimeris glycimeris, 2) Mactra, (extinct) and 3) Cyrtodaria angusta extinct). Half size. (Photo Ari Kárason.)

larch and in addition broad leaved trees such as oak, beech, hazel and holly along with alder, birch and willow. Plant remains therefore suggest a much milder climate than at present. The mean temperature of the coldest month was for instance probably rarely below 0°C. The marine fauna suggests that the sea temperature was at least 5° higher than at present when the layers were being deposited.

The Serripes layers, between Hallbjarnarstaðaá and Höskuldsvík (Figure 24-17) which are associated with the *Serripes grönlandicus* account for just over half of the thickness of the Tjörnes sediments. They consist almost entirely of marine sediments but thin lignite beds occur near the top of them. At the base of the Serripes layers most warm-loving molluscs have disappeared and in their place molluscs suddenly appeared which live in waters of a similar temperature to those at present surrounding Iceland. They include Neptunea, Macoma and Serripes grönlandicus which characterize the deposits.

These radical changes in the marine fauna probably indicate a deteriorating climate. The sea temperature was however higher than at present as shown by the presence of warm-loving species (*Solen ensis*). It is also remarkable that of around 100 species of molluscs in the Serripes layers 25% originate in the Pacific and took part in great fauna migrations from the Pacific to the Atlantic when the sea flooded the Bering Strait for the first time. Among species which took part in this migration were indeed Neptunea, Macoma and Serripes Grönlandicus.

A similar and equally sudden change in the marine fauna is also evident in deposits from the North Sea area where the arrival of Nepunea and Serripes grönlandicus indicates the onset of the Pleistocene. The same should be expected in Iceland and indeed indications of a cold climate-tillite-first appears above this horizon. The arrival of the Serripes grönlandicus and its companion fauna thus represent two turning points. Firstly their arrival in the North Atlantic probably indicates the end of the Tertiary period and the onset of the Pleistocene peri-

256

od. Secondly their arrival marks the separation of the super continents of America and Asia along the Bering Strait. This geological event appears to be well preserved and recorded on Tjörnes, thanks to the lavas.

According to potassium-argon age determinations, the youngest underlying Tertiary basalts are 8 million years old. The lava near the base of the Tapes layers at Kaldakvísl is 4 million years old and the lava which covers the Serripes layers at Höskuldsvík is 2.5 million years old. The division between the Mactra and Serripes layers is thus probably around 3 million years old. From this it is clear that the Tapes and Mactra layers are Pliocene in age while the Serripes layers could be from the oldest stages of the Pleistocene.

The Furuvík beds. A 250 m thick lava series extends from Höskuldsvík northwards to Breiðavík (Stangarhorn). At Furuvík in the middle of this series there are two tillite beds which altogether are about 40 m thick. According to potassium-argon age determinations they are 2 million years old, while according to palaeomagnetic measurements they could be nearly 2.5 million years old. These are the oldest glacial remains at Tjörnes. At Jökuldalur, mid southern Iceland and in the Húsafell and Esja areas there are older tillites from the Pleistocene, the oldest probably being around 3 million years old.

The Breiðavík deposits. At Breiðavík a 150 m thick sedimentary formation, the Breiðavík beds, rests on top of the lavas which cover the Furuvík beds. They constitute tillite beds which alternate with marine fossiliferous beds. There are six tillite beds. Shell deposits commonly occur between them as well as lava flows in places, both formed in interglacial periods. The shells in the marine sediments are mostly the same as those living in the waters around Iceland today, suggesting that between glacial periods there were true warm periods when the climate and sea temperature were similar to today's. In two places in the succession, on top of the tillite

beds, the shell Portlandia arctica has been found, a shell which today lives in the ice cold waters of the Arctic Ocean. They probably lived at the edge of the ice sheet at Breiðavík. Portlandia arctica does not occur in older marine sediments at Tjörnes. In the lower Portlandia arctica bed a gneiss boulder has been found and it is the oldest evidence of drift ice on coasts around Iceland. Plant remains have been found in the Breiðavík beds, especially pollen grains. These are mainly of alder, willow and birch. According to potassium-argon age determinations the lower part of the Breiðavík beds is around 2 million years old while the overlying lava (Mánárbasalt) east of Breiðavík is 1.2 million years old.

The Breiðavík beds can be traced southwards through central Tjörnes to Grasafjöll and Búrfell where they are at a height of 550–600 m. They thus rest unconformably on all the older sequences at Tjörnes. For half the distance there are marine sediments as well as tillites, but farther south lacustrine and fluvial sediments take over. This suggests that during the formation of the Breiðavík deposits Tjörnes was a lowland area and was often below sea level. Tjörnes has since risen and become tilted so that it now forms a horst. All the mountains in the Tjörnes area are thus rather young. This suggests that glacial remains, the tillite layers, at Tjörnes were not formed by local glaciers but rather by quite large ice sheets which originated outside the area. It thus follows that each tillite bed at Tjörnes probably represents a true glacial period and not a short cold spell. The stratigraphical distribution of tillites also supports this.

In the east and south of the Tjörnes area the Breiðavík beds and their corresponding basalt lava flows are overlain by late Pleistocene basalt lavas with sediments in between, especially tillite beds. This succession contains at least 4 tillite beds from the late Pleistocene, i.e. younger than 0.7 million years old.

Figure 24-19. Looking west across Grundarfjörður, Snæfellsnes, W-Iceland. The Búlandshöfði beds underlie lava and móberg (both clearly bedded) uppermost in the screes in Kirkjufell and Stöð on right. Tertiary rocks which underlie them can be seen for instance in the shelf to the south at Stöð and in the dark bed which protrudes from the screes low down in Kirkjufell. The present day landscape is younger than one million years. (Photo Þ.E.)

Búlandshöfði

Towards the base of the mountains on the north of the Snæfellsnes peninsula an almost continuous 20–50 m thick sedimentary horizon can be traced for 30 km from Grundarfjörður, W-Iceland and westwards to Ólafsvík. Good cross sectional outcrops in the sediments can be found at Stöð and Búlandshöfði for example and the sediments are named accordingly, the Búlandshöfði layers. The deposits are generally very similar in composition. At Stöð and Búlandshöfði Tertiary basalts reach from sea level and up to a height of 130 m and some of the surface outcrops are glacially striated (Fig-

ures 24-15 and 24-19). Tillites mixed with marine sediments rest unconformably on the Tertiary basalts. The marine sediments contain fossilized molluscs which suggest an ice cold sea, such as for example Portlandia arctica. On top of this at Búlandshöfði is clay sediment containing "modern molluscs" such as Arctica islandica, Mytilus edulis and Nucella lapillus species. When they existed the sea temperature was similar to that at present and had become much warmer from what it was when the older deposits were being formed. At Stöð the warm marine sediments are missing but in their place there is a foreset bedded delta deposit on top of which is fine grained sand-

Figure 24-20. Svínafellsfjall in the Öræfi district, SW-Iceland. The Svínafell interglacial sedimentary beds can be seen at the bottom of the section, clearly bedded and light in colour. They are overlain by tillite (dark band) and then móberg. (Photo Þ.E.)

stone which was deposited in a lake. The sandstone contains considerable numbers of leaf imprints and pollen grains of alder, willow, birch and heather. The Búlandshöfði sediment then became covered by lava flows which the glaciers of the next glacial period polished and striated. The lava directly on top of the sediments is reversely magnetized and its age according to potassium-argon dating is 1.1 million years. The Búlandshöfði deposits should therefore be similar in age to the upper part of the Breiðavík beds at Tjörnes.

The Búlandshöfði deposits clearly show the great climatic variations during the Pleistocene. The striated bedrock, and representative molluscs of an ice-cold sea indicate an icy glacial period. Interglacial conditions are indicated by the presence of "modern" molluscs and birch and alder forests higher up in the succession. The lavas on top of the sediment were erupted during the same interglacial period signify that the land was ice-free, since lava can only flow under these circumstances. The glacial striæ on the basalt covering the Búlandshöfði deposits show that after the lavas were erupted the climate deteriorated again and an ice sheet covered the area anew. The móberg ridge of Höfðakúlur was built up on Búlandshöfði in erup-

tions under this ice sheet and the rocks are reversely magnetized, making them older than 0.7 million years. Nowhere are Pleistocene climatic variations so clearly demonstrated in geological deposits at one locality as at Búlandshöfði and Stöð.

Some fossiliferous deposits and tillites from the early Pleistocene also occur at Bakkabrúnir in Víðidalur, at Skagi in N-Iceland, in Skammadalskambur in Mýrdalur, in Holt, Hreppar, Flói, Ölfus in S-Iceland, Hvalfjörður, at Húsafell, Esja, W- and SW-Iceland and Jökuldalur, E-Iceland. The tillites for instance have not been dated to the extent that the number of glaciations can be correlated between regions. This is particularly true of deposits and formations from 2–3 million years ago. The tillite beds number between 3 and 9. The nature of the sediments has still to be researched further to ascertain whether all the tillites are indeed proper tillites, for some could be coarse grained fluvial sediments, solifluxion deposits or even mud flow deposits (lahars) from central volcanoes.

The Móberg Formation

The deposits and successions of deposits be-

259

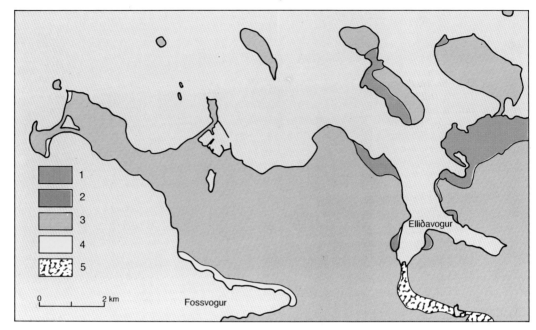

Figure 24-21. A simplified geological map of Reykjavík. Explanation: early Quaternary formations, 2) Elliða-vogur sedimentary beds, 3) Reykjavík interglacial grey basalt, 4) Fossvogur sedimentary beds and 5) Elliðaár-hraun lava, 4600 years old. (Drawing Þ.E. and G.H.I.)

longing to the móberg formation were formed during the late Pleistocene which commenced 0.78 m.y. ago and ended 10,000 years ago, or during the present Brunhes geomagnetic epoch. Belonging to this period are for example the móberg mountains which still strongly dominate the landscape (Figure 8-14 and 24-14). They were formed in subglacial eruptions during glacial periods. Also belonging to this period are the Pleistocene shield volcanoes such as Ok and Mosfellsheiði, W- and SW-Iceland which were formed during interglacial periods. The following sections deal with some noteworthy sites from the late Pleistocene, in particular from late interglacial periods.

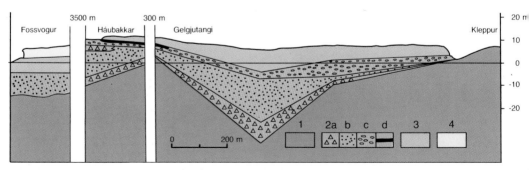

Figure 24-22. Bedrock section in Reykjavík between Kleppur and Fossvogur. Two gaps of 300 m and 3500 m a missing in section. Symbols: 1) early Quaternary formations, 2) Elliðavogur sedimentary layers (a tillite, b siltstor c conglomerate and d peaty lignite), 3) grey basalt and 4) Fossvogur sedimentary layers. (Drawing Þ.E. and G.H.

Figure 24-23. Fossvogur sediments in a cliff section at the head of the Fossvogur inlet in Reykjavík, cf. Figure 24-21. They rest on striated Reykjavík grey doleritic basalt on which a till bed (tillite) lies which in turn is overlain by fossiliferous marine siltstone as the figure shows. The marine sediments were probably formed during the last interglacial of the Pleistocene period, but could also be from the end of the Pleistocene. (Photo Þ.E.)

Svínafell

At the base of Svínafellsfjall in Öræfi district SE-Iceland is a 120 m thick bed of fine grained sandstone which was deposited in a lake (Figure 24-20). Throughout the sandstone there are pollen grains and sparse leaf imprints of alder willow, birch, rowan, blueberry- and crowberry heather, grasses and ferns. Pollen analyses give a similar picture of the vegetation cover during the formation of the Svínafell deposits. Alder was the main tree type.

Above the farm at Svínafell there are good sections in the rocks underlying the sediments. At the base is an approximately 100 metre thick series of grey basalts which are normally or reversely magnetized. After the

261

formation of the lavas a valley just over 100 m deep was cut into the lava succession and it is in this valley that the Svínafell sediments are found. On top of them there is a fairly thick tillite bed and pillow lava and breccia which were probably both formed during the same glacial period. Resting on this is a 50 m thick lava series normally magnetized and a móberg layer, both of which were probably formed during an interglacial period. On top of this is móberg with some pillow lava which forms the summit of the mountain. This was formed by subglacial eruption. The Svínafell deposits were probably formed in the third last interglacial period of the Pleistocene and are probably around 0.5 million years old.

The deposits in the Hvítá gorge are probably of a similar age to the Svínafell deposits. Pollen analyses on the lake sediments under the basalt in the upper step of the waterfall suggest that the vegetation was similar to that at present, i.e. with birch, willow and herbs, but also alder.

Elliðavogur and Fossvogur

Deposits from the youngest periods of geological history are usually better preserved than those from older periods. However, this does not apply to sediments from the more recent interglacials in Iceland though lavas erupted during these periods are widespread. Major sedimentary deposits from the last two interglacial periods have only been found in Reykjavík. One of these deposits, the Elliðavogur layers, is overlain by the Reykjavík late Pleistocene Grey Basalt, which in turn is overlain by the Fossvogur layers (Figure 24-21 and 24-22).

Elliðavogur deposits. At Elliðavogur, 5 km east of Reykjavík town centre, Háubakkar and Ártúnshöfði, sediments occur between the Reykjavík Grey Basalt and early Pleistocene volcanic formations. In an 8 m high section in the sediments at Háubakkar there are 4–5 m of fine grained siltstone. In certain beds there are some molluscs, especially Macoma calcarea. On top of the siltstone are 2–3 m of yellow-brown cross bedded sandstone (fluvial sediment) and on top of this pockets of boulder conglomerate in the northern part of the section. Northwards the sediment disappears underneath the lava flow. Below this comes conglomerate and between this and the basalt is a 20 cm layer of lignite. It contains seeds and fruits of crowberry, bogbean and sedges, as well as pollen grains of birch, willow and various herbs. The flora resembles that of the present day and it is noteworthy that alder is not present. Carbonized plant remains and soil also occur under the same basalt at Ártúnshöfði. It has recently been discovered that there are two Pleistocene basalt lavas north of Gelgjutangi with a lignite seam separating them. The lower of these lavas is below sea level at this location. Underlying the sediments at Ártúnshöfði the early Pleistocene bedrock is glacially striated.

Drilling in Reykjavík has revealed that the Elliðavogur sediment varies greatly in thickness. In places it is missing while in other places it is 30 m thick (Figures 24-21 and 24-22).

The history of formation of the Elliðavogur layers and the Reykjavík late Pleistocene Grey Basalt lavas is briefly as follows: Ice sheets covered the Reykjavík area forming an undulating landscape in the late Pleistocene bedrock. When the ice sheet retreated at the end of the third last glaciation, the sea followed the ice front inland flooding the lowland. Marine sediments accumulated in all the depressions of the bedrock. On top of the marine sediments, fluvial sediments (conglomerate and cross-bedded sandstone) were deposited, the land having risen above sea level. Rivers and streams then cut channels in the sediments while at the same time plants began to colonize the land. These plant remains now form the lignite seam in the Háubakkar section and underneath the basalt at Ártúnshöfði. This vegetation was,

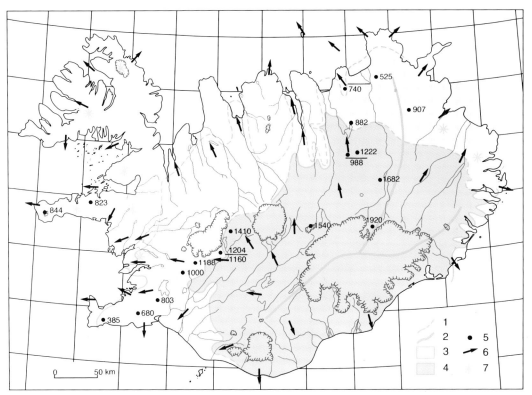

*Figure 24-24. Glacier movement during the last glacial period and re-advance stages during retreat : Symbols:
1) ice front, 2) ice divide, 3) Álftanes ice sheet, 4) Búði ice aheet, 5) table mountains with altitudes in metres,
6) striae, 7) main ice centres in highlands outside the main ice sheet. (Drawing Þ.E. and G.H.I.)*

however, not destined to survive for long, for shortly afterwards, probably only a few thousand years after the first appearance of plants, vigorous lava eruption took place on Mosfellsheiði probably in the Borgarhólar area. This eruption formed the flat late Pleistocene basalt shield volcano of Mosfellsheiði. Extensive lavas flowed westwards from it over the existing flat land of the Reykjavík area and to the sea (as evidenced by pillow lavas at the base of the lava). From the extent of the Reykjavík late Pleistocene Grey Basalt it can be concluded that the landscape of the Mosfellssveit area was more or less in its present form. The basalt flows probably formed a great lava field in the area from Kópavogur northwards to Esja. Seltjarnarnes and the islands in Kolla-

fjörður are remains of this big lava field. During the last interglacial period basalt lavas covered the Reykjavík area from the southeast as can be seen in the late Pleistocene basalt flows at Selás, upper Breiðholt and Heiðmörk (Heiðmerkurgrágrýti) which overlie the Reykjavík Grey Basalt flows.

The Elliðavogur deposits appear to have formed at the end of a glacial stage and at the start of an interglacial, probably the last but one and sometime later in the same interglacial period the Reykjavík Grey Basalt lava flows were formed. This warm period has been called the *Elliðavogur interglacial*.

Fossvogur layers. At the end of the Elliðavogur interglacial period the ice sheet of the following glacial advanced over the Reykjavík area resulting in a landscape which is basically that of today. The retreat of the glacier was followed by a marine transgression in which marine sediments were deposited, the Fossvogur layers (Figure 24-21, 24-22 and 24-23) which now form a 4–5 m high sea cliff in the north of Fossvogur bay, 1 km SE of Reykjavík airport. The Fossvogur layers rest on the glacially striated Reykjavík late Pleistocene Grey Basalt. At their base is most often glacial till but they are mainly comprised of grey siltstones. Some fossilized molluscs also occur, the number of species being much more than in the Elliðavogur deposits and all of them occurring today on the coast of Iceland. The fossils thus show that during the formation of the Fossvogur deposits the sea temperature was similar to that at present. It has long been thought that the Fossvogur layers were formed during the last Pleistocene interglacial, but more recent work suggests that they could be from the end of the last glacial period, about 11,000 years old.

The last glacial stage

All the traces of glaciation which can be seen on the present land surface are the results of glaciers from the last Weichsel glacial and often due to their final movement before they melted. From research on glacial striæ, roche moutonée forms and other glacial traces (cf. chapter 17). It can be concluded that almost the entire country was covered by ice during the last glacial period which began 70,000 or 120,000 years ago and ended 10,000 years ago. Ice sheets covered the greater part of the country and the ice flowed in all directions from the ice divide in the south central highlands, as the N-S orientation of striæ at Kjölur, Sprengisandur and Tungnár-öræfi suggest (Figure 24-24). *The main ice divide and ice centre* probably lay from Torfajökull to the north-east along the Tungnaá mountain range and then eastwards along Vatnajökull and from Kverkfjöll along

Hólsfjöll and out on the Melrakkaslétta peninsula. On the northwest peninsula, Tröllaskagi, N-Iceland, Smjörfjöll, E-Iceland, Skarðsheiði, W-Iceland and the Snæfellsnes peninsula as well as on many other mountain massifs there were isolated ice caps as indicated by glacial striæ which radiate outwards from the highland in all directions.

While the ice sheet was retreating and thinning at the end of the Pleistocene there were also localized, short lived, minor ice centres and divides in mountainous areas at the edge of the ice sheet. Ice flow from these areas had resulted in an irregular distribution of end moraines and in places striæ which cut across older systems of striæ.

From the orientation of the ice divide of the ice sheet during the last glacial period it is clear that, as today, southerly winds were laden with precipitation. The ice flowed northwards from the accumulation area at the ice divide south of the water divide. In the broad valleys of northern Iceland there were outlet glaciers from the ice cap, rather than ice caps, with individual peaks rising above the ice surface, while the snow line was considerably higher on the north of the ice sheet than on the south. Moist southerly winds were dry by the time they reached the north, having lost their moisture on the glaciers in the south. The northerly winds were probably dry having blown across a cover of sea ice. Thus the variation in precipitation in different parts of the country was probably more during glacial periods than at present. The many high mountains on either side of Eyjafjörður were for instance probably ice free. Great valley glaciers which had their origins high at the valley heads flowed out from tributary valleys and joined the ice flow from the central highlands at the mouths of the valleys.

Glacial traces on headlands and offshore islands give clear evidence on the *extent* and *size* of glaciers of the last glacial. There are signs of glacial erosion on all the headlands whether on Garðskagi in southwest Iceland or on Melrakkaslétta in the north-east and also on islands off the coast such as Grímsey although it lies about 40 km offshore (Figure 24-24). From this it is clear that glaciers have everywhere flowed over the coastal shelf, which at the maximum of the last glacial stage was dry land for at least as far out as the 100 m depth line. Recently end moraines have been found off Breiðafjörður between Kolluáll and Víkuráll at a distance of 130 km offshore at a depth of 150–250 m. They were probably formed at the maximum of the last glaciation. The main ice sheet calved off the coastal shelf in many areas except where it is broadest such as off the western fjords and northern Iceland, where it is possible that in a few places there were ice-free areas on dry land although now under the sea.

Evidence of the *thickness of glaciers* of the last glaciation is mainly obtained from research on high mountains. No traces of ice flow can be found on mountains which stood above the ice surface there is often evidence of the upper limit of erosion, for instance terraces formed in meltwater lakes and meltwater channels. On mountains which were ice-covered, glacial traces have, however, often been destroyed by frost weathering or wind erosion. In addition to giving information on glacial thickness, glacial striæ on mountains give more reliable information on the direction of flow than they do on lowland, the landscape having a strong effect on glacial flow.

The altitude of móberg table mountains and móberg ridges also provide useful information about glacier thickness during their period of formation. The móberg ridges did not reach significantly above the glacier surface but the lava caps of the table mountains on the other hand extended well above the glacier. As mentioned earlier the ice centre was in the Tungnáröræfi surface area where there are many móberg ridges but no table mountains. The mountains did not reach above the ice cover even though many of them are over 1000 m in height and

now tower 500–600 m above their surroundings. During their formation the glacier surface was therefore more than 1000 m above sea level and the minimum ice thickness 500–600 m. The glacier surface here was probably higher or at 1500–2000 m and its thickness therefore 1000–1500 m. In other móberg areas table mountains are, however, common, the ice thickness having been less there.

Flora and fauna and the Pleistocene climate

During the formation of the lower Tjörnes beds, the Tapes and Mactra layers in the lower and middle Pliocene period and many of the warm-loving trees typical of the Miocene had already disappeared forever and pine forests with fir, spruce and larch had become dominant. Birch, willow and alder grew amongst these while broad leaved trees flourished, such as oak, beech, hazel and holly. The climate was thus still mild in mid-Pliocene time at the close of the Tertiary although it had started to cool somewhat.

Plant remains in the upper part of the Breiðavík beds give a completely different picture of the vegetation, the onset of the Pleistocene ice age having started by then (late Pliocene). The broad leaved trees and pine forests were gone leaving birch, alder and willow. These trees still survived during the period from 3 million years to around 2.5 million years ago. Major glaciers covered part of the country for the first time during cold periods as indicated by tillite beds of this age in Jökuldalur E-Iceland, Hvalfjörður and the Húsafell area, W-Iceland. Little is known about the size of these first ice sheets in Iceland though it is certain that they reached the Tjörnes peninsula first around 2 million years ago according to the tillite beds in Furuvík. It could well be they were restricted to the active volcanic zones where mountains were highest. It is clear that the climate in these first glacial periods was so

265

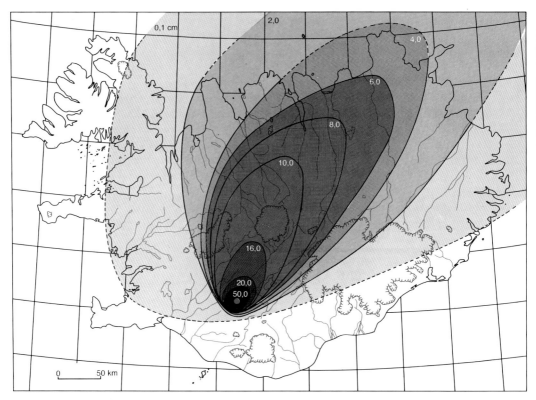

Figure 24-25. Distribution and thickness (centimetres) of the tephra layer H₃ which was deposited in a huge rhyolitic explosive eruption 2800 years ago. (Sigurður Þórarinsson 1961.)

cold that neither broad leaved trees nor co- niferous forests which grew during the for- mation of the Mactra layers in the Pliocene could stand this climatic deterioration. Warm-loving trees died out. They had no re- treat route since the country had already be- come an island in the ocean-if indeed it was always an island-so that they perished and became extinct. None of these warm-loving trees succeeded in becoming established during interglacial periods after this. How- ever it is likely that the climate in intergla- cial periods during the early Pleistocene was sufficiently mild for them to have grown in Iceland, the climate of the first interglacial periods being milder than now. This sug- gests that the water expanse around Iceland was too broad for warm-loving trees to re- turn. This was a different situation to that on

the continents where animals and plants could migrate according to climatic changes.

Vegetation in interglacial periods was then similar until the middle late Pleistocene to what it was during the formation of the Breiðavík layers as the plant at Stöð, Svína- fell, Bakkabrúnir and other areas indicate when there were in Iceland forests of alder, birch and willow. Alder seems to have be- come extinct in the third last glacial period, probably about half a million years ago. During this and the second last glacial peri- od the climate was at its coldest during the Pleistocene as can be concluded from the size of glaciers elsewhere in the world (Fig- ure 23-23). Alder did not return in spite of a warmer climate. Although data are scant on vegetation in the later interglacial periods, it can be assumed that it was similar to at pre-

Figure 24-26. Tephra layers in a bog section at Torfalæk-ur in the A-Húnavatnssýsla district, western N-Iceland. At the top is the tephra layer H_1, from the year 1104, next is H_3, about 2800 years old and at the bottom is H_4 about 4000 years old. The tephra layers are light coloured, i.e. rhyolitic and originate in Hekla. Scale 1 m. (Photo Þ.E.)

sent. Birch was the main forest tree type along with willow and rowan (Sorbus).

In other countries the remains of land animals provides much information on climatic change. In Iceland no such remains have been found from the Pleistocene but on the other hand the evidence is very clear from fossilized marine animals in the Pleistocene sediments. The majority of the most warm-loving shell species became extinct in late Pliocene time (Mactra layers) although some of them still occur in the younger Tjörnes Serripes beds which are probably 3–2.5 million years old. In the Breiðavík beds they have disappeared which suggests that a falling sea temperature and deteriorating climate was quite rapid early in the Pleistocene. With and from the formation of the Breiðavík deposits interglacial sediments only contain species which live at present on

267

Figure 24-27. Pollen grains of grass (1), willow (2) and birch (3). Magnification 500X. (Drawing Iversen.)

the coast of Iceland. It should be noted, however, that Mollusc species originating in the Pacific appeared suddenly in the Serripes layers deposits. They are so numerous that they have probably forced out the pre-existing species as is often the case when new species colonize a new area. It could therefore be that they indicate colder conditions than would be expected. Many Pacific species still flourish along the Icelandic coast today. Shells typical of icy seas are much less common in marine sediments in Iceland than might be expected. Portlandia arctica is first found at the bottom of the Breiðavík deposits some 2 million years ago. It then only occurs in the Búlandshöfði deposits and in sediments from Late glacial time. Portlandia arctica lives at present in ice cold seas such as those off the east coast of Greenland.

Fossils in late Pliocene and Pleistocene sediments thus suggest that the *climate* first started to get markedly colder around 3 million years ago. Around the same time ice sheets began to partly cover the land in cold spells and by 2 million years ago they were so large that they reached the sea at Tjörnes (Furuvík layers). The climate in interglacial periods appears to have been similar to at present. On the other hand during glacial periods the climate was much colder, the mean annual temperature probably being 5–10°C lower than at present. The snow line was 500–1000 m lower. As now, southerly winds were moisture laden and the main ice divide lay somewhat to the south of the water divide.

Late glacial time and the Holocene

The Holocene is generally considered to have begun 10,000 years ago when the climate became as it is now. The division between the Pleistocene and the Holocene in Iceland coincides with the retreat of the ice sheet from Búði end moraines which was around 10,000 years ago.

Deposits from the end of the Pleistocene and the Holocene often form a continuous series and for this reason the stratigraphy of both periods is treated together. Deposits from late glacial time and the Holocene are more complete and therefore better known than from any other period of geological history in Iceland. Sediments and lava flows are extensive and widespread due to the intense volcanic activity as well as to rapid erosion and resulting rapid sedimentation.

In addition to traditional stratigraphical methods for relative dating such as correlating series of strata in localized areas with the regional stratigraphic succession, other methods are applicable to this youngest geological period, including counting of varve clays, tephrochronology and pollen analysis, all of which are supported by radioactive carbon dating.

Tephrochronology

In most volcanic eruptions ash and pumice i.e. tephra are nearly always formed. In flood eruptions the tephra fall is usually insignificant but in explosive eruptions it is often very great. High tephra production is mainly associated with explosive activity where acid magma is erupted such as in Hekla, as well as in subglacial eruptions such as Katla. Acid tephra is usually white or light-coloured, basalt tephra black or dark-coloured. Some tephra layers are distributed over a large area and can be traced in soil profiles over great distances (Figure 24-25). Each tephra layer is a time marker in soil or sediment and of exactly the same age everywhere.

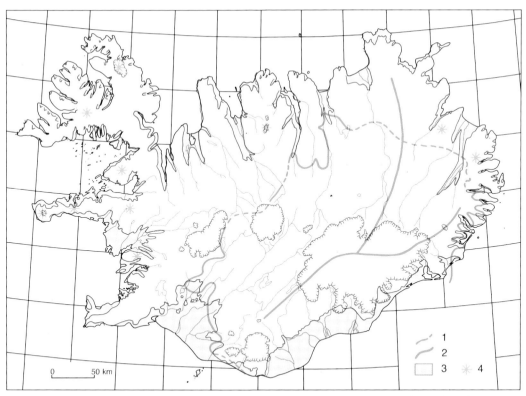

Figure 24-28. Map showing areas under the sea at the end of the Pleistocene and early in the Holocene periods, i.e. about 10,000 years ago. Symbols: 1) limit of the Búði ice sheet, 2) ice divide, 3) land below the sea level at that time, 4) main ice centres in highlands outside the main ice sheet. (Drawing Þ.E. and G.H.I.)

The age of the tephra layers can be determined in various ways. Tephra layers deposited in historical time are for instance dated from historical accounts or archaeological finds, while pre-historical tephra layers in conjunction with their position in soil profiles are dated by pollen analysis or nowadays mostly by radioactive carbon dating. If dating has been carried out in one place the age of the tephra layer in all sections where it is found is then known. Tephrochronology in Iceland is mainly based on the light-coloured acid layers since they are rather few in number and easily recognized as well as being distributed over large areas (Figure 24-25). Four of these light-coloured layers are from Hekla: H_5 (6600 years), H_4 (4000 years), H_3 (2800 years) and H_1 which

was erupted in the "first Hekla fire" of 1104, the tephra from which destroyed the settlements in the Þjórsárdalur valley and the Hrunamannaafréttur district northwest of it. All of these Hekla tephra layers spread northwards and form very clear horizons in the soil sections of northern Iceland (Figure 20-3). Tephra layer H_3 covers around 80% of the country and is found in soil sections over the area from Húnaflói-Reykjavík, W-Iceland, eastwards to Breiðdalur, E-Iceland (Figure 24-25). Icelandic tephra layers are in fact found in soil sections abroad, such as in the Faeroes, Norway, Sweden, N-Germany and the British Isles. All the light-coloured tephra layers from Hekla have been found in most of these countries as well as tephra layers from eruptions at the end of Late gla-

269

cial time and early Holocene which were first found abroad before they were discovered in Iceland.

Tephra layers are of great value in chronological studies whether they be age determinations on lavas, climatic changes as deduced from pollen diagrams, changes in river channels and canyons, advance and retreat of glaciers, archaeological remains as well as in measurements on the history of the accumulation of peat bogs and loessial deposits (Figure 20-4 and 20-5).

Tephra layers increase in thickness towards the volcano and thus give an indication as to their origin. They also provide information on volcanic history, i.e. the number of eruptions in volcanoes as well as on changes in their petrological composition.

Pollen analysis

Each year plants spread an immense quantity of microscopic pollen dust, especially plants which disperse their pollen by wind. The pollen grains are very small, or only 1/100–1/10 mm in size. As well as varying in size, pollen grains are unique to each plant family and even individual species vary in type and shape (Figure 24-27). Pollen grains which fall on dry land are destroyed but those which fall in bogs and lakes are preserved there for ever. The proportion of pollen types in each annual layer of peat corresponds to the vegetation which flourished in the bogs or surroundings at the time. Thus the pollen distribution records the history of the environment and the method of interpretation is known as pollen analysis. Samples are taken at 5–10 cm intervals from the bog section. They are then boiled in potassium hydroxide and acid and examined under the microscope and 200–1000 pollen grains analysed and counted, The percentage of pollen types from each sample is then calculated and plotted on a pollen diagram, from which the vegetation history can be deduced and from it the climatic history. The

scarcity of plant species and isolation of the country means that the value of pollen analysis as a dating method is rather limited in Iceland. There is, however, a clear indication with the advent of birch in pollen diagrams around 8500–9000 years ago in the south and west and of sharp vegetation changes with settlement of the country. In spite of the scarcity of the Icelandic flora, a reasonable picture of the vegetation and climatic changes from the end of the Pleistocene has been obtained by pollen analysis (Figure 24-31 and 24-32).

Late glacial time[8]

About 18,000 years ago the world climate became milder after the bitter cold of the last glacial period and the ice sheets began to melt. Climatic change for the better was, however, not without some readvances. The evidence of two cold spells and associated glacier advance is two large, though admittedly incomplete end moraines, the Álftanes and Búði end moraines (Figure 24-24).

Just over 12,000 years ago, with the milder climatic conditions, the ice sheet boundary retreated to within the present day coastline in the southwest, west and north-east of the country. Around this time the weather conditions become suddenly colder again and the glacier advanced, pushing up an end moraine which can be traced from Álftanes south of Reykjavík – the presidential residence at Bessastaðir stands on the end moraine ridge – across the mouth of Hvalfjörð-

---

8 The period from when the edge of the ice sheet moved inland of the present day coast – in the south it extended on to the coastal shelf however and up until it started to retreat from the Búði end moraine at the start of the Holocene is here called *late glacial time*, although this is not in accordance with other nomenclature in this book.

In this book uncorrected carbon dates are used, corrections on ages of plant remains based on dendrochronology or on shells are not used. These corrections are thought to be around 370 years less on Icelandic samples.

Figure 24-29. The Vindheimamelar gravel terraces in the Tungusveit district in Skagafjörður, N-Iceland, which were deposited at the highest shoreline at the end of the Pleistocene period. They are at a height of 45 m a.s.l. Looking towards the southeast. Sólheimafjall in the background. (Photo Þ.E.)

ur and Skorholtsmelar in the Melasveit district W-Iceland and the mouth of the southern Borgarfjörður valleys. The sea kept pace with the retreating glacier and flooded the lowland which had been depressed by the glacier load. Discontinuous end moraines also run from Hrútafjörður eastwards to Blönduós, west N-Iceland, which were probably pushed up during the Álftanes cold spell (Figure 24-24). Farther east in northern Iceland the glacier extended far out into the fjords and for instance almost to the mouth of Eyjafjörður. Fnjóskadalur was ice-free but valley glaciers in Eyjafjörður and Bárðardalur blocked the passes Dalsmynni and Ljósavatnsskarð forming a large ice-dammed lake. The lake drained to the north over Flateyjardalsheiði. There is a coll at a height of 200 metres which fits well with gravel terraces in the mountain alope at 200 m in the north and 250 m in the south of the

valley. In the mountains of mid northern Iceland valley and corrie glaciers were common during the Álftanes cold stage and the same applies to the eastern fjords, the Snæfellsnes peninsula, NE-Iceland and other areas. In the south the ice sheet extended over the coastal shelf and calved into the sea. The Álftanes readvance probably took place about 12,000 years ago. New research supported by many new C^{14} dates indicate that the bigger part of these end moraines are locally 10,600 years old. The same applies to the "ice-dammed" lakes in Fnjóskadalur.

Sediments from the warm spell preceding the Álftanes cold spell are at present only found at Kópasker, NE-Iceland and in the Melasveit district and Hvalfjörður, W-Iceland. This is marine sediment containing shells and underlies till layer. The age of the shells is 13,000–12,300 years. This warm period could be termed the Kópasker interstadial.

271

Following the cold spell which caused the glacier advance in the Álftanes stage, came a warm spell of about 1000 years. The ice sheet then retreated inland. Marine sediments from this period, which abroad is known as the Allerød period are for instance found at Melar in Reykjavík and underlying glacial till from the Búði cold spell at the Kaldá river in Hnappadalur, W-Iceland and at Saurbær in the Dalasýsla district, W-Iceland. Shells from the sediments are around 11,200 years old. This period could be named after Saurbær and called the *Saurbær interstadial*.

The climate then deteriorated again with the last cold spell during Late glacial time. The ice sheet advanced pushing up big end moraines (Figure 24-24) which can be traced in the south from Keldur in Rangárvellir right across the southern lowlands to the mountain Efstadalsfjall at Laugardalur. The glacier boundary lay across Þjórsá just above Árnes at the Búði waterfall from which the stage gets its name. The glacier boundary ran northwards from Efstadalsfjall along the mountain ranges in the Biskupstungur area and from there along the base of Bláfell and Langjökull to Hveravellir and from there eastwards to the eastern Jökulsá river inland of Skagafjörður. The end moraines of the Búði glacier are known as the *Búðaröð*. In northern Iceland an incomplete end moraine can be traced from Ljósavatnsskarð at the mouth of Reykjadalur north of Mývatn through Möðrudalur and eastwards to Hauksstaðir in Jökuldalur, E-iceland. This moraine was probably also pushed up by the Búði ice sheet. In the east of the southern lowlands, east of Eyjafjallajökull, the glaciers extended into the sea across the coastal shelf. In the Árnessýsla and Rangárvallasýla districts, S-Iceland, in Reykjadalur in the S-Þingeyjarsýsla district, N-Iceland and in the Fljótsdalur district and eastern fjords glacier tongues reached the sea (Figure 24-28). It should, however, be borne in mind that sea level was then at its highest and the bays into which the glaciers extended are now dry land due to isostatic uplift of the land. On the Snæfellsnes peninsula, in the western fjords, in the mountains between Skagafjörður and Skjálfandi, valley glacier tongues extended from the ice sheet at the valley heads down-valley and in places into the sea. Actually it is now widely thought that the Búði ice sheet at the outset extended as far as the Álftanes end moraines and the glaciers at this stage were thus much larger than was previously thought.

Around 10,000 years ago, or 9700 according to C^{14} dating corrected for sea water influence, the glaciers retreated from the Búði end moraine. The climatic improvement was so rapid that the ice sheet was completely gone from the Tungnáróræfi area, mid southern highlands, around 8000 years ago where it had been thickest. The big Þjórsárhraun lava was erupted from a fissure which runs NE at Hófsvað on the Tungná river and flowed uninterrupted 130 km to the sea between the Þjórsá and Ölfusá rivers.

Shoreline changes

At the maximum of the last glacial period sea level was about 100–150 m lower than at present much of the earth's water resources being bound up in glaciers as has always been the case during glacial periods. Already, towards the end of the last glacial period, the climate became steadily warmer so that glaciers retreated greatly throughout the world. As a result of the great volume of meltwater which was added to the world's oceans sea level rose rapidly.

In Iceland the rise in sea level was for a long time more rapid during Late Glacial and early Holocene Time than the uplift of the land since the response of the earth's crust is always slower. The sea therefore kept pace with the retreating ice front and flooded first the coastal shelf and then the lowlands. The highest shoreline in the country appears to be of similar age or somewhat older than the Búði end moraine or more

Figure 24-30. Submarine peat on the beach at Seltjarnarnes, western Reykjavík area. The peat contains a layer of small birch stems from the early birch period. The peat suggests that land subsidence of 5 m has occurred in the Reykjavík area during the last 3000 years. (Photo Þ.E.)

than 10,000 years old. At that time the rise in sea level equalled the uplift of the land. This situation lasted for some time though not quite simultaneously as is clearly indicated by well defined wave-cut platforms and extensive gravel terraces corresponding to the highest shoreline.

The height of the highest shoreline varies in different parts of the country. They are highest inland in valleys, especially in the south of the country since the ice pressed down more on the land where it was thick than on headlands where it was thin. Thus the highest shoreline inland in the Árnessýsla and Rangárvallasýsla districts is just over 100 m above present sea level, at Hjalli in the Ölfus district 55 m, at Hvaleyrarholt in Hafnarfjörður 32 m, at Öskjuhlíð in Reykjavík 43 m, while in many other areas it is 30–60 m.

As mentioned earlier the highest shorelines are generally indicated by clear wave-cut platforms and gravel terraces-ancient storm beaches and deltas (Figure 24-29). In places gravel bars were also attached to

them such as Ölduhryggur on southern Snæfellsnes. Below the shoreline glacial till is widely wave-washed and the boulders rounded, while in valleys thick deposits of varved silts are widespread which have accumulated where the water depth was more. This fine-grained sediment originated mainly in the suspended sediment of glacial rivers. Overlying the varved silts in many areas is sand and gravel which rivers have deposited as sea level was falling. Great outwash plains or sandur (Icel.) have also been deposited by glacial rivers, especially along the boundary of the Búði glacier in southern Iceland. Thus the extensive sands of the Hvolshreppur and Rangárvellir district were deposited from glacial rivers in the front of the Búði glacier.

While sea level was reaching its maximum and remained there and also while it fell again through uplift of the land, a large area of the present day lowland was beneath the sea, while the valleys were broad bays. The southern lowlands were entirely be-

273

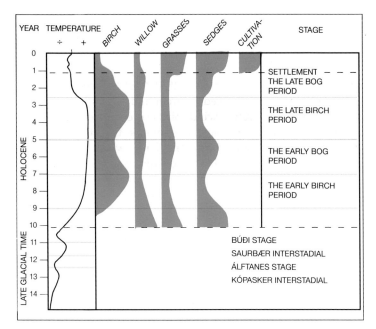

Figure 24-31. Changes in mean annual temperature and vegetation from late glacial time and the Holocene in Iceland. Furthest to the left thousands of years. The curves show proportional changes in vegetation and apply mainly to the south of the country. (Drawing Þ.E.)

neath sea level as far inland as the limit of the highland (Figure 24-28 and 18-7). In the Reykjavík area the present day headlands and islands lay under sea level. The hills Öskjuhlíð and Háaleiti were islands while the main landmass began inland of the Elliðaá river. The majority of cultivated land in Iceland and at least 3/4 of the farms of the country are on former sea floor. The majority of concrete aggregate, road building material and infill aggregate is obtained from gravel terraces from this period.

The marine sediments, especially varved silts contain widespread shells and gastropods. Portlandia arctica is one of the few molluscs found in the marine sediments and which no longer lives in Icelandic waters, but in the N-Arctic ocean. Marine sediments in the Faxaflói Bay area and on the southern lowlands contain numerous scallops (Chlamys islandicus), which are now rare in warm waters are common in the colder waters of Breiðafjörður in NW-, N- and E-Iceland. This suggests that the sea temperature was somewhat lower than at present when the sediment was being deposited.

While the ice front was at the Búði end moraine, the uplift of the land inland in southern Iceland was 20 m more than the increase in sea level. Uplift was then very rapid. In the south the shoreline was 15 m lower than at present when the Þjórsárhraun lava was erupted 8000 years ago. Inland in northern Iceland the strand line changed from 100 m above sea level and to 15 m below the present sea level in around 2000 years so that uplift has exceeded sea level rise by about 5 m per century on average over this period.

During the period 9000 to 3000 years ago the coast lay further out than at present. In the early part of the period sea level was still rising since the huge ice sheet of N. America was only completely melted 5000 years ago. The Icelandic crust was at this time fully recovered. Evidence of a higher shoreline from this time are only found at western Húnaflói, from Hrútafjörður to Steingrímsfjörður, where the *Nucella layers* occur up to 5 m above present sea level. These deposits seem to be 3000–5000 years old. The index fossil is Nucella lapillus, which did not live on the north coast during past centuries but began to

274

appear there from around 1920 due to improving weather conditions and increase in sea temperature. During the deposition of these layers the water temperature on the north coast was at least as high as at present and considerably higher than in previous centuries.

In the last few thousand years the land has begun to subside again, probably due to slow vertical movements. A good example is the Seltjarnarnes submarine peat (Figure 24-30). Peat was still forming in the Seltjörn bog 3000 years ago. Some time later the peat formation ceased and at the time of settlement 1000 years ago there was a lake (hence the name). There is now a sea inlet there. Subsidence in the Reykjavík area has probably been around 5 m in the last 3000 years which corresponds to 15 cm per century on average and the coast line change in past centuries. Marine peat is common along the south and west coast and is in fact found in other parts of the country which suggests that the entire country is although sinking very slowly. It is now thought, however, that the crust south of Vatnajökull at Hornafjörður is rising as a result of decreased load weight due to melting of Vatnajökull, adversely affecting the harbour entrance.

Vegetation and climate in the Holocene

For a long time there has been divided opinion as to the origin of the present flora in Iceland. Up until the 1940's it was generally thought that during the last glacial period the country was entirely ice-covered to the extent that only nunataks appeared above the surface and the ice cold conditions had destroyed life entirely (tabularasa theory). According to this view the flora first became established when the ice sheet started to melt. The Icelandic flora comprises about 450 species of higher plants. It is now widely believed by many researchers that half of these survived the cold conditions of the last glacial period in ice-free areas. It has recently been shown that the outermost promontory between Dýrafjörður and Önundarfjörður, NW-Iceland, was ice-free during the last glacial period. It is thought that of the remaining half at least 90 species were introduced by man and others by ocean currents, wind, birds or even icebergs. Botanical research suggests that the centres of spreading for plants which survived the hard climatic conditions are in NW-, E- and in particular in central northern Iceland, where for meteorological, georaphical and topographical reasons, the largest ice-free area is to be expected.

Because of the southerly position of the ice divide during the last glacial period the climate of ice-free areas in the northern part of the country was much more continental than at present. Precipitation was rather low and sunshine effective. Conditions on the ice-free areas would not have been worse than at present in N.E. Greenland north of 80° N (Peary Land) which is ice-free due to a lack of precipitation. In this cold inhospitable corner of the world around 100 plant species thrive at present. The climate was then probably warmer in ice-free areas. In Iceland and conditions more like those in the Esjufjöll mountains which form nunataks in the Breiðamerkurjökull glacier, an outlet glacier from S-Vatnajökull (Figure 17-1). Their base is at a height of 800 m and their highest peaks 1500 m. Around 100 plant species now flourish in this area.

The ice sheet melted rather rapidly as mentioned earlier. Already during the Álftanes stage quite large areas, some on lowland, were already ice-free. (Figure 24-24 and 24-28). As the land became free of the ice load the vegetation spread outwards from the nunataks and ice-free areas, while in addition seeds were introduced from across the sea, by wind, birds, ocean currents or even icebergs. Those that found favourable conditions for survival immediately put down roots and from them have come all the members of the Icelandic plant kingdom.

275

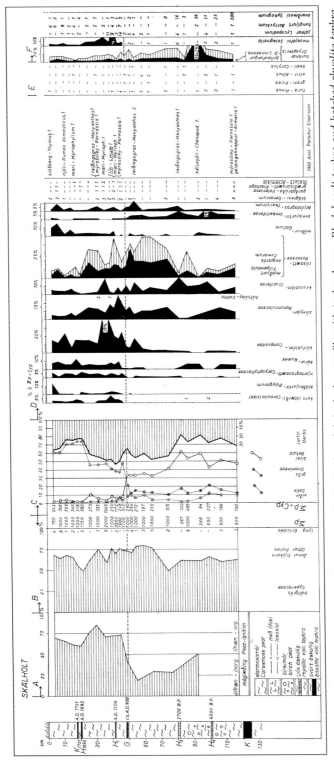

Figure 24-32. Pollen diagram from Skálholt, S-Iceland. Furthest left is the bog profile with tephra layers. Black basalt tephra and hatched rhyolite tephra. Column A shows the proportion of organic material (right) in the peat. Column B shows the percentage of sedges (Cyperaceae) against other pollen grains. Column C shows the percentage of various other pollen grains and column D of various plants with sedges subtracted. Two columns give individual rare pollens. Column E shows the number of pollen grains originating in other countries. Column F shows the percentage of spores (left) and the number of rare spores. (Drawing P.E.)

276

Figure 24-33. Icelandic birch forest as it probably was at the time of settlement and during prehistoric Holocene. Gatnaskógur at Hallormsstaður. (Photo Sigurður Blöndal.)

According to pollen analysis of Icelandic peat bogs the vegetation history of the country since the glaciers started to melt, late in the last glacial period, can be divided into six main parts. Their names are mainly based on vegetation changes as indicated by pollen analysis in peat bogs and lake sediments (Figure 24-31 and 24-32).

Late glacial time and earliest Holocene. The first period of the vegetation history began when the glaciers started to melt from dry land in late glacial time. Sedges, grasses, willow and various flowering plants appear in·this period. Birch is missing in the south, west and west of northern Iceland and it could thus be termed the *birch-free period* there. In the north-east on the other hand birch appears to have grown at this time although this has yet to be proved. The occurrence of birch in the north in this period

277

Figure 24-34. Bog section at Borgarmýri, Ártúnshöfði in East-Reykjavík. Tephra layers: At shovel blade, Katla tephra 5000 years old. The light layer with the knife blade, Hekla 2800 years ago. Light layer at upper knife blade, tephra from 900 A.D., the settlement tephra horizon, above which aeolian material increases. The thick black tephra layer is from Katla 1500 A.D. after which wind borne material is replaced by peat, since the land had become barren due to wind erosion. (Photo Þ.E.)

could suggest it survived in nunatak areas there during the last glacial period. From the end of this period and up to the settlement very few, if any, new plant species appear to have been added to the Icelandic flora.

The early birch period. The second period is known as the early birch period, which began when birch spread rapidly over the entire country just about 9000 years ago. Birch woods and shrubs rapidly covered all the lowland except the most waterlogged bogs. The lower tree stem layer was formed in this period. During this period the climate was warm and dry.

The early bog period. From 7000–8000 years ago precipitation increased so that the peat bogs became wetter and the woods were forced out or new bogs were formed where none had been before. The type plant of this wet period was Sphagnum moss. Its spores during this period are usually more numerous than the pollen grains and spores of other plants added together. Sphagnum moss now barely lives in Iceland. This shows that the climate was mild although it was humid.

The late birch period. Around 5000 years ago precipitation decreased with the result that birch spread again and invaded the peat bogs. This was the start of the late birch period which lasted until 2500 years ago. The

upper tree stem layer in Icelandic peat bogs is from this period. The climate was then at its best in Iceland during the Holocene. The annual mean temperature was probably 2–3°C higher than at present, the summers milder and the winters shorter and milder. During this period at least 3/4 of the country was covered with vegetation and half of it forested The forest limit was at least 600 m at which height the uppermost forest remains are found in Austurdalur in Skagafjörður and in Fróðárdalur east of Langjökull. It is probable that even the highland areas Sprengisandur and Ódáðahraun were covered with vegetation at this time.

The late bog period. Around 2500 years ago or at the transition between bronze age and iron age transition in Scandinavia the climate suddenly worsened, the temperature fell and precipitation increased. This marked the end of the *warm period (climatic optimum)* of the Holocene which began with the early birch period 9000 years ago. The climate has since either been similar to that of today or become slightly worse up until the 19th century. During the climatic optimum glaciers were practically non-existent in Iceland except on the highest mountains such as Eyjafjallajökull, Snæfell, Öræfajökull and the Vatnajökull summits. With the worsening climate 2500 years ago these mountain glaciers advanced suddenly and their snouts extended farther than during recent centuries. The huge ice caps which now dominate began to form at this time and have gradually increased in size since. They were at their maximum at the end of the last century. Associated with the climatic change was a change in the vegetation. The birch forest declined as the bogs became wetter while at the same time the forest limit became lower. This period could be termed the late bog period and it continues today. It is appropriate to divide it into two. The second part corresponds to historical time, i.e. the last 1100 years which is clearly delimited from a vegetation point of view the effects of settlement suddenly becoming very apparent (Figure 24-31 and 24-32).

Settlement and historical time. At that time Iceland was grown between the mountains and the sea, according to Ari the learned Þorgilsson in the Íslendingabók, i.e. The Book of Icelanders, in his description of the country at the outset of settlement, written about 1120 A.D. Admittedly the woods had declined in the bogs by then and had been replaced by mire vegetation. Well drained land was on the other hand covered with dense woods.

The birch forest was at a disadvantage because of the deteriorating climate and declined rapidly after settlement of the country began, this being completed in 60 years. Some districts such as Húnavatnssýsla and Skagafjörður, western N-Iceland, were already nearly bare of forest in the early centuries. The causes of the extensive and rapid forest destruction are several but the most important are: Since the time of settlement and for a long time afterwards, the woods were heavily exploited for charcoal production. Wood was needed in quantity for bog iron ore smelting as the majority of iron used for making of utensils, tools, weapons etc., was obtained from bog ore up until the 15th century. Also up until the 19th century charcoal was produced for iron working and beating of scythe blades. The best timber was used for house construction even though imported timber and driftwood were also used. Wood felling was very intensive and over large areas, since the amount of timber per hectare was low in Icelandic woods. Grazing is another factor. Sheep grazing in Iceland has for a long time been carried out at the expense of the land. Winter grazing was especially damaging to the woodland and where wood felling had been practised the sheep ensured that the wood did not manage to become re-established. It should also be pointed out that thin wood charcoal beds are usually found widely in soil profiles around farms and deserted farms at the start of settlement. These wood charcoal beds suggest that the first settlers burnt shrubs, trees and withered grass around the farms. They were unconcerned about the woods, having been used to conditions at home in Norway where the dark pine forests were an obstacle to all cultivation. Burning of woodland and withered grass was more suitable on the fertile loessial soil in Iceland than on the acid pine forest soils of western Norway.

In the light of this it is clear that the birch forest, which covered half the country 2500 years ago and probably just over one quarter at the start of settlement, has in a few centuries suffered badly because of the unchecked encroachment of man and livestock, a situation aggregated by the climate. In areas close to tephra producing volcanoes the ash and pumice have led to the destruction of the vegetation. The words of Ari the learned are thus closer to the truth than generally believed and show how rapid the vegetation changes have been. At present only 1% of the country is covered by woodland and shrubs.

Another major factor in the vegetation changes which occurred at the time of settlement is the *increase in grass cover*. The grass pollen increases in direct proportion to the decrease in birch pollen, suggesting that the

Figure 24-35. Wind eroded banks in the northwest of Tungufell, east of Gullfoss, S-Iceland. The picture clearly shows surface run off and aeolian erosion of the soil. Water channels run downslope (down picture) while the wind has eroded the soil along the hill. The northeasterly wind (from left of picture) has been mainly responsible. Aerial photo taken from NW in Sept. 1970. (Photo Þ.E.)

grass increased at the expense of the forest. The enormous increase in grass cover could be for two reasons. When the wood was felled or burned, the grass species which grew underneath had more space and better growing conditions with the result that they spread greatly. In addition it is likely that the first settlers were simply sowing grass seed of new species which they had brought with them. It could well be that both some species were brought by man and also that the Icelandic species had more space when the forest was destroyed.

Pollen analysis provides some information on the *cultivation* of plants. A few pollen grains have been found, for instance, of bog myrtle (Myria gale), mugworth (Artemisia vulgaris) and wormwood (A. absithium) from early in historical time. Neither of

these plants grows today in Iceland but they were used in mead ale brewing and for healing while the wormwood was also used as mothballs in clothes. Pollen grains of flax (Linum) and valerian have also been found.

Pollen grains of barley (Hordeum) appear in pollen diagrams from many sites early in historical time. In addition to the evidence of pollen analysis for *cultivation of barley* in early times there is abundant evidence for this in the sagas, annals, early letters, church records, place names as well as from archaeological remains for instance in Reykjavík, at Bergþórshvoll and in the deserted farm of Gröf at Hof in the Öræfi district, where barley was found on the straw. The farm was deserted during the eruption of Öræfajökull in 1362. From this evidence it can be concluded that barley cultivation was seldom practised in the north and east, but was common in the south of the country but came to an end not later than in the 16th century. Much has been written and many hypotheses proposed for the decline and end of barley cultivation in Iceland. The main ideas are: famine, hard times due to black death and crop failure and seed shortage, changed living habits such as land division and associated work shortage, declining skill, changing trade patterns and last but not least worsening climate. Of these, the worsening climate and changing trade patterns appear to be the most likely causes.

With the settlement various plant species were introduced which accompany man wherever he colonizes or cultivates land. These plants are known generally as weeds. All weeds have in common that they need good soil and plenty of light. Many of these plants are originally steppe plants or coastal plants which have accompanied man for thousands of years from country to country. Some of the weeds which appear with the settlement are though Icelandic in origin such as sea plantain which grew by the sea before the settlement and then moved and established itself around farms. Also with the settlement pollen grains of sheep sorrel first become apparent in number as well as common sorrel (Rumex) although both grew in Iceland before the settlement.

Soil erosion and denudation followed in the wake of the vegetation changes with the settlement and had already become significant in many areas in early centuries. The ash content of the soil increases for example immediately after the settlement. The causes of the increased mineral content are mainly that in most districts denudation began early in historical time and the soil dust settles in the bogs. In the Reykjavík area the ash content increases immediately after the settlement in soil profiles but decreases sharply after 1500 which suggests that most of the soil and vegetation had been stripped off and were already completely denudated by

then. A colour change due to the soil denudation can be discerned in bog sections in many areas. Peat formed before the settlement is usually dark in colour while peat formed later is coloured yellow by the addition of the wind-borne soil material (Figure 24-34).

The causes of denudation lie in the rapid vegetation changes which took place with the arrival of man when the forest had to make way for grass land. Meltwater from snow in forests percolates to a large extent down through the soil. On the other hand on sloping grass land the most of the meltwater runs off rapidly on the surface and cuts channels in the soil cover (Figure 24-35). Soil erosion and denudation spread out from the channel banks. The wind-borne soil material then caused thickening and dried out the soil making the work of the wind easier. Denudation has in places, equally in settled areas as well as on highlands not only blown soil from dry land but also caused denudation in bogs. Tephra eruptions have caused denudation. Examples are the Hekla eruptions of 1104, 1693 and 1766–68 which are partly to blame for soil and denudation in the grasslands of the Árnessýsla, Landsveit and Rangárvellir districts in southern Iceland (Figure 20-3 and 20-4). It is, however, doubtful that the volcanic tephra would have resulted in such damage on wooded land which prevents wind erosion.

Evidence on *climatic change* during the first few centuries of settlement in Iceland and up to 1550 is otherwise rather sparse. Drift ice reached the coast from time to time from the ocean to the north brought by the East Greenland current. From the frequency of drift ice and famine years it can be estimated that for the first few centuries the climate was similar to that of the last few decades but around 1200 it became colder. After that the climate became somewhat warmer late in the 14th century and in the 15th century. Drift ice is first of significance from around 1600. During the next few centuries drift ice was very common and sometimes covered

Figure 24-36. Remains of the Tertiary peneplain in the Tertiary Basalt Formation between Skagafjörður and Eyjafjörður, south of Öxnadalur and Norðurárdalur, N-Iceland. The "alpine" landscape, i.e. the deep valleys and cirques, was formed during the Pleistocene period. (Photo Þ.E.)

the area from NW-Iceland northwards and eastwards as far as the south-east coast, similar to the situation in the spring of 1968. The coasts were often closed by drift ice well into the summer and the weather conditions were so cold that the grass crop failed as well as the livestock. Shortly before the end of the last century glaciers were at their maximum and they have never been so extensive since the beginning of the Holocene. Otherwise little is known about glacier advance in past centuries but they had started to increase greatly in size in the late 16th century ages. Around 1700, for instance, Breiðamerkurjökull encroached on the farm lands of Breiðá and Fjall. Today the glacier has retreated from the farm locations but where once there was cultivated land there is now only barren glacial moraine.

Holocene volcanism

Volcanism during the Holocene is limited to the same areas as during the late Pleistocene or in other words Reykjanes-Langjökull, Vestmannaeyjar-Melrakkaslétta and the Snæfellsnes volcanic zones and Öræfajökull (Figure 8-1). On average eruptions have occurred every 5 years in Iceland and some 40–50 volcanoes have been active (cf. chapters 7 and 8.)

Volcanism has been very varied and the magma has often broken its way to the surface through a circular feeder conduit (shield volcanoes, strato volcanoes), but mainly through fissures. Shield volcanoes and fissure eruptions naturally occurred repeatedly in the same areas, such as Reykjanes, Hellisheiði, Veiðivötn and the area east of lake Mývatn. They are by definition monogenetic features, each site erupting only once. Strato volcanoes have on the other hand each erupted many times. Hekla has for instance erupted 18 times and volcanoes in Hekla's vicinity have erupted at least 5 times since the settlement, Katla probably 20 times and Grímsvötn 20 times. Eruptions have also occurred in the sea. Vestmannaeyjar have for instance been built up in submarine eruptions, mainly during the Holocene, the last being Surtsey.

During the early Holocene, basalt flood eruptions appear to have been very common but explosive eruptions rare. During this time most shield volcanoes were formed as for example Skjaldbreiður and Trölladyngja. The last large shield volcano to erupt was Ketildyngja in the Ódáðahraun area which was formed 3500 years ago and in which the older Laxárhraun lava flowed down to Lake Mývatn and from there along the valley of Laxárdalur and to Aðaldalur, a distance of about 70 km. The lava cap on Surtsey is also a shield volcano. Shield volcanoes occur mainly in two areas, the Reykjanes-Langjökull zone and in the Ódáðahraun area. In some shield volcano eruptions very large amounts of lava were produced, such as in Trölladyngja and Skjaldbreiður where it is probably 15 km^3.

Fissure eruptions have on the other hand been frequent and constant ever since the end of the Pleistocene and large volumes of lava have been produced in some of them. The Laki lava in the southern highlands which was erupted from the Laki crater row in 1783 covers for example 580 km^2 and the volume of volcanic products is around 12 km^3. The Þjórsárhraun lava which was erupted in the Tungná area 8000 years ago covers just over 900 km^2. Only basalt magma has been produced in basalt flood eruptions.

Explosive eruptions appear to have become more common as the Holocene progressed. The first large phreatic eruption was the Hekla eruption H$_5$, 6600 years ago, although the largest was the Hekla eruption

H$_3$, 2800 years ago in which around 12 km^3 of tephra were produced, or the equivalent of 3 km^3 of solid rock. In the largest explosive eruptions only rhyolite magma has been produced (Hekla, Öræfajökull 1362 and Askja 1875), but basalt tephra has been produced mainly in eruptions in tephra ring craters (Hverfjall, Vatnaöldur) and in subglacial eruptions (Katla, Grímsvötn) and in submarine eruptions (Surtsey).

Lava flows erupted in the Holocene cover just over 10,000 km^2 or 10% of the country. The total amount of basalt lavas is estimated to be about 320 km^3, intermediate lavas some 25 km^3 (mainly andesite from Hekla) and rhyolite lavas around 2 km^3. The total amount of basalt tephra as solid rock is estimated as 40 km^3, andesite tephra 4 km^3 (mainly from Hekla) and rhyolite tephra about 11.5 km^3. Altogether therefore the total amount of volcanic products produced since the end of the Pleistocene in Iceland is about 400 km^3.

Geomorphology: the shaping of the landscape

Both exogenic and endogenic forces have been responsible for producing the landscape in Iceland. Volcanism builds up mountains and extensive lava series which already during their period of formation had started to dip and become faulted through crustal movements. The fault strike then often controls the landscape formation by exogenic forces such as fluvial, glacial and marine processes.

The surface of the Tertiary Basalt Formation was rather flat at the end of the Tertiary period although crater-rows, shield volcanoes and strato volcanoes stood above the surroundings. Valleys were rather shallow and the landscape being gently sloping and most rivers were spring-fed. Both factors naturally have a strong influence on the erosive capability of the rivers. Remnants of the late Tertiary "peneplain" are still widespread in the landscape. In the northwest the high plateau is the most complete remnant of this peneplain. It is now a fairly gently rolling high plateau admittedly modified by Pleistocene glaciers. It is generally at a height of 700 to 900 m and practically equally smooth right to the most extreme promontory. The situation is similar in northern Iceland from Miðfjörður to Bárðardalur although the "peneplain" is more dissected there. Smooth mountain summits occur in this area at a height of 900–1300 m (Figure 24-36). In the east of Iceland remains of such a peneplain also occur although it is now very dissected and with many peaks. Summits occur at a height of 900–1100 m. According to observations on the belted distribution of amygdales 500–1000 m appear to have been removed from the top of the Tertiary Basalt Formation in the east before the present landscape of valleys and fjords was formed. Since the late Tertiary peneplain remnants widely reach the most extreme promontories it can be concluded that it extended further than at present, or probably as far as the present day coastal shelf. With the denudation of the Tertiary lava pile during the Quaternary epoch it was attacked by marine erosion while rivers and glaciers cut deep and broad valleys into it. The debris which was removed lightened the crust with the result that the peneplain was gradually uplifted. The Tertiary peneplain thus probably lay much nearer sea level at the end of the Tertiary period than at present.

During the Pleistocene the effects of external forces were much greater than they were in the Tertiary for several reasons. During the Tertiary the bedrock had become quite impermeable because of amygdule infillings and diagenesis of the interbasaltic sediments. With valley deepening the rivers therefore flowed on constantly more impervious rock. As a result less water percolated down through the bedrock and the surface run off increased. Thus the surface run off

gradually changed in character. Spring-fed rivers became less common and direct run off rivers more so. With the formation of the ice sheets glacial rivers made their appearance. The erosive capability of direct run off rivers and glacial rivers is much more than spring-fed rivers so that landscaping processes were more rapid during the Quaternary than in the Tertiary. In addition, flooding was rare in the warm climate of the Tertiary, but during interglacial periods of the Pleistocene and meltwater was very common, the country being snow-covered during the winters and spring-and autumn floods became very common. Rivers cut canyons and valleys in the surface strata often in accordance with the fault strike. The valleys became gradually broader and deeper, largely due to the erosion by glaciers during glacial periods. The inter-valley ridges were gradually destroyed and broad valleys were formed such as Borgarfjörður, Breiðafjörður, Skagafjörður and Fljótsdalshérað. Marine erosion eroded the headlands and smoothed the valley bottoms forming broad strandflats such as on the southern coast of the Snæfellsnes peninsula, in Borgarfjörður (Mýrar), and in the eastern Skaftafellssýsla district. Eustatic shoreline changes due to the glacial-interglacial cycles as well as subsidence and uplift due to isostatic crustal changes associated with fluctuating glaciers also helped the strandflat formation, wave action eroding a broader shelf than otherwise would have been formed. The coastal shelf was also widened by sediment deposits as for instance off the south and southeast coasts.

The history (development) of landscape formation is, however, not easily interpreted everywhere, especially since volcanism has interrupted the external forces in many places. In some areas the younger lavas make geomorphological research easier especially where lavas have flowed in ancient valleys. From lavas of this type in the west of northern Iceland it is for instance obvious that the landscape had to some extent reached its present appearance in the early Pleistocene although rivers and glaciers have of course deepened and broadened the valleys since. Examples are Víðidalur, Svínadalur-Langidalur, Skagi and Skagafjörður where early Pleistocene lavas form the valley floor such as at Bakkabrúnir and Borgarvirki in Víðidalur. On the other hand the present day landscape on the northern side of the Snæfellsnes peninsula provides a good example of very rapid landscape development. The Grundarfjörður valley is for instance less than one million years old although it is 600–700 m deep compared to surrounding lava and móberg horizons which were undissected up until the present geomagnetic epoch which started 0.7 million years ago. The most youthful landscape is found in the present active volcanic zone such as the Hekla area, the Mývatn area, the Ódáðahraun area, the Tungnáröræfi-Þórisvatn area and on the Reykjanes peninsula where volcanism has been practically the only process at work for the past few thousand years. Precipitation in the active volcanic areas percolates downwards and escapes as ground water causing no surface erosion except during spring thaw when the ground is frozen.

The present landscape was practically fully developed at the start of the Holocene except in the active volcanic zones where volcanic landforms are most conspicuous. Most canyons were formed after the melting of the ice at the end of the Pleistocene, although some of the largest were formed before the last glacial as for example the Þjórsá canyon in the Gljúfurleit region. In contrast the Hvítá canyon below the Gullfoss waterfall is 3 km in length and has been formed following the melting of the Búði glacier 10,000 years ago (Figure 16-9). Lava eruptions have also had a widespread effect on river channels and controlled erosion. Before the Þjórsárhraun lava erupted 8000 years ago the Þjórsá and Hvítá rivers entered the sea as one somewhere between the present day river mouths. The lava divided the rivers and the Þjórsá river has for instance cut a gorge along the eastern edge of the lava at the Urriðafoss waterfall at the Þjórsá bridge. The Ölfusá river on the other hand has cut a gorge along the western edge of the lava at Selfoss and east and south of the Hestfjall mountain. Marine erosion has also been important and wave action has formed many high cliffs. Glacial erosion has also been an important agent in forming the landscape during the Holocene, especially valley glaciers and outlet glaciers, as can be deduced from moraine deposits of modern glaciers and the thickness of the fluvioglacial deposits (cf. chapter 17).

The Icelandic bedrock and crust

As mentioned earlier in this chapter and in chapter 12, Iceland is situated on a spreading ocean ridge, the Mid Atlantic ridge where the North American and Eurasian plates are drifting apart. At the spreading axis, or ocean ridge, new crust is constantly being produced from rising magma which is added to the plates as well as accumulating on top of them as they drift laterally. The sea floor is consumed at converging plate margins in ocean trenches and beneath fold mountains. The rate of drift at spreading ridges in Iceland is about 1 cm per year in each direction

Magma production is not evenly spread along the length of the ocean ridges but is rather more in certain areas, so called *hot spots*. One such hot spot is located under Iceland since nowhere in the world is magma production and volcanism more than here. Hot spots are not confined to only ocean ridges, however. An example are the Hawaiian islands which are situated in the middle of the Pacific plate. Due to the high volcanic production at hot spots, the newly formed crust is thicker there than on either side along the ridge axis and a result islands or land masses stand out of the sea in these areas. Iceland is an example of this, being by far the largest island on an ocean ridge. Through volcanism over a long period thickening of the sea floor or a ridge transverse to the ocean ridge is formed. One such ridge is the Greenland-Iceland-Faeroes-British Isles ridge which was formed in the Cainozoic era and is still being formed in Iceland.

Some 60 million years ago the North Atlantic began forming by continental drift when the North American (including Greenland) plate on the one hand and the Eurasian plate on the other drifted apart. This was accompanied by volcanism on either side of this "narrow" early Atlantic ocean, in the British Isles and in Greenland, but especially in the space between them on the spreading ridge, the Reykjanes ridge and its continuation the Ægir ridge which is now extinct, but lies between Iceland and Norway. The latter ridge was thus active from the start of the Cainozoic 60 million years ago and up to the mid Cainozoic era around 25 million years ago (cf. Figure 24-4).

When drifting and volcanism ceased on the Ægir ridge, spreading and volcanism shifted to the Kolbeinsey ridge off the east coast of Greenland. It runs from Iceland northwards to the fracture zone west of Jan Mayen. Spreading and volcanism have continued there and on the Reykjanes ridge. The build-up of Iceland began at this time so that the oldest basement rocks could be 25 million years old although none older than 14 million years old are known to be above sea level.

One or two volcanic zones have since been active in Iceland and volcanism has steadily built up the country. Within the volcanic zones there is "constant" spreading while at the same time magma rises from below to solidify either as intrusions at depth in the "fractures" between the plates or on the surface where it solidifies as volcanic rock (lava and tephra). Because of the build up of volcanic products and their weight the centre of the volcanic belt subsides at the same time as the newly formed crust drifts constantly laterally. Iceland has thus gradually been built up and increased in size in spite of the fact that erosive agents are probably nowhere as active as here and have prevented the country from becoming as big as it otherwise would have been through volcanic production and the spreading rate.

The crust beneath Iceland is thought to be divided into two layers. The upper layer is 3–6 km thick underneath the Tertiary areas, thickest under the south of W-Skaftafellssýsla, but much thinner in the volcanic zones. The thickness of the lower layer and depth to the Moho discontinuity underneath Iceland is not known with any certainty but is believed to be from 8 to 15 km depth, least in the volcanic zones.

The uppermost rock sequences in the crust underneath Iceland is composed of strata belonging to the Pleistocene Móberg Formation and Grey Basalt Formation as well as to the Tertiary Basalt Formation. The lower part of the crust is probably mainly composed of dikes and intrusions and altered rocks. The upper most part of the mantle, or lower part of the plates underneath Iceland is probably very thin, the asthenosphere (low velocity layer) being at shallow depth, 10–20 km underneath the volcanic zones as is the case everywhere underneath the ocean ridges. This makes interpretation of seismological data in the Icelandic area more difficult with the result that information about the crust and mantle beneath Iceland is in many respects scant and unclear since partially melted rock occurs at shallow depth, as well as semifluid magma layers or magma reservoirs beneath the volcanic zones (cf. chapter 12).

Epilogue

This book, Rocks and Landscapes – Geology of Iceland, is the fifth revised and modified edition of my earlier books on geology. The first book was published in 1968, later editions were abridged and revised versions. All editions have been published in two printings. The most recent edition appeared in 1991. The book is intended, not only as a text book in secondary schools up to university level in Iceland, but also as a handbook for the general public. The main changes in the 1991 edition from the earlier ones are that most chapters have been added to in line with developments and research results both here and abroad, in particular regarding volcanism, plate tectonics and historical geology. The order of individual chapters was changed from earlier versions so as to enhance the text flow. For the most part interpretation of geological data follows traditional lines. Sometimes, opinions are divided as regards the most recent research results. In such cases the author obviously, takes a personal stand. The book was translated practically unchanged into English and German and no chapters were left out, even though foreigners might find some of them to be of marginal interest. Most place names mentioned in the book can be found on maps, both topographic and geological in the scales 1:250,000 and 1:500,000. The Icelandic characters Þ, þ and Ð, ð are retained in place names throughout the book. They are not found in English although they represent similar sounds. The letter Ð, ð is pronounced like the „th" in brother. Þ, þ is pronounced like „th" in thorn. Alphabetically Ð comes after D and Þ comes after Z.

The book describes both the internal and external forces of Nature and outlines the geological history of Iceland. The chapter on historical geology should enhance the understanding of the evolution of life and the environmental equilibrium in the world. An emphasis should be placed on the chapter on the geological history of Iceland where the reader will find information on the geological development and formation of Iceland. This emphasis should also be placed on the changes in flora, fauna, climate and the effects of the appearance of man in Iceland. Attention should be drawn to the geological maps of Iceland in the scale of 1:250,000 of which seven out of nine maps have been published. There is also a new geological map of Iceland on a single sheet in the scale 1:500,000.

I have had advice from numerous individuals, teachers, students and general readers and have been informed of many things that could be improved. A number of photographs have been added and I should like to thank the owners for their use. Illustrations from earlier versions were redrawn and new illustrations were added in the 1991 edition. All this work is by the geographer Gunnar H. Ingimundarson. Professor Sigurður Steinþórsson, Dr. Sveinn P. Jakobsson and Dr. Kristinn J. Albertsson made valuable contributions to the chapters on petrology and internal forces and Dr. Hreggviður Norðdahl contributed to the chapters on external forces. Dr. Georg Douglas translated the book into English and Dr. Lúðvík E. Gústafsson into German. Dr. Kristinn J. Albertsson updated and translated the indexes, epilogue and bibliography into English. Sigurður Svavarsson, editor at Mál og menning, supervised the work for which the author and translators are deeply grateful.

Selected bibliography

The bibliographical list is chiefly for those who might want further information on the various geological topics. The reading material here contains comprehensive lists of references. This list furthermore contains a few foreign textbooks in geology from which some support has been drawn. Much geological information can be found in the Icelandic periodical Náttúrufræðingurinn, published by the Icelandic Natural History Society since 1931. Even though Náttúrufræðingurinn is in Icelandic most articles have an English summary. Another periodical is Jökull, the annual publication of the Icelandic Glaciological Society, published since 1951. Most of Jökull is written in English and it carries a lot of geological material. A number of geological papers have been published in the two series, Rit and Greinar by the Icelandic Science Society and in Acta naturalia Islandica, published by the Natural History Institute. A multitude of reports published by the National Energy Authority, Science Institute of the University of Iceland, The Icelandic Meteorological Office and various other institutions contain a lot of geological information and data. The Icelandic Museum of Natural History and the Icelandic Geodetic Survey have jointly published 7 sheets (out of 9 planned) in the scale 1:250,000 and in 1989 they published a geological map of Iceland in the scale 1:500,000.

Akhmetiev, M.A., Bratseva, G.M., Giterman, R.E., Golubova, L.V. & Moiseva, A.I. (1978): Late Cenozoic stratigraphy and flora of Iceland. – Trans. Acad. Sci. USSR. 316, 188 pp. Moscow. (In Russian).

Ari Trausti Guðmundsson (1986): Íslandseldar. – 168 pp. Reykjavík. (In Icelandic).

Árni Hjartarson & Ólafur Ingólfsson (1988): Preboreal glaciation of Southern Iceland. – Jökull 39, 1-16.

Árný Erla Sveinbjörnsdóttir, Jón Eiríksson, Heinemeier, J. & Rud, N. (1993): The Fossvogur marine sediments in SW Iceland – confined to the Allerød/ Younger Dryas transition by AMS ^{14}C dating. – Boreas 22, 147-157.

Áslaug Geirsdóttir (1991): Diamictites of late Pliocene age in western Iceland. – Jökull 40, 3-25. Reykjavík.

Axel Björnsson (1976): Jarðhræringar við Kröflu. – Náttúrufræðingurinn 46, 177-198. Reykjavík. (With an English summary).

Axel Björnsson, Guðni Axelsson & Ólafur Flóvenz (1990): Uppruni hvera og lauga á Íslandi. – Náttúrufræðingurinn 60, 15-

38. Reykjavík. (With an English summary).

Axel Kaaber & Kristján Sæmundsson (1988): Íslenskir steinar. – 143 pp. Reykjavík. (In Icelandic).

Bragi Árnason (1976): Groundwater systems in Iceland traced by deuterium. – Soc. Sci. Islandiae Rit 42, 236 pp. Reykjavík.

Bailey, E.B. & Weir, J. (1939): Introduction to geology. – 498 pp. London.

Betechtin, A.G. (1974): Lehrbuch der speziellen Mineralogie. – 683 pp. Leipzig.

Björck, S., Ólafur Ingólfsson, Hafliði Hafliðason, Margrét Hallsdóttir & Anderson, N.J. (1992): Lake Torfadalsvatn: A high resolution record of the North Atlantic ash zone I and the last glacial-interglacial environmental changes in Iceland. – Boreas 21, 15-22.

Douglas, G.R. (1993): Geomorphology in Iceland. – Evolution of geomorphology. 201-208. London.

Escher, A. & Watt, W.S. (ed.) (1976): The geology of Greenland. – 603 pp. Copenhagen.

Eysteinn Tryggvason (1986): Multiple magma reservoirs in a rift zone volcano. Ground deformation and magma transport during the September eruption 1984 of Krafla, Iceland. – J. Volc. Geotherm Res. 28, 1-44.

Francis, P. (1976): Volcanoes. – 368 pp. Harmondsworth.

Freysteinn Sigurðsson & Kristinn Einarsson (1988): Groundwater resources of Iceland. Availability and demand. – Jökull 38, 35-54. Reykjavík.

Friedrich, W. (1966): Zur Geologie von Brjánslækur (Nordwest-Island) unter besonderer Berücksichtigung der fossilen Flora. – Sonderveröff. d. Geol. Inst. d. Univ. Köln, 10, 108 pp. Cologne.

– – & Leifur A. Símonarson (1981): Die fossile Flora Islands und die Thule Landbrücke. – Spektrum der Wissenschaft, 10. Oct 22-31. Heidelberg.

Grétar Guðbergsson (1974): Myndun móajarðvegs í Skagafirði. – Íslenskar landbúnaðarransóknir 7, 20-45. (In Icelandic).

Guðmundur G. Bárðarson (1945): Ágrip af jarðfræði. – 3. útgáfa. Reykjavík. (In Icelandic).

Guðmundur Kjartansson (1943): Árnesinga saga. Yfirlit og jarðsaga. – 250 pp. Reykjavík. (In Icelandic).

– – (1980): Fold og vötn. – Greinasafn. 223 pp. Reykjavík. (In Icelandic).

Guðmundur P. Ólafsson (1990): Perlur í náttúru Íslands. – 419 pp. Reykjavík. (In Icelandic).

Guðmundur Pálmason (1974): Crustal structure of Iceland from explosion seismology. – Soc. Sci. Islandiae Rit 40, 187 pp. Reykjavík.

Guðmundur Pálmason & Kristján Sæmundsson (1974): Iceland in relation to the Mid-Atlantic ridge. – Am. Rev. Earth and Planet. Sci. 2, 25-50.

Guðmundur E. Sigvaldason (1968): Structure and products of subaquatic volcanoes in Iceland. – Contrib. Mineral. Petrol. 18, 1-16.

– – (1992): Recent hydrothermal explosion crater in an old hyaloclastic flow, central Iceland. – J. Volcanol. 54, 53-63.

Guttormur Sigbjarnarson (1968): Áfok og uppblástur. – Náttúrufræðingurinn 39, 68-118. Reykjavík. (With an English summary).

Halldór Pétursson (1991): The Weichselian glacial history of west Melrakkaslétta, northeastern Iceland. – Environmental Changes in Iceland: Past and Present. 49-65. Dordrecht.

Haukur Jóhannesson (1981): Jarðlagaskipan og þróun rekbelta á Vesturlandi. – Náttúrufræðingurinn 50, 13-31. Reykjavík. (With an English summary).

Haukur Tómasson (1993): Jökulstífluð vötn á Kili og hamfarahlaup í Hvítá í Árnessýslu. – Náttúrufræðingurinn 62, 77-98. Reykjavík. (With an English summary).

Helgi Björnsson (1988): Hydrology of ice caps in volcanic regions. – Soc. Sci. Islandiae Rit 45, 139 pp. Reykjavík.

Holmes, A. (1972): Principles of physical geology. – 2. útgáfa. 1288 pp. London.

Hospers, J. (1954). The geology of the country between Akureyri and Mývatn in northern Iceland. – Geol. Mijnbouw 16, 491-508.

Hreggviður Norðdahl (1983): Late Quaternary stratigraphy of Fnjóskadalur North-Iceland. – Lundqua thesis 12, 78 pp. Lund.

– – (1990): Late Weichselian and Early Holocene deglaciation history of Iceland. – Jökull 40, 27-50.

– – & Hafliði Hafliðason (1992): The Skógar Tephra, a Younger Dryas marker in North Iceland. – Boreas 21, 23-41.

Hreinn Haraldsson (1981): The Markarfljót sandur area, Southern Iceland: sedimentological, petrological and stratigraphical studies. – Striae 15, 65 pp. Uppsala.

Jón Eiríksson (1981): Lithostratigraphy of the upper Tjörnes sequence North-Iceland, The Breiðavík group. – Acta nat. Islandica 29, 37 pp. Reykjavík.

– – (1985): Facies analysis of the Breiðavík group sediments, North Iceland. – Acta nat. Islandica 31, 56 pp. Reykjavík.

– – & Áslaug Geirsdóttir (1991): A record of Pliocene and Pleistocene glaciations and climatic changes in the North Atlantic based on variations in volcanic and sedimentary facies in Iceland. – Marine Geol. 101, 147-159.

– – , Áslaug Geirsdóttir & Leifur A. Símonarson (1992): A review of the late Pleistocene stratigraphy of Reykjavík, Iceland. Quaternary International, 10-12, 143-150.

Kjartan Thors & Guðrún Helgadóttir (1991): Evidence from southwest Iceland of low sea level in early Flandrian times. – Environmental Changes in Iceland: Past and Present. 93-104. Dordrecht.

Kristinn J. Albertsson (1978): Um aldur jarðlaga á Tjörnesi. – Náttúrufræðingurinn 48, 1-10. Reykjavík. (With an English summary).

– – (1981) On Tertiary tillites in Iceland. – The Earth's pre-Pleistocene glacial record, 562-565. London.

– – & Þorleifur Einarsson (1982): Um aldur jarðlaga efst á Breiðadalsheiði. – Eldur er í norðri, 206-210. Reykjavík. (In Icelandic).

Kristján Sæmundsson (1980): Outline of the geology of Iceland. – Jökull 29, 7-28. Reykjavík.

– – (1982): Öskjur á virkum eldfjallasvæðum á Íslandi. – Eldur er í norðri, 221-239. Reykjavík.

– – (1991): Jarðfræði Kröflukerfisins. – Náttúra Mývatns, 24-95. Reykjavík.

– – (1992): Geology of the Thingvallavatn area. – Thingvallavatn, Oikos, 40-68. Copenhagen.

Leifur A. Símonarson (1980): On climatic changes in Iceland. – Jökull 29, 44-46. Reykjavík.

– – (1981): Íslenskir steingervingar. – Náttúra Íslands, 157-173. Reykjavík.

– – (1990): Fyrstu landspendýraleifarnar úr íslenskum tertíerlögum. – Náttúrufræðingurinn 59, 189-195. Reykjavík. (With an English summary).

Leó Kristjánsson (ed.) (1974): Geodynamics of Iceland and the North Atlantic area. – 323 pp. Dordrecht.

– – (1982): Geomagnetic polarity mapping of Icelandic lavas: Comparison with ocean-floor magnetic lineations. – Earth Evolution Series 2, 126-129.

Lindström, M., Lundqvist, J. & Lundqvist, Th. (1991): Sveriges geologi från urtid til nutid. – 398 pp. Lund.

Lúðvík E. Gústafsson (1992): Geology and petrography of Dyrfjöll central volcano, eastern Iceland. – Berliner Geowiss. Abh. (A) 138, 98 pp. Berlin.

McDougall, I., Kristján Sæmundsson, Haukur Jóhannesson, N. Watkins &

Leó Kristjánsson (1977): Extension of the geomagnetic polarity time scale to 6.5 m. y.: K-Ar dating, geological and paleomagnetic study of a 3500 m lava succession in W-Iceland. – Geol. Soc. Am. Bull. 88, 1-15.

– – Leó Kristjánsson & Kristján Sæmundsson (1984): Magnetostratigraphy and geochronology of northwest Iceland. – J. Geophys. Res. 89, 7029-7060.

Margrét Hallsdóttir (1987): Pollen analytical studies of human influence on vegetation in relation to the landnám tephra in southwest Iceland. – Lundqua thesis 18, 45 pp. Lund.

Níels Óskarsson, Sigurður Steinþórsson & Guðmundur E. Sigvaldason (1985): Iceland geochemical anomaly: Origin, volcanotectonic, chemical fractionation and isotope evolution of the crust. – J. Geophys. Research 90. B 12, 10011-10025.

Ólafur G. Flóvenz & Karl Gunnarsson (1991): Seismic crustal structure in Iceland and surrounding area. – Tectonophysics 189, 1-17.

Ólafur Ingólfsson (1988): Glacial history of the lower Borgarfjörður area, western Iceland. – Geol. Fören. Förh. Stockholm 20, 239-309.

Páll Einarsson (1989): Intraplate earthquakes in Iceland. – Earthquakes at North Atlantic passive margins: Neotectonics and postglacial rebound. 329-344. New York.

Price, R. J. (1973): Glacial and fluvioglacial landforms. – 242 pp. London.

Rasmussen, J. & Noe-Nygaard, A. (169): Beskrivelse til geologisk kort over Færøerne. – 370 pp. Copenhagen.

Richter, D. (1986): Allgemeine Geologie. – 412 pp. Berlin.

Schmidt, K. & Walter, R. (1990): Erdgeschichte. – 307 pp. Berlin.

Schminke, H.-U. (1986): Vulkanismus. – 163 pp. Stuttgart.

Schutzbach, W. (1985): Island: Feuerinsel am Polarkreis. – 3. útgáfa. 272 pp. Bonn.

Schwarzbach, M. (1971): Geologenfahrten in Island. – 104 pp. Ludwigsburg.

– – (1974): Das Klima der Vorzeit. 380 pp. Stuttgart.

Sigurður R. Gíslason & Stefán Arnórsson (1988): Efnafræði árvatns á Íslandi og hraði efnarofs. Náttúrufræðingurinn 58, 183-197. Reykjavík. (With an English summary).

Sigurður Steinþórsson (1981): Ísland og flekakenningin. – Náttúra Íslands, pp. 29-63. (In Icelandic).

Sigurður Þórarinsson (1962): Uppblástur á Íslandi í ljósi öskulagarannsókna. – Ársrit Skógræktarfélags Ísl., 17-54. Reykjavík. (In Icelandic).

– – (1964): Surtsey – the new island in the North Atlantic. – 63 pp. + 46 figs. Reykjavík.

– – (1968): The eruption of Hekla in historical times. A tephrochronological study. – The Eruption of Hekla 1947-48. I. 183 pp. Reykjavík.

– – (1974): Vötnin stríð. Saga Skeiðarárhlaupa og Grímsvatnagosa. – 254 pp. Reykjavík. (In Icelandic).

– – (1981): Jarðeldasvæði á nútíma. – Náttúra Íslands, 81-120. Reykjavík. (In Icelandic).

– – & Kristján Sæmundsson (1980): Volcanic activity in historical time. – Jökull 29, 7-28. Reykjavík.

Sigurjón Rist (1956): Íslenzk vötn. – 127 pp. Reykjavík. (In Icelandic).

– – (1990): Vatns er þörf. – 248 pp. Reykjavík. (In Icelandic).

Sigurvin Elíasson (1977): Molar um Jökulsárhlaup og Ásbyrgi. – Náttúrufræðingurinn 47, 160-179. Reykjavík. (With an English summary).

Skinner, J.S. & Porter, S.C. (1987): Physical geology. – 750 pp. New York.

Stanley, S.M. (1989): Earth and life through time. – 689 pp. New York.

Stefán Arnórsson & Sigurður R. Gíslason (1990): Um uppruna lághitasvæða á Íslandi. – Náttúrufræðingurinn 60, 39-56. Reykjavík. (With an English summary).

Strauch, F. (1970): Die Thule-Landbrücke als Wanderweg und Faunenscheide zwischen Atlantik und Skandik im Tertiär. – Geol. Rund. 60, 381-417, Stuttgart.

Sveinbjörn Björnsson (ed.) (1967): Iceland and mid-ocean ridges. – Soc. Sci. Islandiae Rit 38, 209 pp. Reykjavík. (A collection of papers by various authors on the geology and geophysics of Iceland and the relationship with mid-ocean ridges.)

– – (1975): Jarðskjálftar á Íslandi. – Náttúrufræðingurinn 46, 110-133. Reykjavík. (With an English summary).

– – & Páll Einarsson (1981): Jarðskjálftar. Náttúra Íslands, 121-173. Reykjavík. (In Icelandic).

Sveinn Jakobsson (1972): Chemistry and distribution pattern of recent basaltic rocks in Iceland. – Lithos 5, 365-386.

– – (1979): Petrology of recent basalts of the eastern volcanic zone, Iceland. – Acta nat. Islandica 26, 103 pp. Reykjavík.

– – (1980): Outline of the petrology of Iceland. – Jökull 29, 57-73. Reykjavík.

Trausti Einarsson (1957): Magneto-geological mapping in Iceland with the use of a compass. – Phil. Mag. Suppl. 6, 232-239.

– – (1972): Eðlisþættir jarðar og jarðsaga Íslands. – 267 pp. Reykjavík. (In Icelandic).

Trond Forslund & Ágúst Guðmundsson (1991): Crustal spreading due to dikes and faults in southwest Iceland. – J. Struct. Geol. 13, 443-457.

Walker, G.P.L. (1959): Geology of the Reydarfjördur area, eastern Iceland. – Q. J. Geol. Soc. London 114, 367-391.

– – (1960): Zeolite zones and dike distribution in relation to the structure of the basalts of eastern Iceland. – J. Geol. 68, 515-527.

Walker, G.P.L. (1963): The Breiðdalur central volcano. – Q. J. Geol. Soc. London 119, 25-63.

– – (1964): Geological investigations in E-Iceland. – Bull. Volcanol. 27, 1-15.

– – (1966): Acid volcanic rocks in Iceland. – Bull. Volcanol. 29, 375-406.

Þorleifur Einarsson (1961): Pollenanalytische Untersuchungen zur spät- und postglazialen Klimageschichte Islands. – Sonderveröff. d. Geol. Inst. d. Univ. Köln, 6, 52 pp. Cologne.

– – (1965): The Surtsey eruption. – 30 pp. + 23 figs. Reykjavík. (Published in Icelandic, Danish, English and German).

– – (1968): Jarðfræði – saga bergs og lands. – 335 pp. Reykjavík.

– – (1974): The Heimaey eruption. – 56 pp. + 32 figs. Reykjavík. (In Icelandic, Norwegian, English, German and Polish).

– – (1982): Saga Hvítárgljúfurs og Gullfoss í ljósi öskulagarannsókna. – Eldur er í norðri, 443-451. Reykjavík. (In Icelandic).

– – & Edda Lilja Sveinsdóttir (1984): Nýtt kort af Skaftáreldahrauni og Lakagígum. – Skaftáreldar, 37-48, Reykjavík. (With an English summary).

– – & Kristinn J. Albertsson (1988): The glacial history of Iceland during the past three million years. Phil. Trans. R. Soc. London B 318, 637-644.

Þorvaldur Thoroddsen (1905-6): Island. Grundriß der Geographie und Geologie. – Petermanns Geogr. Mitteil. 152-153, 358 pp. Gotha.

– – (1908-11): Lýsing Íslands. – 1038 pp. Copenhagen. (In Icelandic).

– – (1925): Die Geschichte der isländischen Vulkane. – 458 pp. Copenhagen.

Þórdís Ólafsdóttir (1975): Jökulgarður á hafsbotni út af Breiðafirði. – Náttúrufræðingurinn 45, 31-36. Reykjavík. (With an English summary).

Place name index

Subject index

Glossary of Geographical Terms

The Icelandic terms in this glossary are almost exclusively nouns. They are shown in singular and plural. Many of the words occur in place names.

akur, akrar	cultivated field (grainfield)
apalhraun, apalhraun	aa lava
austur (adverb, noun)	east, noun: the East
á, ár	river, stream
áll, álar	narrow, deep channel
ás, ásar	rise, narrow, elongated
bakki, bakkar	1) riverside, 2) bank (riverbank), bluff
berg, -	cliff, rock
bjarg, björg	rock, cliff
borg, borgir	1) rocky hill, 2) town
brekka, brekkur	slope, hillside
bunga, bungur	dome, rounded hill
býli (see jörð)	farm
bær, bæir	1) farm, farmstead, farmhouse, 2) town
dalur, dalir	valley (dale)
djúp, djúp	deep
djúpur (adjective)	deep
drangur, drangar	isolated pillar of rock, pinnacle
efri (adjective)	upper
eldur, eldar	fire
endi, endar	behind (usually rounded)
ey, eyjar	island
eyja, eyjur	island
eyri, eyrar	sand- or gravel bank, sandspit
fell, fell	fell, mountain (usually isolated, rounded)
fjall, fjöll	mountain
fjallgarður, fjallgarðar	mountain range
fjara, fjörur	1) beach, 2) low tide

fjörður, firðir	fiord
fljót, fljót	big, large river
flóð, flóð	1) flood, 2) high tide
flói, flóar	1) bay, 2) fen, marsh
flöt, flatir	level (grass) land
foss, fossar	waterfall
gil, gil	ravine, guly, gorge
gígur, gígar	crater
gjá, gjár	fissure, rift
gljúfur, gljúfur	gorge, canyon
grunn, grunn	shoal, shallow, fishing bank
gufa, gufur	steam
haf, höf	sea, ocean
háls, hálsar	long hill, long low mountain
hamar, hamrar	cliff, precipice, (bluff)
heiði, heiðar	heath
helluhraun, -hraun	pahoehoe lava
hlíð, hlíðar	slope, hillside, mountain side
hn(j)úkur, hn(j)úkar	peak (usually rounded)
holt, holt	hill (originally a clearing)
hóll, hólar	hill
hólmi, hólmar	islet
hraun, hraun	lava, lava field, lava flow
vhreppur, hreppar	rural community
hryggur, hryggir	ridge
hver, hverir	hot spring
hvoll, hvolir	hill
hæð, hæðir	hill (low)
höfði, höfðar	head, headland, cape, promontory
höfn, hafnir	harbour
innri (adv.)	inner
ís	ice
jökulá, -ár	glacier river
jökulgarður, -garðar	moraine
jökulhlaup, -hlaup	glacier outburst
jökulís	glacier ice
jökull, jöklar	glacier
jörð, jarðir	1) earth, 2) farm
kaldur, kaldir (adj.)	cold
kaupstaður, -staðir	town, urban community
kauptún, kauptún	village
kjarr	scrub, bush
klettur, klettar	rock, crag (esp. plur. cliffs)
kot, kot	small farm, croft
kvísl, kvíslar	branch (of a stream), fork
land, lönd	1) land, land area, 2) country
laug laugar	warm spring
lind, lindir	spring
lítill, litlir (adj.)	small

litli, litlu	small
lón, lón	lagoon
lækur, lækir	brook, creek
melur, melar	gravel, gravel flat, (shingle)
mór, móar	1) peat, 2) heath, heathland
múli, múlar	mountain
mýri, mýrar	bog, (moor)
mörk, merkur	woodland
neðri (adv.)	lower
nes, nes	peninsula
norður (adv., noun)	north (noun: the North)
núpur, núpar	peak (usually rounded)
oddi, oddar	tongue of land, point
ós, ósar	1) river mouth, river head
pollur, pollar	1) pool, 2) puddle
reykur, reykir	1) smoke, 2) steam
rif, rif	reef
sandur, sandar	1) sand (only sing.), 2) sands, 3) outwash plain
sjór	sea, ocean
skagi, skagar	peninsula
skarð, skörð	1) pass, 2) gap
skál, skálar	corry, cirque, basin
skógur, skógar	wood(s)
skriða, skriður	1) scree, 2) landslide, rockslide
skriðjökull, -jöklar	outlet glacier
slétta, sléttur	plain
sprungar, sprungur	fissure, crack, crevice
staður, staðir	place (in many names of prominent farms, e.g. Bessastaðir)
stór(i), stórir (stóru)	adj.big, large
straumur, straumar	current
strönd, strendur	ccoast, shore
suður (adv., noun)	south (noun: the South)
sund, sund	sound, strait
sýsl, sýslur	county, (province or disrict) (rural admin. units made up of hreppar)
tangi, tangar	narrow point (projecting into lake or sea)
tindur, tindar	peak, summit
tjörn, tjarnir	pond
tún, tún	home field, cultivated hay field
uppspretta, -sprettur	spring
varmi (masc.), varma (fem.)	warm
vatn, vötn	1) water (only sing.), 2) lake
vegur, vegir	road
vestur (adv., noun)	1) west (noun: the West)
vík, víkur	inlet, cove

vogur, vogar	small bay inlet (estuary)
ytri (adv.)	outer (closer to sea), farher west
þverá, þverár	tributary
ölkelda, ölkeldur	mineral spring
völlur, vellir	1) level field, plain, 2) flat grassland

Directions etc.

austur	efri	neðri
norður	innri	ytri
suður	litli	stór(i)
vestur	lítill	

Water, rivers, lakes, ocean, islands

á	foss	straumur
áll	grun	strönd
djúp	hafn	sund
djúpur	hólm	tjörn
ey	höfni	uppspretta
eyja	kvísl	vatn
fjara	lind	vík
fjörður	lón	vogur
fljót	lækur	þverá
flóð	ós	ölkelda
flói	sjór	

Geothermal features

gufa	laug	varmi
hver	reykur	

Glaciers etc.

ís	jökull	skriðjökull
jökulís	kaldur	

Volcanism, tectonics

apalhraun	gjá	hraun
eldur	helluhraun	sprunga
gígur		

Land, landscape, landforms, topography

ás	háls	nes
bakki	hamar	núpur
berg	heiði (also veg.)	oddi
bjarg	hlíð	rif
borg	hn(j)úkur	sandur
brekka	holt	skagi
bunga	hóll	skarð
dalur	hryggur	skál
drangur	hvoll	skriða
fell	hæð	slétta
fjall	höfði	strönd
fjallgarður	jörð	tangi
flöt	klettur	tindur
gil	land	völlur
gljúfur	melur (also veg.)	múli

Vegetation

akur	mór	skógur
flói	mýri	tún
heiði	mörk	völlur
kjarr		

Administration, farms, misc.

býli	kaupstaður	staður
bær	kauptún	sýsla
hreppur	kot	vegur
jörð		